W9-CHQ-708

Golfing in Washington

The _Complete_ guide to
Washington's golf facilities

Eleventh Edition

by
Daniel MacMillan

Published by

M A C Productions
Golf Guides Since 1986

Carnation, Washington

Waiver on Accuracy
We have gone to great lengths to provide the golfer with an up-to-date, accurate and comprehensive guide to golfing facilities in the state of Washington; nevertheless, we all slice it out of bounds from time to time. Each course reserves the right to change their prices and policies at any time and the author & publisher will not be held liable for any inaccuracies presented in this book.

Copyright © 1996 by Daniel MacMillan
All rights reserved. The course layouts, map grids and format are all protected under United States copyright laws. Unlawful use of this material will result in prosecution to the full extent of the law. No part of this publication may be stored in a retrieval system or transmitted, in any form, or by any means, electronically, mechanically, by photocopying, recording, facsimile, or otherwise, without the prior written permission of the publisher and author.

Library of Congress Cataloging-in-Publication Data
MacMillan, Daniel E.
Golfing in Washington
1. Golf Course guide
2). Travel-golf related in Washington State

Printed in Canada

Cover photos courtesy of:
Avalon Golf Club; Burlington, Washington (front)
Echo Falls Country Club; Snohomish, Washington (back)

Cover photos: by John R. Johnson ©

First Edition, April 1986	Seventh Edition, March 1992
Second Edition, May 1987	Eighth Edition, March 1993
Third Edition, May 1988	Ninth Edition, March 1994
Fourth Edition, April 1989	Tenth Edition, March 1995
Fifth Edition, March 1990	Eleventh Edition March 1996
Sixth Edition, March 1991	

ISBN 1-878591-18-5

Published by:
MAC Productions
PO Box 655; Carnation, Washington 98014 USA
(206) 333-4641

Preface

In this the eleventh edition of **"Golfing in Washington"** I hope it will
be the most complete golf guide in the state published to date. We have
completely upgraded the book and added new features to help with
planning your golf trips. The size is designed with the idea that the
book will more easily fit in your glove box or golf bag. We have also
provided small map inserts along with the driving directions to help you
get to the golf facilities. As always you will find new courses, par 3's,
and ranges just opened or due to open later in the season. Layouts,
prices and yardage have been revised to reflect any changes that have
occurred since last year. I hope you enjoy this years book, see you on
the links!

Acknowledgements

A special thanks to all the pros, owners and course managers who
have been so helpful in providing us access to their courses and current
information. Thanks to the Oregon Department of Transportation,
Washington Department of Transportation and the Idaho Department
of Transportation for the endless supply of maps needed in doing this
project.

Bob Valentine and Valco Graphics for the tremendous support on this
labor of love project over the years. Thanks Robert!!!

Jeff Shelley for his help and personal support on these projects.

This book would not have been possible without the tremendous support
of my entire family and my friends. I thank each and every one of them
for the special interest they have shown in the golf books.

To my children Joshua Daniel, Sarah Gene and the new addition
Christian Rogers for showing me what really is important in life.

Thanks to my loving wife Kristi Gene. Words cannot express the love
and support she has given me on this project. I feel blessed to have a
wife whom provided a loving, caring, Christ like atmosphere in which
to produce this book in. Thanks Kristi Gene. Most importantly my Lord
Jesus, for his gentle hand and firm grip with my life and this company.

Daniel

Daniel MacMillan has been an avid golfer for the past 11 years. He enjoys researching and playing the various golf courses of the Pacific Northwest (if it were only that easy!!). *Golfing in Washington* was the brainchild of Daniel and his previous partner Mark Fouty who, one day while playing a round at Snohomish Golf Course, discussed finding a guide to use themselves. When no such guide was available this one was written. The book has taken on many stages. It was originally called *Golfing in Western Washington*, which encompassed only the more populous half of the state. In 1988 it expanded to *Golfing in Washington* (now in it's eleventh edition). Meanwhile Mark pursued a career in New York so Daniel bought out Mark's share of the company. The company has therefore become a real family operation. Daniel drags his wife Kristi and their three children throughout the Pacific Northwest seeking information on new courses and facilities for upcoming publications. We hope all the thousands of miles and endless phone calls have paid off. This guide is designed to have all the information a golfer wants and needs to know about playing a course, and as a golfer Daniel has done just that.

Golfing in Oregon is the second book published by MAC Productions and written by Daniel. Now in its sixth edition it also is published on an annual basis. This book too has taken many forms it was originally called *Golfing in Oregon & Idaho*. In 1992 the book was changed to reflect the new format and now only includes the state of Oregon.

Golfing in Idaho & Montana is the third book published by MAC Productions and written by Daniel. The first edition of this book was called *Golfing In Idaho* and was published in 1994. The new book which will be out in spring of 1996 will include the great state of Montana and will be called *Golfing In Idaho & Montana* look for it in a pro shop or book store near you.

New territories are always being explored for writing golf course guides such as this. It takes many man hours and attention to detail to produce books of this nature. From start to finish a new book takes about two years to produce. Currently five more are in the works with many more in the initial planning stage. Look for the new publications at a pro shop or book store near you. Daniel's hope is that you will find this to be the best golf guide of its kind on the shelf.

Contents

Abbreviations, Explanatory notes and Disclaimers

Executive Course: An executive course is usually longer than a typical par 3 short course but shorter than a regulation course.

Private Course: A course that is not open to public play.

Semi-private Course: courses are closed to the public at certain times during the week.

Tees: T-Tour; C-Championship; M-Men; W-Women.

Greens fee: W/D-Weekday; W/E-Weekend.

N/A: Not available, either services or information not available.

Course rating: This rates the degree of difficulty of course in the NW and refers to the average number of shots per round a scratch golfer ought to shoot. It is figured by rating teams who factor in terrain, length and hazards of each course. The higher the rating the more difficult the course. Course ratings courtesy of the *Pacific Northwest Golf Association & Oregon Golf Association.*

Slope: This is similar to the course rating but it considers other factors as well. The slope rating takes into consideration the playing difficulty of a course for handicaps above scratch. The higher the number, the more difficult the course. Slope ratings courtesy of the *Pacific Northwest Golf Association & Oregon Golf Association.*

Greens fee: prices are subject to change at any time. Because a number of Eastern Washington courses close for the winter, the prices may reflect those of last year. When two prices are given, the first refers to the 18 hole fee, the second to the 9 hole fee. "Reciprocates" refers to the practice of private courses allowing members of other private courses to play their courses. However, because some courses only reciprocate with a limited number of other courses, it's best to call first.

Trail fee: the fee a course charges an individual to use their own power cart on the course.

Reservation policy: This refers to the maximum number of days the course allows reservations to made in advance under normal circumstances.

Winter condition: Dry, damp, wet refers to the club pro's opinion of the course's condition in rainy conditions.

Terrain: flat, flat some hills, relatively hilly, very hilly.

Tees: Grass or mats are the alternatives.

Temporary greens: When "yes" is stated, one *may* find some greens either under repair or susceptible to damage during inclement weather, thus a temporary in play.

Course layouts/yardage: My intent is to show tees in relation to greens, obvious hazards and other holes. Some hazards may not be adequately represented, nor are trees shown.

Map 1

Map 1 ⛳ Denotes Approximate Golf Course Location **Golfing in Washington**

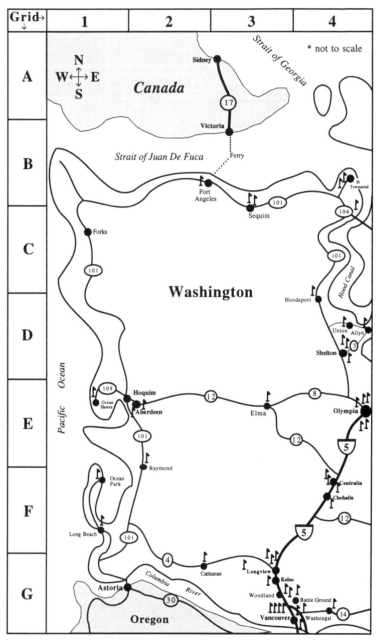

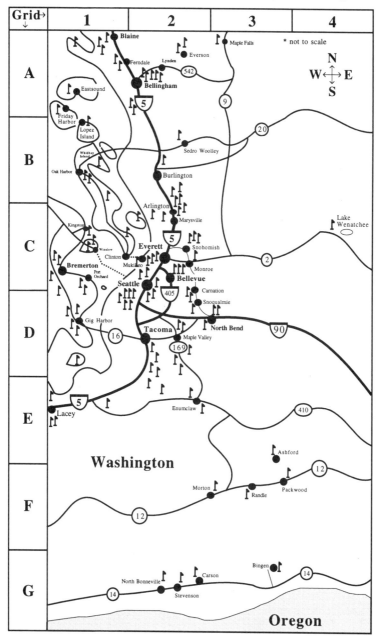

Map 3

Denotes Approximate Golf Course Location

Golfing in Washington

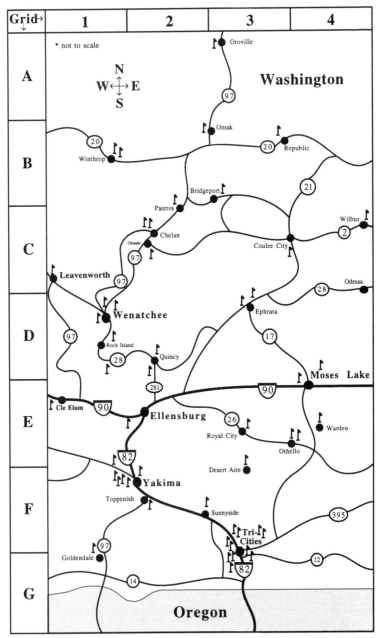

Grid→	1	2	3	4

* not to scale

N
W←↔→E
S

Washington

Oroville

97

Omak

20

Republic

20

Winthrop

Bridgeport

21

Pateros

Wilbur

Chelan

2

Orondo

Coulee City

97

Leavenworth

Odessa

97

28

Wenatchee

Ephrata

Rock Island

17

Quincy

Moses Lake

28

281

90

Cle Elum

90

Ellensburg

26

Royal City

Warden

82

Othello

Yakima

Desert Aire

Toppenish

Sunnyside

395

Tri-Cities

Goldendale

97

12

82

14

Oregon

Map 4

Denotes Approximate Golf Course Location   **Golfing in Washington**

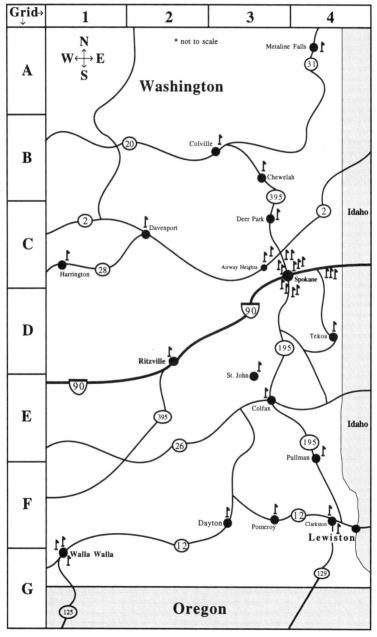

| Grid→ | 1 | 2 | 3 | 4 |

N
W ←→ E
S

* not to scale

Metaline Falls

31

Washington

20

Colville

Chewelah

395

Deer Park

2   **Idaho**

2

Davenport

Airway Heights

Spokane

Harrington

28

90

Tekoa

195

Ritzville

St. John

90

395

Colfax   **Idaho**

26

195

Pullman

Dayton   Pomeroy   12   Clarkston

12   **Lewiston**

Walla Walla

129

125

Oregon

Alderbrook Golf & Yacht Club (semi-private)
E 300 Country Club Drive E; Union,WA 98592; (360) 898-2560
Pro: Mike Fields, PGA. Superintendent: Dwane Ehrich. 18 hole course.
Rating/Slope: C 70.9/122; M 69.6/120; W 72.2/125. **Course record:** 64.
Green fees: W/D $25/$15; W/E $30/$18; Sr. rates $18 (M-F); M/C, VISA.
Power cart: $22/$13. **Pull cart:** $3/$1.50. **Trail fee:** $9.
Reservation policy: yes, 3 weeks for members & guests; 1 week for the public.
Winter condition: open, dry. **Terrain:** flat, some hills. **Tees;** grass.
Temporary greens: no. **Services:** club rentals, lessons, snack bar, beer, pro shop,
club fitting, tennis courts, driving range. **Comments:** Picturesque setting above
Hood Canal and the beautiful Olympic Peninsula. Well stocked pro shop that will
service all your golfing needs. Golf course has excellent drainage for winter play.

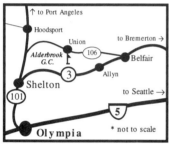

Directions: from I-5 N&S cut off for
Highway 101 (exit 104) to Shelton/Port
Angeles. Bypass Shelton, continuing
approximately 5 miles to Twanoh State
Park/Bremerton turn (Hwy 106). Follow
for approximately 4 miles (along Hood
Canal) to Union. The course will be on
your right, across from the Alderbrook Inn
on Hood Canal. Look for signs.

Course Yardage & Par:

C-6326 yards, par 72.
M-6037 yards, par 72.
W-5500 yards, par 73.

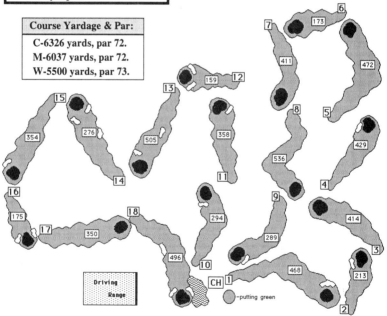

Allenmore Golf Club (public)
2125 South Cedar; Tacoma, WA 98405; (206) 627-7211
Pro: Don Mojean, PGA. Supt.: Arne Smith. 18 hole course, driving range.
Rating/Slope: M 69.2/121; W 73.8/129. **Course record:** 60.
Green fees: $20/$14.50 all week long; Jr. & Sr. rates (M-F); no credit cards.
Power cart: $20/$10. **Pull cart:** $3/$2. **Trail fee:** $3 for personal carts.
Reservation policy: yes, for weekends and holidays only, 1 week in advance.
Winter condition: open, dry. **Terrain:** relatively hilly. **Tees:** grass.
Temporary greens: rarely. **Services:** club rentals, lessons, snack bar,
pro shop, lockers, showers. No knob shoes, 5-somes OK if they play fast.
Comments: Great golf course for hosting tournaments and special events.
Good public course that gets a great deal of play during the summer months so
make your tee times well in advance for weekend or holiday play.

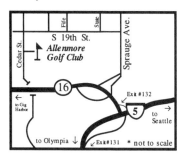

Directions: from I-5 N&S exit to Hwy
16W(Gig Harbor-Bremerton). Proceed for
a short distance to the Sprague Avenue
exit. Continue on Sprague for .4 miles to
S 19th St. Take a left on S 19th. Proceed
to Cedar Street. left on Cedar Street. Golf
course entrance will be located on your
left. Look for signs marking your turn.

Course Yardage & Par:
C-6355 yards, par 71.
M-6064 yards, par 71.
W-5906 yards, par 75.

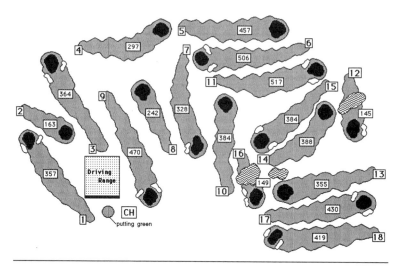

Alta Lake Golf Course (public)

PO Box 85; Alta Lake Road; Pateros, WA 98846; (509) 923-2359
Owners: Don & Susan Barth. 18 hole course.
Rating/Slope: C 71.3/125; M 69.5/121; W 69.9/118. **Course record:** 71.
Green fees: $18/$11 all week long; VISA, M/C.
Power cart: $18/$10. **Pull cart:** $3/$2. **Trail fee:** $4.
Reservation policy: yes, you may call ahead for a tee time, (a must in summer).
Winter condition: golf course is closed from November to mid March.
Terrain: relatively hilly. **Tees:** grass. **Temporary greens:** not in use.
Services: club rentals, snack bar, beer, pro shop, motel on the 9th green.
Comments: links type course designed after the links of Scotland. Rolling terrain
and the desert framing each fairway make this course a special place to play.

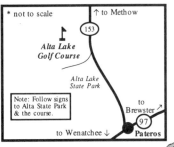

Directions: the golf course is located
southwest of Pateros, Washington. From
Highway 97 follow the signs to Alta Lake
State Park where the course is located.
(this is approximately 57 miles north of
Wenatchee). From Highway 153 the golf
course will be located 2 miles north of
Pateros, Washington.

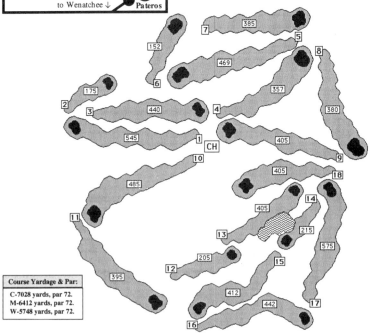

Course Yardage & Par:
C-7028 yards, par 72.
M-6412 yards, par 72.
W-5748 yards, par 72.

Apple Tree Golf Course (public)

8804 Occidental Avenue; Yakima, WA 98903; (509) 966-5877
Pro: George Price Jr, PGA. 18 hole course, driving range. Course record: 65.
Rating/Slope: T 73.3/129; C 72.0/127; M 70.7/124; S 68.0/118; W 72.0/124.
Green fees: Monday thru Thursday $35 (+tax); Friday thru Sunday $50 (+ tax).
Power cart: $24 (plus tax). **Pull cart:** $4 (plus tax). **Reservation policy:** please
call ahead for tee time info (30 days). **Trail fee:** $5. **Winter condition:** open,
weather permitting. **Terrain:** flat, some hills. **Tees:** grass. **Services:** club rentals,
lessons, snack bar & grill, pro shop, driving range, restaurant, banquet facilities.
Comments: Fantastic layout with an island green on the 17th hole in the shape
of a "Washington Apple". If you are looking for a golf course that is a pleasure to
play I highly recommend this top rate facility. This track is worth a special trip so
make sure you include Apple Tree in any eastern Washington golf vacation.

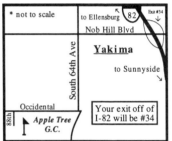

Directions: From I-82 take the Nob Hill
exit #34. Follow W Nob Hill westbound
to 64th Ave. Turn left on S 64th Avenue.
Proceed on S 64th Ave to Occidental Ave.
Turn right on Occidental Ave. Follow to
88th Ave. Left to the clubhouse. The golf
course will be on both sides of Occidental
Ave. Look for signs marking your way.

Course Yardage & Par:

T-6892 yards, par 72.
C-6618 yards, par 72.
M-6311 yards, par 72.
S-5857 yards, par 72.
F-5428 yards, par 72.

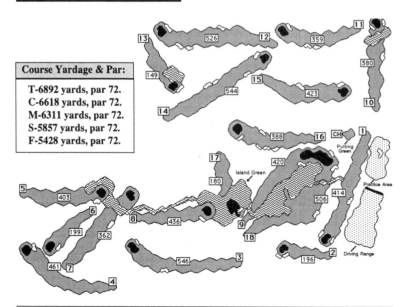

Auburn Golf Course (public)

29630 Green River Road SE; Auburn, WA 98092; (206) 833-2350
Pro: Doug Campbell, PGA. Superintendent: Kevin Van. 18 hole course.
Rating/Slope: C 69.0/121; M 66.7/116; W 72.0/123. **Course record: 63.**
Green fees: $16.25/$12.25; Jr. and Sr. rates (weekdays only); no credit cards.
Power cart: $18/$10. **Pull cart:** $3/$2. **Trail fee:** $5 for personal carts.
Reservation policy: yes, please call ahead up to 1 week in advance for times.
Winter condition: course is open, wet. **Terrain:** flat, some hills. **Tees:** grass.
Temporary greens: occasionally during the winter months. **Services:** club rentals,
lessons, snack bar, beer, pro shop. **Comments:** the golf course is pleasant to walk
with a few hills throughout. Water and sand comes into play on several holes. The
front nine is fairly wide open. The back nine is more hilly with trees coming into
play throughout. The well stocked pro shop will serve all your golfing needs.

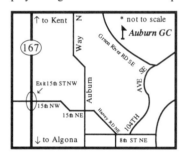

Directions: from I-5 N&S take exit #147
(S 272nd St.). Go east on S 272nd for 2.4
miles to Hwy 167 S. S for 2 miles to 15th
St NW exit. Go east on 15th NW for 1 mile
to Harvey Rd. South for .5 miles to 8th NE.
East for .4 mile to 104th SE. Go north for
.8 miles to SE 307th Pl-Green River Road.
Proceed for 1 mile to the course.

Course Yardage & Par:
C-6020 yards, par 71.
M-5571 yards, par 71.
W-5571 yards, par 73.

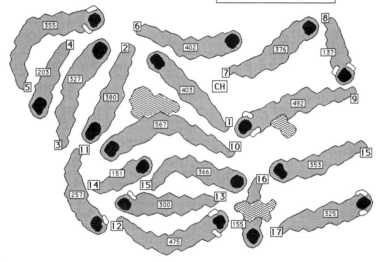

Avalon Golf Club (public)

1717 Kelleher Road; Burlington, WA 98233; (360) 757-1900; 1-800-624-0202
Pro: Brian Kruhlak, PGA. Supt.: Randy Letellier. 27 hole course. Record: 69.
Rating/Slope: South/West: T 71.8/129; C 70.0/124; M 68.7/118; W 72.2/122.
Green fees: Mon.-Thur. $27.50; Fri. $32; Sat.-Sun. & Hol. $35/$23 (all+tax).
Power cart: $23. **Pull cart:** $3. **Trail fee:** $23. **Reservation policy:** yes, call
up to 5 days in advance or no time limit if payment in advance by credit card.
Winter condition: dry, no temp. greens. **Terrain:** flat, some hills. **Tees:** grass.
Services: club rentals, lessons, restaurant, beer, wine, pro shop, driving range,
caddy service in season, putting green. **Comments:** First rate golfing facility.
This 27 hole Robert Muir Graves designed golf course offers spectacular views of
the Skagit Valley and surrounding countryside. If you are looking for top rate golf
course with a friendly staff try Avalon, you will not be disappointed. Great track.

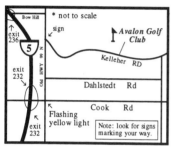

Directions: from I-5 N&S take exit #232
(Cook Road).Turn east and go for 1 block
to the traffic light. Turn left and go north
on old Hwy 99. When you reach Kelleher
Road turn right. Go beyond the Humane
Society and a make a left at the Avalon
sign and proceed to the golf course.

Rating/Slope:
North/South: T 73.1/132; C 71.3/127; M 69.6/124; W 73.2/127.
North/West: T 72.3/125; C 70.3/121; M 69.6/124; W 71.6/122.

Course Yardage & Par:

<u>North:</u> T-3396 yards, C-3189 yards,
M-2989 yards, W-2726 yards, par 36.
<u>South:</u> T-3375 yards, C-3205 yards,
W-3005 yards, W-2808 yards, par 36.
<u>West:</u> T-3201 yards, C-3001 yards,
M-2797 yards, W-2510 yards, par 36.

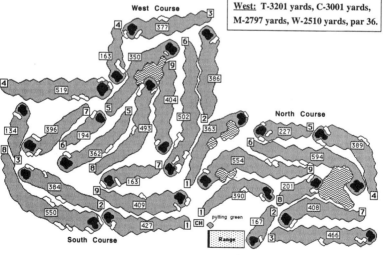

Badger Mountain Golf Course (public)

Reata Road & Badger Mt. Blvd.; Tri-Cities, WA; for info (206) 564-7942
Pro: N/A. **18 hole course, driving range. Course is in a (509) Area code**
Rating/Slope: the course is to new to have been rated. **Course record:** N/A.
Green fees: all fees to be determined. **Power cart:** to be determined.
Pull cart: to be determined. **Reservation policy:** to be determined.
Winter condition: closed in winter. **Terrain:** flat, some hills. **Tees:** grass.
Services: club rentals, lessons, lounge, restaurant, snack bar, beer, wine, liquor,
showers, lockers, pro shop, driving range, 18 hole putting course, rec. center,
mini water park, training facility. **Comments:** championship course set up to be
challenging or forgiving for all golfing abilities. A public golf course with a private
course feel and service. Look for this course is open in spring or summer of 1996.

Directions: from I-82 take the Badger
Road exit. Proceed on Badger Road to
Leslie Road. Proceed to Reata Road and
look for signs indicating your turn to
Badger Mountain Blvd. Note: as of this
publication date some of these roads have
not been constructed.

Course Yardage & Par:

T-6960 yards, par 72.
C-6455 yards, par 72.
M-6070 yards, par 72.
W-5675 yards, par 72.

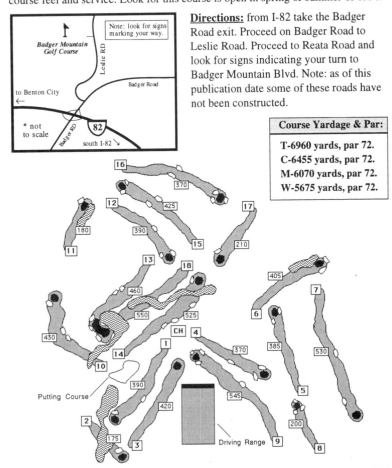

Ballinger Park Municipal Golf Course (public)

23000 Lakeview Drive; Mountlake Terrace, WA 98043; (206) 775-6467
Managers: Jan Japar, Mimi Racicot. **Superintendent:** Rick McDow.
Rating/Slope: M 64.2/100; W 66.9/105. **Course record:** 28. **9 hole course.**
Green fees: W/D $8.50; W/E $9; additional 9 holes $7; winter, twi-lite, Jr & Sr
rates; VISA, MC. **Power cart:** none. **Pull cart:** $2. **Trail fee:** none (seasonal
restrictions). **Reservation policy:** yes, summer all week, winter weekends only.
Winter condition: open, wet. **Terrain:** flat. **Tees:** grass & mats, off season only.
Temporary greens: no. **Services:** club rentals, restaurant, beer, wine, golf shop
featuring discount golf apparel & equipment. **Comments:** greens well maintained.
The course offers a well stocked pro shop for all your golfing needs Clubhouse
offers catering and rental of the Lakeview room for special occasions.

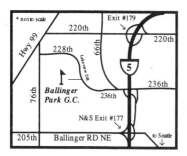

Directions: I-5 N take exit #177 to 236th
SW. Go west on 236th which becomes
Lakeview DR for .7 miles. I-5 S take
exit #179 to 220th SW. Go west on 220th
SW to 66th Ave. Go south for 1 mile to
Lakeview DR. Go west on Lakeview DR
to the golf course. Note: the golf course is
located on Lake Ballinger adjacent to the
tennis courts, picnic area and athletic field.

Course Yardage & Par:
M-2656 yards, par 34; W-2466 yards, par 34.

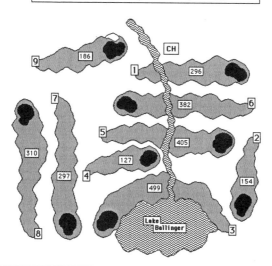

Banks Lake Golf Club (public)

Airport Road; PO Box 11; Grand Coulee, WA 99133; (509) 633-0163
Manager/Pro: John W Combs Jr. 9 hole course, dual tees for 18 holes.
Rating/Slope: M 68.1/103; W 70.2/110. **Course record:** 68.
Green fees: $16/$14 all week long; no special rates; VISA, M/C.
Power cart: $20/$12. **Pull cart:** $1. **Trail fee:** $5 for personal carts.
Reservation policy: yes, you may call in advance for a tee time, no restrictions.
Winter condition: the golf course is closed December through February.
Terrain: flat, some hills. **Tees:** grass. **Temporary greens:** no, not in use.
Services: lessons, driving range, snack bar, pro shop, putting green.
Comments: rolling lush terrain situated in the midst of the "desert" in eastern
Washington. The golf course is relatively new and kept in excellent condition.
The course sports dual tees for those wanting a different look on the 2nd nine.
Good 9 hole tract that offers the golfer a very friendly atmosphere.

Directions: the golf course is located two
miles south of Electric City off of Hwy
155. There is a sign on Highway 155
marking the turn to the golf course. The
golf course is located by the airport. You
will turn on Airport Road to the golf
course which will be located on your left
hand side of the road.

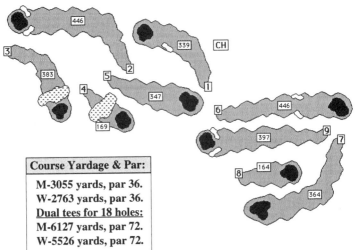

Course Yardage & Par:
M-3055 yards, par 36.
W-2763 yards, par 36.
Dual tees for 18 holes:
M-6127 yards, par 72.
W-5526 yards, par 72.

Battle Creek Golf Course (public)

6006 Meridian Ave. N; Marysville, WA 98271;1-800-655-7931, (360) 659-7931
Pro: Jim Pulliam, PGA. Supt. Chuck Nolan. 18 hole reg., 9 hole par 3, range.
Rating/Slope: C 71.4/125; M 69.5/121; W 70.9/124. **Course record:** C 68; M 66.
Green fees: W/D $18/$12. W/E $23/$14. Jr. & Sr. rates (M-F); VISA, MC.
Green fees for the par 3 course: W/D $11/$7; W/E $14/$8. **Power cart:** $21/$12.
Pull cart: $3/$2. **Trail fee:** $10. **Reservation policy:** yes, call 7 days in advance.
Winter condition: open, dry, good drainage. **Terrain:** some hills. **Tees:** grass.
Services: club rentals, lessons, cafe, beer, wine, pro shop, grass tees in practice
area, driving range, club memberships. **Comments:** excellent, scenic golf course
that wanders thru woodlands and wetlands. Greens have improved dramatically
over the last few years so be sure to add Battle Creek to your weekend outings.

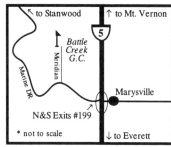

Directions: from I-5 N&S take exit #199
(Tulalip-Marysville). Go west on Marine
DR for 2.75 miles. Turn right on Meridian
Avenue. Travel north for .75 miles to the
course. Note: look for a sign at your turn.

Course Yardage & Par:
C-6575 yards, par 73.
M-6153 yards, par 73.
W-5286 yards, par 73.

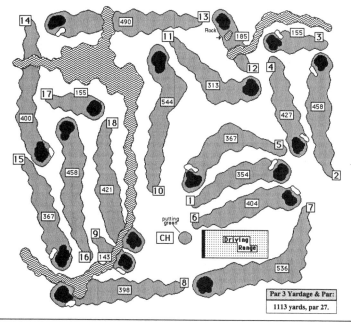

Par 3 Yardage & Par:
1113 yards, par 27.

Beacon Rock Golf Course (public)

Box 189; Hwy 14; North Bonneville, WA 98639; (509) 427-5730, 800-428-5730
Managers: James & Linda Borup. 9 hole course, dual tees for 18 holes.
Rating/Slope: M 67.5/115; W 69.7/109. **Course record:** 29.
Green fees: $18/$9 (plus tax); Senior rates on Tues.,Wed., Thur.; M/C, VISA.
Power cart: $9 per nine holes. **Pull cart:** $3/$2. **Trail fee:** $5.
Reservation policy: yes, you may call 7 days in advance for a tee times.
Winter condition: open year round, wet. **Terrain:** flat. **Tees:** grass.
Temporary greens: no. **Services:** club rentals, restaurant, beer, pro shop.
Comments: this excellent walking golf course features tree lined fairways with
medium to small greens. Dual tees are available for a different look on your second
nine. The golf course is very playable throughout the entire year.

Directions: the golf course is located
west of North Bonneville off of Hwy 14.
Exit at Grenia Street to the course. Watch
for a sign on the highway marking your
way to the course. If coming from I-205
N&S be sure to exit to Hwy 14 (exit #27)
going eastbound (Lewis & Clark Hwy).

Course Yardage & Par:
M-2746 yards, par 36.
W-2540 yards, par 36.
Dual tees for 18 holes:
M-5580 yards, par 72.
W-5154 yards, par 72.

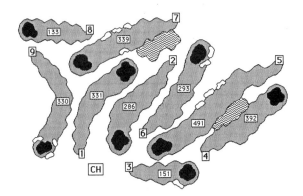

Bear Creek Country Club (private)

13737 202nd Avenue NE; Woodinville, WA 98072; (206) 881-1350
Pro: Roger Rockefeller, PGA. Supt.: Scott Rippel. 18 hole course. Record: 68.
Rating/Slope: T 74.9/136; C 72.1/130; M 69.8/125; W 71.9/124.
Green fees: private club, members & guests only; Jr. rates; VISA, M/C.
Power cart: private club, members & guests only. **Pull cart:** members only.
Reservation policy: private club, members & guests of members only.
Winter condition: open, dry. **Terrain:** relatively hilly. **Tees:** grass.
Temporary greens: N/A. **Services:** club rentals, lessons, snack bar, beer, wine,
liquor, pro shop, lockers, showers, driving range. **Comments:** very difficult golf
course where shot placement is a must. Hilly terrain gives the golfer a wide variety
of lies. Out of bounds comes into play a nearly every hole. Excellent private course.

Directions: from I-405 N&S take exit #20B
(NE 124th) to NE 124th. Travel eastbound for
4.25 miles to Avondale Road. Go North for .1
miles (your turn will come up quickly, veer
left) to NE 132nd. Go east for .3 miles to NE
133rd. Go eastbound on 133rd until you reach
202ND Ave NE, take a left to the golf course.

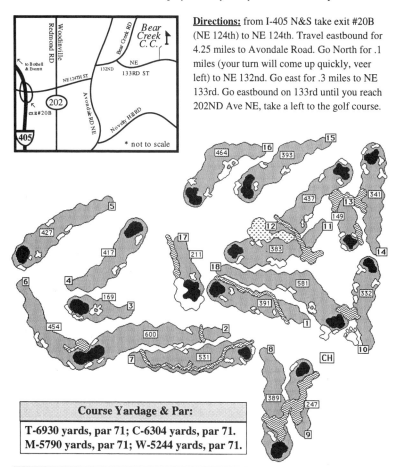

Course Yardage & Par:		
T-6930 yards, par 71; C-6304 yards, par 71.		
M-5790 yards, par 71; W-5244 yards, par 71.		

Bear Creek Golf Course (public)
Route 1, Box 275; off of Hwy 20; Winthrop, WA 98862; (509) 996-2284
Managers: Ashley & Linda Court. 9 hole course, dual tees for 18 holes.
Rating/Slope: M 68.9/117; W 69.4/113. Course record: 65.
Green fees: W/D $16/$11; W/E $18/$12; no credit cards.
Power cart: $19/$10. Pull cart: $2. Trail fee: $2.50.
Reservation policy: yes, call in advance for weekends and holidays only.
Winter condition: the golf course is closed from November to March.
Terrain: relatively hilly. Tees: grass. Temporary greens: no. Services: club
rentals, snack bar, beer, practice green, pro shop. **Comments:** beautiful view of
the North Cascades. Fairways are well-kept, lush and green. Water, and trees are
the primary hazard from the tee and on your approach shots. If you are looking for
nice 9 hole course in a great area of Washington try Bear Creek.

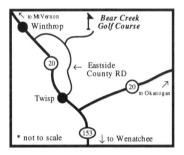

Directions: the golf course is located
north of Twisp and east of Winthrop.
From Hwy 20 go 7 miles north on
Eastside County Road. The golf course
is located 3/4 of a mile up the first paved
road on the right hand side. Look for signs
marking your way to the golf course

Course Yardage & Par:
M-3114 yards, par 36.
W-2706 yards, par 37.
<u>Dual tees for 18 holes:</u>
M-6173 yards, par 72.
W-5309 yards, par73.

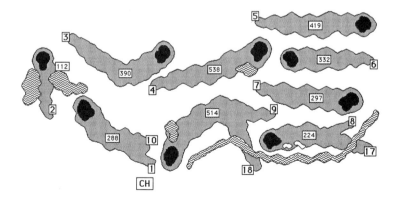

Bellevue Municipal Golf Course (public)

5500 140th NE; Bellevue, WA 98005; (206) 451-7250
Pros: Marty Raab, PGA. Casey Anderson, PGA. Steve Hubbard, PGA.
Superintendent: Mark Blechen. 18 hole course, driving range.
Rating/Slope: M 66.5/110; W 68.6/111. Course record: 60.
Green fees: $18; Jr. & Sr. rates (Weekdays); no credit cards.
Power cart: $21/$13.50. **Pull cart:** $3. **Trail fee:** not allowed.
Reservation policy: 1 week in advance, call Mon. for Fri., Sat. and Sun. tee times.
Winter condition: the golf course is open all year long, wet conditions.
Terrain: flat, some hills. **Tees:** grass (mats in winter). **Temporary greens:** yes.
Services: club rentals, lessons, snack bar, beer, wine, pro shop, driving range.
Comments: one of state's busiest golf courses. For being such a busy municipal course it can be found to be in excellent condition. Greens are generally in great shape during the peak season. Covered range for those wanting to practice.

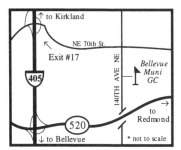

Directions: from I-405 N&S take exit #17 to NE 70th St. Proceed to 140th Ave NE and turn left. Follow 140th Ave NE until you reach the course, which will be on your left. From I-5 N&S take exit to Hwy 520 eastbound. Go east to 148th Ave NE. Go north on 148th for .8 miles to NE 40th. West for .5 miles to 140th NE. Travel north for 1 mile to the course.

Course Yardage & Par:

M-5535 yards, par 71.
W-5081 yards, par 71.

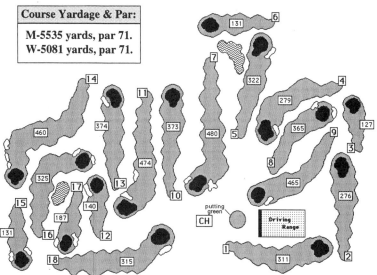

Bellingham Golf & Country Club (private)

3729 Meridian; Bellingham, WA 98225; (360) 733-5381
Pro: Dean Russell, PGA. Superintendent: William Fulton. 18 hole course.
Rating/Slope: C 71.0/123; M 69.8/120; W 72.7/124. **Course record: 65.**
Green fees: private club, member & guests only; reciprocates; no credit cards.
Power cart: private club, member & guests only. **Pull cart:** private club.
Trail fee: private club, members only. **Reservation policy:** private club.
Winter condition: open, dry. **Terrain:** flat, some hills. **Tees:** grass.
Temporary greens: yes (winter). **Services:** lessons, lounge, beer, wine, liquor,
pro shop, lockers, showers, driving range. **Comments:** Excellent private facility
for members and guests only. The course features tree lined fairways with small
well bunkered greens that create difficulty in scoring.

Directions: from I-5 N&S take exit #256
(Meridian St.) to Meridian St. Travel west
on Meridian St for .2 miles to the golf
course which will be on your right hand
side. Course located right off of I-5.

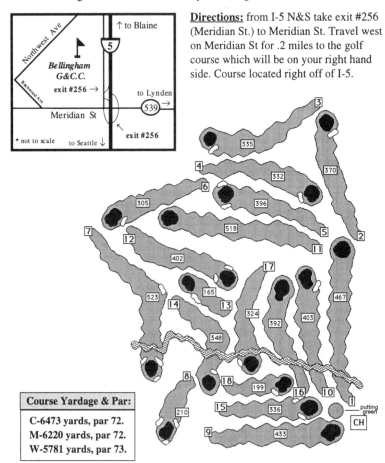

Course Yardage & Par:

C-6473 yards, par 72.
M-6220 yards, par 72.
W-5781 yards, par 73.

Big Bend Golf & Country Club (public)

P.O. Box 162; Golf Course Road; Wilbur, WA 99185; (509) 647-5664
Pro: Mark Hatala. 9 hole course, dual tees for 18 holes.
Rating/Slope: C 68.5/109; M 67.4/107; W 73.6/120. **Course record:** 30 (9 holes).
Green fees: W/D $13/$9; W/E $15/$10; All day $17.50. VISA, MC.
Power cart: $15/$10. **Pull cart:** $1.75/$1. **Trail fee:** $3.50.
Reservation policy: call in advance for tee times. **Winter condition:** the golf course is closed from November to March. **Terrain:** flat, some hills. **Tees:** grass.
Temporary greens: no. **Services:** club rentals, snack bar, lounge, beer, wine, liquor, driving range, pro shop, showers. **Comments:** well maintained. One of the best 9 hole golf courses in the state with water and sand coming into play throughout. Lush fairways. Two sets of tees for a full 18 hole variation. Try Big Bend if you are looking for quick 9 hole round on a beautiful golf course.

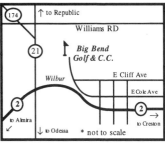

Directions: the course is located south of the junctions of Hwys 21 and 174, just northwest of Wilbur. The golf course is on the east side of Hwy 21. Look for a sign on the highway marking the way to the course. If traveling from Spokane take Highway 2 to Wilbur.

Course Yardage & Par:
M-2985 yards, par 36.
W-2875 yards, par 37.
Dual tees for 18 holes:
M-5942 yards, par 72.
W-5705 yards, par 74.

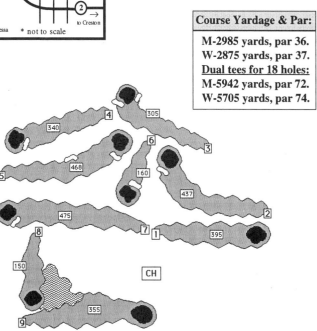

Birch Bay Village Golf Course (private)

8169 Cowichan Road; Blaine, WA 98230; (360) 371-2026
Manager: Galen Reimer. 9 hole executive course.
Rating/Slope: the golf course is not rated. **Course record:** 30.
Green fees: private golf course, members & guests only; no credit cards.
Power cart: private golf course, members & guests only. **Pull cart:** private golf
course. **Trail fee:** not allowed. **Reservation policy:** yes, no time limit. Must be a
property owner or guest. **Winter condition:** closed from November to February.
Terrain: relatively hilly, flat areas. **Tees:** grass. **Temporary greens:** occasionally.
Services: club rentals, lessons, pro shop. **Comments:** the course reciprocates for
club professionals. Adjacent to Birch Bay in Whatcom County, the course houses
three ponds which are in play for the majority of the round.

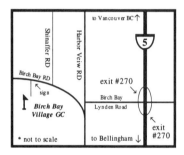

Directions: from I-5 N&S take exit
270 (Lynden-Birch Bay Road), to
Lynden-Birch Bay Road. Travel west for
3.7 miles to Harbor View Road. Go south
for .2 miles to the road paralleling the
bay. Go north for 1.3 miles to the course
entrance. Look for a sign marking your
turn to the private entrance.

Course Yardage & Par:
C-2120 yards, par 33.
M-1785 yards, par 30/32.
W-1605 yards, par 30.

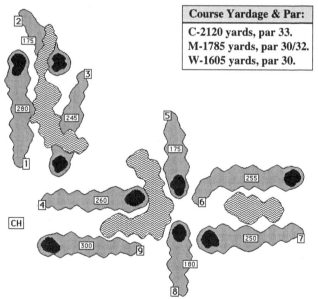

Blue Boy West (public)

27927 Florence Acres Road; Monroe, WA 98272; (360) 793-2378
Managers: Ernie & Doug Smith. **Superintendents:** Ernie & Doug Smith.
Rating/Slope: course is not rated. **9 hole executive course. Course record:** 29.
Green fees: W/D $14/$8; W/E $17/$10; Jr. & Sr. rates (Monday thru Friday).
Power cart: $8. **Pull cart:** $3/$2. **Trail fee:** personal carts not allowed.
Reservation policy: yes, please call 14 days in advance for tee times.
Winter condition: open all year, damp. **Terrain:** flat, with some rolling hills.
Tees: grass. **Temporary greens:** not in use. **Services:** lessons (@ Iron Eagle
Sports Center), snack bar, pro shop, full service clubhouse to serve all your needs.
Comments: beautiful scenery, many views of the mountains and flowers. This
short golf course is very challenging. Water comes into play on five holes. If you
are looking for a course to take the whole family to, try Blue Boy West.

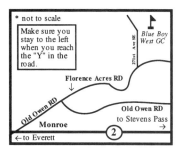

Directions: from Hwy 2 in Monroe, turn
up Old Owens Road. When you come to
a "Y" in the road veer to your left. This
will be Florence Acres Road. Proceed for
approximately 4 miles to the golf course.
The golf course will be located on the left
hand side of the road. Look for signs that
are posted indicating your turns.

Course Yardage & Par:
M-2300 yards, par 33.
W-2300 yards, par 33.

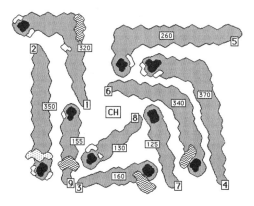

Bowyer's Par 3 Golf, Inc. (public)

11608 NE 119th; Vancouver, WA 98662; (360) 892-3808
Owner: Elwin Bowyer. 9 hole par 3 golf course.
Rating/Slope: the golf course is not rated. **Course record:** 21.
Green fees: $6.50; Sr. rates (weekdays $5.50); no credit cards.
Power cart: not available. **Pull cart:** $1.50. **Trail fee:** not allowed.
Reservation policy: none. **Winter condition:** damp. **Terrain:** flat. **Tees:** mats.
Temporary greens: no. **Services:** club rentals, snack bar, club memberships,
small, limited pro shop. **Comments:** this short par 3 course is well maintained
with many fir trees towering above the fairways. Greens are of medium size and
can challenge you at every turn. If you are looking for a course to challenge your
short iron play, try Bowyer's Par 3 Golf.

Directions: From I-205 N&S exit at NE
119th and travel eastbound on 119th to the
golf course which will be located on your
left hand side. Look for signs indicating
your turn to the golf course.

Course Yardage & Par:
M-1015 yards, par 27.
W-1015 yards, par 27.

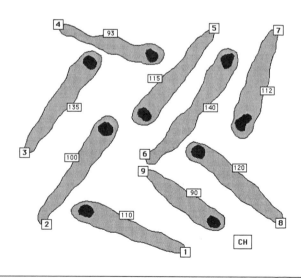

Brae Burn Golf & Country Club (private)

2409 182nd Avenue NE; Redmond, WA 98052; no phone listed
Pro: none. **Superintendent:** Todd Tibke. **9 hole executive course.**
Rating/Slope: the golf course is not rated. **Course record:** 25.
Green fees: private, club members & guests only.
Power cart: none. **Pull cart:** none. **Trail fee:** not allowed.
Reservation policy: none. **Winter condition:** damp.
Terrain: flat, some hills. **Tees:** grass. **Temporary greens:** no.
Services: very limited services, pool for property owners only.
Comments: a scenic executive golf course which is situated in a very attractive housing development . One creek and a few sand traps come into play throughout this short yet challenging track. Excellent greens during the peak golfing season.

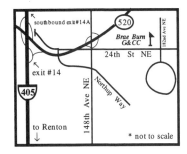

Directions: from I-405 N&S take exit #14 (northbound) 14A (southbound) to Hwy 520E. Take the 148th Avenue NE exit and turn left on NE 24th St. (It is the first light). Proceed on 24th St. to 182nd. Clubhouse is on your immediate left. There is a sign at the entrance to the golf course.

Course Yardage & Par:
M-1283 yards, par 28.
W-1216 yards, par 29.

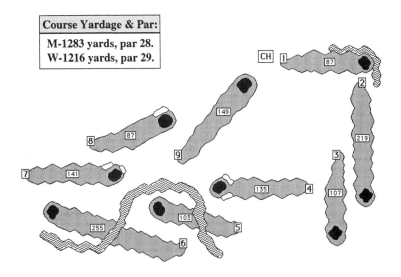

Broadmoor Golf Club (private)

2340 Broadmoor Drive E; Seattle, WA 98112; (206) 325-8444
Pro: Bill Tindall, PGA. Superintendent: Jerry Hilperts. 18 hole course.
Rating/Slope: M 70.5/123; W 74.7/131. **Course Record:** 61.
Green fees: private club members & guests only; reciprocates, very limited.
Power cart: private club. **Pull cart:** complimentary. **Trail fee:** not allowed.
Reservations policy: private club, members only. **Winter condition:** open, dry.
Terrain: flat, some hills. **Tees:** grass. **Temporary greens:** not in use.
Services: lessons, snack bar, lounge, restaurant, beer, wine, liquor, pro shop,
lockers, showers, driving range. **Comments:** Course built in 1926. One of the
finest private courses in the state, set among tree lined fairways and stately homes.
Greens are very fast, well bunkered, small and hard to hold. Great golf course.

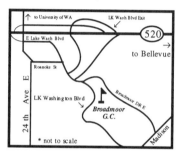

Directions: from I-5 N&S take exit #168B
to Hwy 520E. Exit at Montlake Blvd.
Travel east through the light to E Lake
Washington Blvd. Travel east for .5 miles
to Foster Island Road. Go left on Foster
Island Road to the course entrance which
will be on your right. Note: course located
near arboretum. If coming from Hwy 520
westbound take Montlake Blvd exit and
follow the above directions.

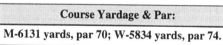

Course Yardage & Par:
M-6131 yards, par 70; W-5834 yards, par 74.

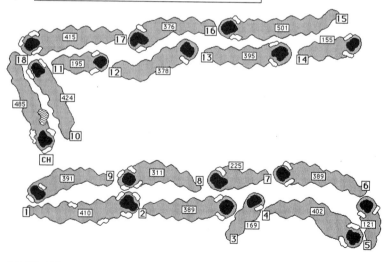

Brookdale Golf Course (public)

1802 Brookdale Road E; Tacoma, WA 98445; 1-800-281-2428; (206) 537-4400
Pro: Tom Parkhurst, PGA. Superintendent: Jeff Gallagher. 18 hole course.
Rating/Slope: C 69.6/112; M 68.4/110; W 72.2/116. **Course record:** 60.
Green fees: $20/$14 every day; Jr. and Sr. rates (M thru F only); M/C, VISA.
Power cart: $19/$12. **Pull cart:** $3. **Trail fee:** $5 for personal carts.
Reservation policy: yes, call up to 1 week in advance for tee times.
Winter condition: open, dry. **Terrain:** flat, some slight hills. **Tees:** grass.
Temporary greens: yes. **Services:** club rentals, lessons, restaurant, beer, wine,
pro shop, lockers, showers. **Comments:** the golf course's excellent drainage
system provides dry play during winter. Good greens and excellent fairways make
this course a local favorite. Outside tournaments are welcome so be sure to call.

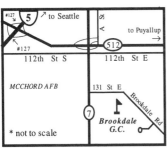

Directions: from I-5 N&S take exit #127
to Hwy 512E. Travel eastbound on Hwy
512 to Hwy 7. Exit at Hwy 7. Proceed
southbound on Hwy 7 for 1.3 miles to
131st Street. Go eastbound on 131st
Street for 1.3 miles to the golf course.
Note: 131st Street will be become
Brookdale Road. Look for signs marking
your way to the course.

Course Yardage & Par:
C-6425 yards, par 71.
M-6201 yards, par 71.
W-5847 yards, par 74.

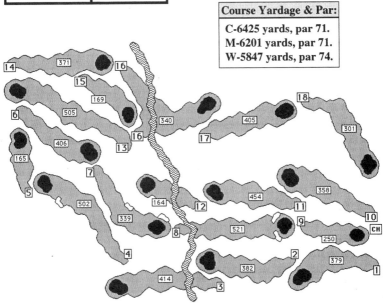

Buckhorn Par 3 & Driving Range (public)
W 13404 Hwy 2; Airway Heights, WA 99010; no number listed.
Pro: N/A. **PGA. Superintendent:** N/A. **9 hole par 3 course.**
Rating/Slope: the golf course is not rated. **Course record:** 23.
Green fees: $7 all week long; no credit cards.
Power cart: N/A. **Pull cart:** $1.50. **Trail fee:** personal carts not allowed.
Reservation policy: advance tee times are not required. First come first served.
Winter condition: closed. **Terrain:** flat, easy to walk. **Tees:** grass & mats.
Temporary greens: no. **Services:** club rentals, miniature golf, lighted driving range. (closed during the winter months), vending machines, small pro shop.
Comments: very short par 3 course that is great for family entertainment. Good driving range to practice your shot making and short iron play on.

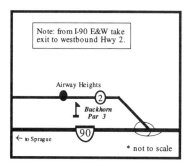

Directions: the golf course is located off Hwy 2 West. If traveling toward the Fairchild AFB the course will be on your left in the town of Airway Heights. Look for the yellow golf sign indicating your turn to the golf course.

Course Yardage & Par:
M-907 yards, par 27.
W-907 yards, par 27.

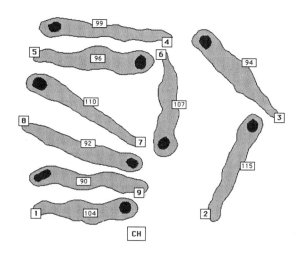

Camaloch Golf Club (public)

326 NE Camano DR; Camano Is., WA 98292; (360) 387-3084, 800-628-0469
PGA Director of Golf: Gary Schopf. Supt.: Felix Revira. 18 hole course.
Rating/Slope: C 70.0/125; M 68.7/122; W 70.9/122. **Course record:** 65.
Green fees: W/D $16/$12; W/E & holidays $23/$15; Jr. & Sr. rates (M-F).
Power cart: $20/$12. **Pull cart:** $3. **Trail fee:** $10 for personal carts.
Reservation policy: reservations recommended, walk-ons are welcome.
Winter condition: dry, excellent drainage. **Terrain:** only 2 hills, very walkable.
Tees: grass. **Temporary greens:** no. **Services:** club rentals, lessons, snack bar,
deli, pro shop, driving range. **Comments:** This well maintained golf course lies in
the banana belt of Washington State. The area receives less rainfall than many
places in western Washington. If you want a dry course in winter, try Camaloch.

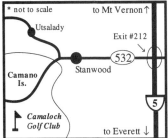

Directions: from I-5 N&S take exit #212
(Stanwood Hwy 532). Go west on Hwy
532 through Stanwood. Continue to the
golf course which will be on your left
hand side of the road. (The golf course
is located about 12 miles from I-5). The
course is very easy to find.

Course Yardage & Par:

C-6125 yards, par 71.
M-5807 yards, par 71.
W-5239 yards, par 71.

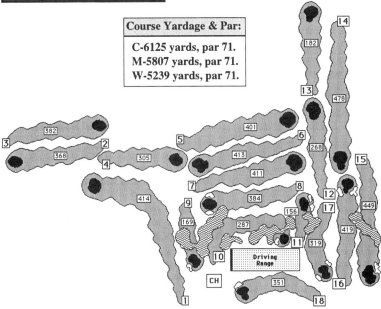

Canterwood Golf & Country Club (private)

4026 Canterwood Drive NW; Gig Harbor, WA 98335; (206) 851-1745
Pro: Doug Gullikson, PGA. Supt.: Mark Cupit. 18 hole course. Record: 64.
Rating/Slope: T 75.8/141; C 73.8/137; M 72.0/131; W 73.3/130.
Green fees: private club, members & guests only, reciprocates; VISA, MC.
Power cart: private club. **Pull cart:** private club. **Trail fee:** monthly basis.
Reservation policy: yes, up to 1 week in advance. **Winter condition:** dry.
Terrain: relatively hilly. **Tees:** grass. **Temporary greens:** no.
Services: lessons, snack bar, restaurant, lounge, beer, wine, liquor, pro shop,
lockers, showers, driving range. **Comments:** very scenic, difficult course with
undulating greens, bunkers and water hazards. Designed by Robert Muir Graves.

Directions: from I-5 N&S take exit #132
for Hwy 16W (Gig Harbor-Bremerton)
Proceed to the Purdy exit and to 144th NW.
Travel east for 1 mile to 54th. Turn south
to the entrance to the Golf & Country Club.
Note: look for signs to Canterwood G&CC
indicating your turn.

Course Yardage & Par:
T-7175 yards, par 72.
C-6705 yards, par 72.
M-6245 yards, par 72.
W-5538 yards, par 73.

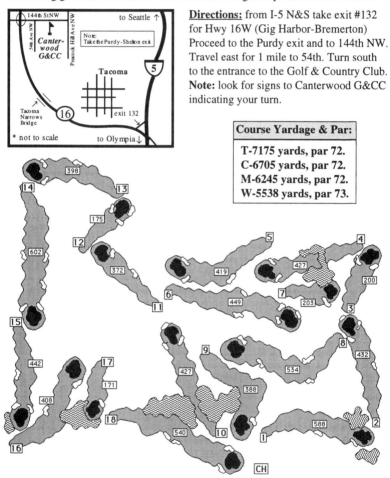

Canyon Lakes Golf Course (public)

3700 West Canyon Lakes Drive; Kennewick, WA 99337; (509) 582-3736
Pros: Brad Graff, Terry Graff, PGA. **18 hole course. Course record:** 63.
Rating/Slope: T 73.4/127; C 71.2/124; M 69.2/120; W 72.0/124.
Green fees: W/D $20; W/E $20 **Power cart:** $24/$12. **Pull cart:** $2.
Trail fee: $8. **Reservation policy:** 1 week, in advance. **Winter condition:** dry.
Terrain: relatively hilly. **Tees:** grass. **Temporary greens:** no. **Services:** club
rentals, lessons, snack bar, restaurant, beer, wine, pro shop, driving range.
Comments: a links style course, Canyon Lakes is set in the desert area of Eastern
Washington. A difficult course where water comes into play on many of the holes.
One of the top ten public courses in the Pacific Northwest. If you get a chance to
play Canyon Lakes you will not be disapointed. Excellent track.

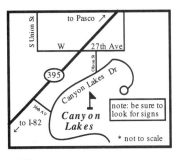

Directions: from Hwy 395S exit south
to W 27th. Proceed to Canyon Lakes
RD. From this point follow signs to the
golf course the way is well marked.

Course Yardage & Par:
T-6973 yards, par 72.
C-6505 yards, par 72.
M-6067 yards, par 72.
W-5565 yards, par 72.

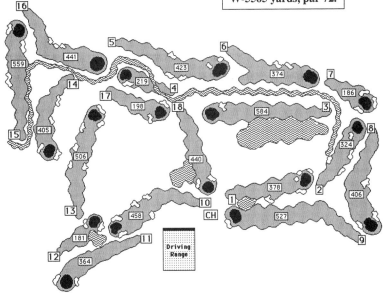

Capitol City Golf Club (public)

5225 Yelm Highway SE; Lacey, WA 98513; (360) 491-5111
Pro: Tim Walsh. Superintendent: Mark Wigren. 18 hole course.
Rating/Slope: C 70.6/121; M 69.2/118; W 71.2/116. **Course record:** 62.
Green fees: W/D $15; W/E $25; Jr. & Sr., military rates (M-F). VISA, MC.
Power cart: $20/$15. **Pull cart:** $3. **Trail fee:** $8. **Reservation policy:** yes,
up to 1 week in advance. **Winter condition:** dry. **Terrain:** flat. **Tees:** grass.
Temporary greens: no. **Services:** club rentals, lessons, lounge, beer, wine, pro
shop, lockers, showers, driving range. **Comments:** "One of the state's finest and
driest courses year round," beautiful view's of Mt. Rainier. Greens are kept in
excellent condition throughout the season. Fantastic facility that is worth the trip.

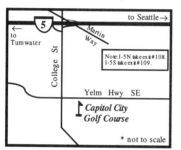

Directions: from I-5N exit #108 College
St. Proceed to College St. and take a right.
Follow College St. for 3 miles to the Yelm
Hwy. Take a left and follow for .4 miles
to the course which will be on your right.
From I-5S take exit #109. Take left on
College St. and follow the same directions.

Course Yardage & Par:
C-6536 yards, par 72.
M-6224 yards, par 72.
W-5510 yards, par 72.

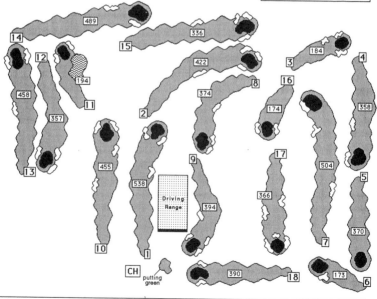

Carnation Golf Course (public)

1810 W Snoqualmie River Road NE; Carnation, WA 98014
(206) 333-4151 or 583-0314. 18 hole course, range. Course record: 64.
Director of Golf: Dan Tachell, PGA. Pro: Chad Tachell, PGA.
Manager/Tournament Director: Stephanie Jackson.
Rating/Slope: C 67.6/113; M 65.1/104; W 65.0/103.
Green fees: M-Thur. $22/$14; Fri.-Sun. $25; Jr/Sr rates, M-Thursday; VISA, MC.
Power cart: $20/$12. **Pull cart:** $2. **Trail fee.** $5. **Reservation policy:** yes, no
time limit. **Winter condition:** open, damp. **Terrain:** flat. **Tees:** all grass.
Services: club rentals, lessons, driving range, restaurant, beer, wine, pro shop,
catering, memberships. **Comments:** the course is flat, easy to walk and in good
condition. It sits in a peaceful setting along the Snoqualmie River. Very friendly.

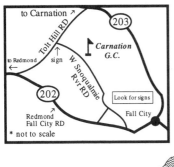

Directions: from I-5 N&S exit to 168B
(Hwy 520E). Proceed eastbound on Hwy
520 to Hwy 202 in Redmond (Redmond-
Fall City RD). Go east on Hwy 202 for 8
miles to Tolt Hill RD. Turn left on Tolt Hill
RD. Proceed for 2.5 miles. Take a right on
W Snoqualmie River Road NE. The golf
course will be located on your left.

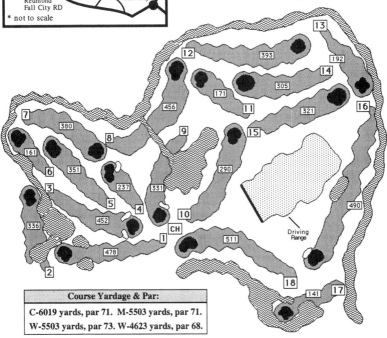

Course Yardage & Par:
C-6019 yards, par 71. M-5503 yards, par 71.
W-5503 yards, par 73. W-4623 yards, par 68.

Cascade Golf Course (public)

14303 436th Avenue SE; North Bend, WA 98045; (206) 888-0227
Managers: Fred & Carol Lawrence, Leroy & Joyce Jorgenson.
9 hole course, dual tees for 18 hole play.
Rating/Slope: M 62.8/93; W 66.4/107. **Course record:** M 69; W 84.
Green fees: W/D $18/$12; W/E $20/$14; Jr/Sr rates W/D's; no credit cards.
Power cart: $18/$10. **Pull cart:** $3/$2. **Trail fee:** $4/$2.
Reservation policy: yes, no time limit from March 1st to October 31. Walk-ons
rest of the year. **Winter condition:** dry course, drains very well. **Terrain:** flat.
Tees: grass. **Temporary greens:** no. **Services:** club rentals, restaurant, beer,
pro shop. **Comments:** Excellent drainage provides dry fairways and greens for
winter play. A family run course where you can usually walk on during the week.
Home of the "Tony Burger." Great course to take the family to. Very friendly.

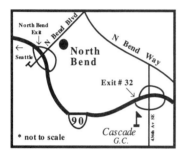

Directions: from I-90 E&W take exit
#32 to 436th SE. Proceed for .1 mile to
the course which will be on your right.
The golf course is located 2 miles east
of the city of the North Bend.

Course Yardage & Par:
Red Tees-2331 yards, par 36.
White Tees-2581 yards, par 36.
Blue Tees-2696 yards, par 36.
<u>Dual tees for 18 holes:</u>
Red Tees-4662 yards, par 72.
White Tees-5162 yards, par 72.
Blue Tees-5392 yards, par 72.

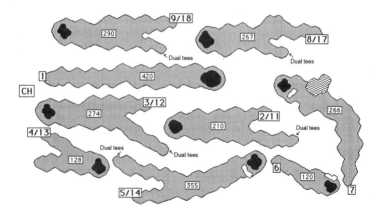

Cedarcrest Municipal Golf Course (public)

6810 84th Street NE; Marysville, WA 98270; (360) 659-3566
Pro: Don Shaw, PGA. Superintendent: Michael Robinson. 18 hole course.
Rating/Slope: M 65.4/110; W 67.8/110. Course record: 60.
Green fees: $14/$11 all week long; no credit cards.
Power cart: $20. Pull cart: $3. Trail fee: $3 for personal carts.
Reservation policy: yes, up to 1 week in advance. Winter condition: damp.
Terrain: flat, some hills. Tees: grass. Temporary greens: not in use.
Services: club rentals, lessons, restaurant, beer, wine, liquor, lockers, showers, pro shop, weekends 4-somes only. Comments: well conditioned course that can offer a wide variety of fairway lies and approach shots to greens. If you are looking for a good course at very affordable price try Cedarcrest. The golf course could be remodled during the the 1996-97 golfing season so be sure to call first.

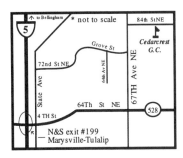

Directions: from I-5 N&S take exit #199 (Marysville-Tulalip) to Hwy 528E (4th St.). Continue on 4th St which becomes 64th St. NE. Proceed to 67th Avenue NE. Turn left on 67th Ave. Travel north on 67th until you reach 84th St NE. Turn right on 84th. The golf course will be on your right.

Course Yardage & Par:
M-5390 yards, par 70.
W-5086 yards, par 72.

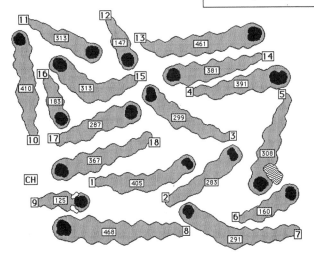

Cedars Golf Club, The (public)

15001 NE 181 Street; Brush Prairie, WA 98606; (360) 687-4233
Pro: Ron Blum, PGA. Supt.: Steve Brown. 18 hole course, driving range.
Rating/Slope: C 71.3/127; M 69.9/125; W 71.7/117. **Course record:** 68.
Green fees: W/D $16/$9; W/E $18/$10; no credit cards.
Power cart: $20/$11. **Pull cart:** $2/$1.50. **Trail fee:** not allowed.
Reservation policy: yes, call up to 1 week in advance. **Winter condition:** wet.
Terrain: flat, some slight hills. **Tees:** grass. **Temporary greens:** no.
Services: club rentals, lessons, restaurant, bar, lockers, showers, pro shop,
driving range, putting & chipping greens. **Comments:** picturesque setting, cedar
trees, lakes and trout stream surround challenging golf. Greens are well bunkered
and can putt very tough at times. Good golf course that can get very busy during
the summer months.

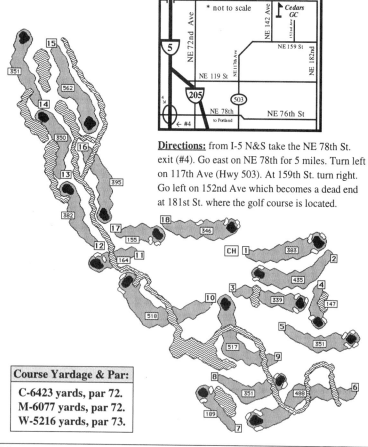

Directions: from I-5 N&S take the NE 78th St.
exit (#4). Go east on NE 78th for 5 miles. Turn left
on 117th Ave (Hwy 503). At 159th St. turn right.
Go left on 152nd Ave which becomes a dead end
at 181st St. where the golf course is located.

Course Yardage & Par:
C-6423 yards, par 72.
M-6077 yards, par 72.
W-5216 yards, par 73.

Centralia Public Golf Course (public)

1012 Duffy; Centralia, WA 98531; (360) 736-5967
Owners: Michael & Renee Ray. **9 hole course, dual tees for 18 holes.**
Rating/Slope: M 67.3/121; W 70.8/125. **Course record:** 32 (9 holes).
Green fees: W/D $9/$6; W/E $12/$8; Jr. rates; no credit cards.
Power cart: $14/$8. **Pull cart:** $2. **Trail fee:** $4.
Reservation policy: please call ahead, no time limit. **Winter condition:** dry.
Terrain: relatively hilly, walkable. **Tees:** grass. **Temporary greens:** no.
Services: club rentals, beer, wine, restaurant, snack bar, limited pro shop.
Comments: tight fairways puts an emphasis on your shot placement. The golf
course offers a dual tee layout for 18 hole play. Creeks come into play on several
holes. Course is much improved with a new pond on the 8th hole.

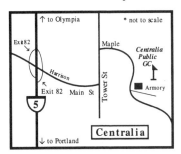

Directions: from I-5 N&S take the
Centralia/Harrison Ave/Mellen Street.
(exit #82) Follow the city center signs.
Proceed to Tower Street and turn left
(east). When you reach E Maple Street
turn right. Go up the hill on Seminary
Road, thru the intersection at the Armory,
and down the hill to the golf course. Look
for signs that are posted along the way.

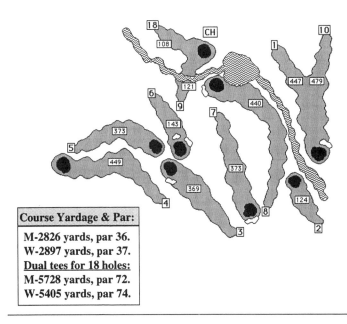

Course Yardage & Par:

M-2826 yards, par 36.
W-2897 yards, par 37.
<u>Dual tees for 18 holes:</u>
M-5728 yards, par 72.
W-5405 yards, par 74.

Chevy Chase Golf Club (public)

7401 Cape George Road; Port Townsend, WA 98368
(360) 385-0704; In Washington: 1-800-385-8722
Manager/Pro: Garth Richards, PGA. 9 hole course, dual tees for 18 holes.
Rating/Slope: M 69.4/115; W 70.7/119. **Course record:** 65.
Green fees: W/D $17/$12; W/E $19/$13; Sr. rates; VISA, M/C.
Power cart: $20/$14. **Pull cart:** $3/$2. **Trail fee:** $10.
Reservation policy: yes, you may call in advance for a tee time.
Winter condition: dry. **Terrain:** flat, some hills. **Tees:** grass. **Temporary greens:** no. **Services:** club rentals, lessons, snack bar, beer, banquet room, pro shop, lockers, waterfront rental cabins, driving range. **Comments:** course provides a beautiful, peaceful setting for golf on the Olympic Peninsula. Good course that drains well during the winter months. With the historic town of Port Townsend only seven miles away play golf in the morning and window shop in the afternoon. The golf course is planning to expand into a 18 hole track in the near future.

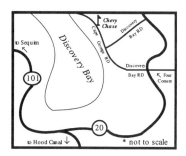

Directions: from any of the Seattle ferries proceed to the Hood Canal Bridge and Hwy 104. Follow Hwy 104 to Hwy 101. Exit to Discovery Bay/ Port Townsend (Hwy 20). Follow Hwy 20 around Discovery Bay to Cape George Road and to the golf course.

Course Yardage & Par:
M-3045 yards, par 36.
W-2675 yards, par 36.
<u>Dual tees for 18 holes:</u>
M-5985 yards, par 72.
W-5281 yards, par 72.

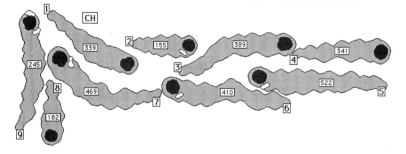

Chewelah Golf & Country Club (semi-private)
Box 407; Sand Canyon Road; Chewelah, WA 99109; (509) 935-6807
Pro: Kim Walker, PGA. 18 hole course, driving range.
Rating/Slope: C 70.9/125; M 69.9/123; W 72.7/120. **Course record:** 65.
Green fees: W/D $13.50/$9; W/E $15/$10; Jr & Sr rates; no credit cards.
Power cart: $20/$10. **Pull cart:** $2. **Trail fee:** $3. **Reservation policy:** call
up to 7 days in advance for a tee times. **Winter condition:** course is closed from
mid November to March. **Terrain:** flat. **Tees:** grass. **Temporary greens:** no.
Services: club rentals, lessons, snack bar, pro shop, beverage cart, driving range.
Comments: narrow fairways, numerous sand traps trees, and three ponds make
this course play difficult. Well run golf course. RV parking available on-site.

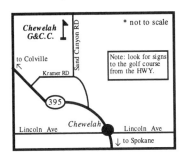

Directions: from Spokane travel on
Hwy 395N for approximately 45 miles
to Chewelah Washington. When in
Chewelah look for and follow signs to
the golf course.

Course Yardage & Par:
C-6511 yards, par 72.
M-6161 yards, par 72.
W-5672 yards, par 74.

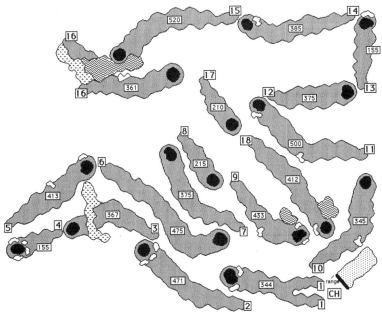

Christy's Golf Range & Par 3 (public)

37712 28th Avenue S; Federal Way, WA 98003; (206) 927-0644.
Pro: George Christy. 9 hole par 3 course, covered driving range.
Rating/Slope: the golf course is not rated. **Course record:** 24.
Green fees: W/D $11/$6*; W/E $11/$6*; Sr rates. (*prices may change)
Power cart: not available. **Pull cart:** $1*. **Trail fee:** personal carts not allowed.
Reservation policy: tee times are on a first come first served basis.
Terrain: flat, some hills. **Tees:** grass and mats. **Temporary greens:** not in use.
Services: club rentals, lessons, full service pro shop, excellent driving range.
Comments: challenging par 3 golf course that is great for the whole family.
Great course to practice your short irons on. Excellent on course pro shop that
will service all your golfing needs. The facility also includes a lighted and
covered driving range that is open seven days a week.

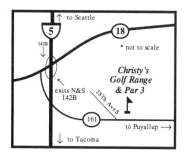

Directions: from I-5 N&S take exit 142B.
Proceed westbound for .2 miles to Hwy
161S. Turn south for 1.6 miles to 28th
Avenue S. Turn left on 28th Avenue S to
the golf course. Look for a sign.

Course Yardage & Par:
M-905 yards, par 27.
W-905 yards, par 27.

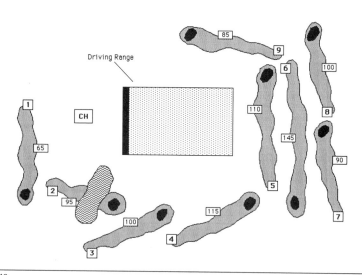

Clarkston Golf & Country Club (private)

1676 Elm Street; Clarkston, WA 99403; (509) 758-7911
Pro: Vicki Mallea, PGA. 18 hole course, driving range.
Rating/Slope: C 72.3/122; M 71.5/121; W 74.4/128. **Course record:** 63.
Green fees: private club, members & guests only; reciprocates; VISA, M/C.
Power cart: private club, members only. **Pull cart:** private. **Trail fee:** private.
Reservation policy: yes, up to 1 week in advance. **Winter condition:** dry.
Terrain: flat, some hills. **Tees:** grass. **Temporary greens:** occasionally.
Services: club rentals, lessons, restaurant, lounge, beer, wine, liquor, lockers,
showers, driving range. **Comments:** beautiful setting along the Snake River with
the Palouse Mountains nearby. Water, trees and well bunkered greens abound.
This well kept private facility will test your skill at every turn.

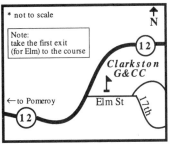

Directions: travel to Clarkston via
Hwy 12. The golf course is located
north of Clarkston near Hwy 12 which
parallels the golf course. Take the first
exit (for Elm Street) to the golf course.

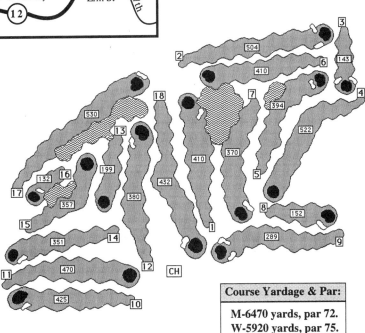

Course Yardage & Par:
M-6470 yards, par 72.
W-5920 yards, par 75.

Classic Country Club (public, 18 hole course, driving range)

4908 208th Street E; Spanaway, WA 98387; (206) 847-4440; (206) 622-4653
Manager/Head Pro: Lorie Isaac. Supterindent: Pete Echols.
Rating/Slope: C 73.6/133; M 71.6/130; W 73.3/128. **Course record:** 67.
Green fees: May 1st to Sep. 30th W/D $30/$15, W/E & Holidays $45/$25;
October to April 30th W/D $20; W/E & Holidays $30; twilight $15,
Jr.& Sr. rates (Monday through Wednesday), AMEX, MC, VISA.
Power cart: $23/$15. **Pull cart:** $5. **Trail fee:** $23/$15 for personal carts.
Reservation policy: yes, please call 7 days in advance for tee times.
Winter condition: open, dry. **Terrain:** flat, some hills. **Tees:** all grass.
Services: club rentals, lessons, snack bar, restaurant, lounge, beer, wine, liquor,
pop, pro shop, lockers, showers, driving range, putting green & chipping greens.
Comments: *Golf Digest* magazine just rated the Classic Country Club #7 in the
state of Washington on their list of America's best 500 places to play golf in 1996.

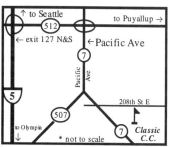

Directions: from I-5 N&S take exit #127
to Hwy 512. Follow Hwy 512 to Hwy 7.
Exit to Hwy 7 southbound. Follow Hwy 7
southbound until you reach 208th St E go
left. The course will be located 2 miles
ahead on the right hand side.

Course Yardage & Par:
C-6793 yards, par 72.
M-6387 yards, par 72.
M-6008 yards, par 72.
W-5580 yards, par 72.

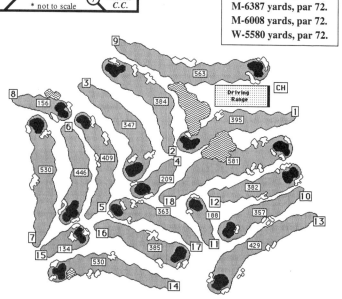

Clover Valley Golf Course (public)

5180 Country Club Way SE; Port Orchard, WA 98366; (360) 871-2236
Pro: Patrick J. Nixon, PGA. 18 hole course, driving range.
Rating/Slope: M 64.9/102; W 66.8/106. Course record: 63.
Green fees: W/D $12.50/$9; W/E $16/$11; Jr. and Sr. rates; VISA, MC.
Power Cart: $18/$10. Pull Cart: $3. Trail fee: none.
Reservation policy: yes, you may call in advance for a tee time (no restrictions).
Winter Condition: open, wet. **Terrain:** moderately flat with some hills.
Tees: grass. **Services:** banquet hall, snack bar, beer, pro shop, driving range.
Comments: located near Bremerton in Port Orchard on the Olympic Peninsula.
Water comes into play on several holes throughout the course. Very friendly golf
course that has improved every year. The facility now sports an on course range.
The 9th hole, a 228 yard par 3 is one of the toughest par 3's you will ever find.

Directions: from Hwy 16 take the Port
Orchard-Sedgewick Road (Hwy 160) exit.
Proceed 3 miles on Sedgewick Road until
you reach Long Lake Road then turn right.
While on Long Lake Road take your first
right onto Country Club Way to the golf
course. **Note:** look for signs from Hwy 16
indicating the exit to the golf course.

Course Yardage & Par:

M-5341 yards, par 69.
W-4824 yards, par 70.

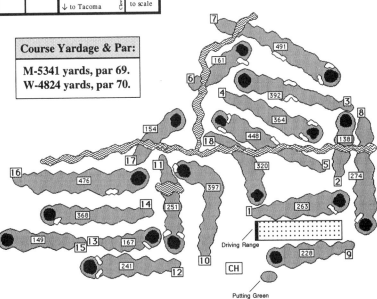

Cloverdale Golf Club (public)
26718 115th NE; Arlington, WA 98223; (360) 435-2539
Manager: Rick Witscher. 9 hole course.
Rating/Slope: the golf course has not been rated yet.
Green fees: W/D $10* for 9 holes; W/E $20* (subject to change) .
Power cart: $15/$7.50*. **Pull cart:** $2*. **Trail fee:** to be determined.
Reservation policy: policy for advance tee times to be determined.
Winter condition: the golf course is open weather permitting, wet to damp.
Terrain: flat, some moderate hills. **Tees:** grass. **Temporary greens:** not in use.
Services: upon completion the course will offer the golfer a full service club-
house, snack bar and pro shop. **Comments:** the course is set on 200 acres in the
beautiful Stillaguamish River Valley. A family owned course that plans to open
the second 9 for play sometime in late 1996 with the grand opening in 1997.

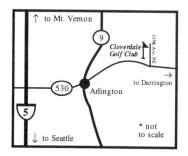

Directions: from I-5 N&S take exit #208
(Hwy 530). Proceed on Hwy 530 eastbound (toward Arlington). Proceed into
and out of the town of Arlington toward
Darrington still on Hwy 530. Travel until
you reach 115th Ave NE where you will
turn left. Proceed for .3 miles to the golf
course. (Look for a black & white sign
marking your turn). The golf course is
located 7.6 miles east of your I-5 exit.

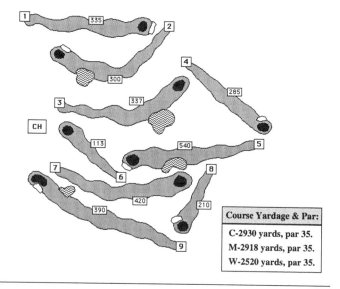

Course Yardage & Par:
C-2930 yards, par 35.
M-2918 yards, par 35.
W-2520 yards, par 35.

Club Green Meadows (private)

7703 NE 72nd Ave; Vancouver, WA 98661; (360) 256-1510 or (503) 230-1461
Pro: Russ Thurick. 18 hole course, practice range.
Rating/Slope: C 70.9/119; M 70.0/117; W 73.4/125. **Course record:** 65.
Green fees: private club, members & guests only; reciprocates.
Power cart: private club. **Pull cart:** private club. **Trail fee:** private club.
Reservation policy: members only. **Winter condition:** open, damp.
Terrain: flat. **Tees:** grass. **Temporary greens:** yes. **Services:** lessons,
snack bar, lounge, restaurant, beer, wine, liquor, pro shop, practice range.
Comments: course has narrow tree lined fairways with ponds and greenside
bunkers coming into play on nearly every hole. Athletic club is on site.

Directions: from I-5 N&S take exit #4 to
NE 78th. Go east on NE 78th to NE 72nd
Ave. Go south on NE 72nd Ave.While on
NE 72nd Ave. turn east to the golf course.
From I-205 N&S take exit #32. Go west
on NE 83rd. Take a left on Andersen RD.
When you reach NE 78th St. turn left.
Proceed to 72nd Avenue NE turn right.

Course Yardage & Par:
C-6486 yards, par 72.
M-6246 yards, par 72.
W-5831 yards, par 76.

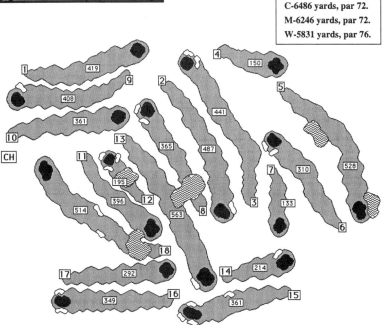

Colfax Golf Club (public)

off Cedar Street; Route 1, Box 46-A; Colfax, WA 99111; (509) 397-2122
Manager: Ron Olson. 9 hole course, dual tees for 18 holes.
Rating/Slope: M 67.9/117; W 70.9/115. **Course record:** M/63; W/73.
Green fees: $15/$10 all week long; no special rates; no credit cards.
Power cart: not available. **Pull cart:** $1.50. **Trail fee:** no charge.
Reservation policy: yes, for weekend play only. Call 1 week in advance.
Winter condition: the golf course is open all year long, dry conditions.
Terrain: flat (easy walking). **Tees:** all grass. **Temporary greens:** not in use.
Services: club rentals, lessons, pro shop, driving range net, putting green.
Comments: easily walked golf course. The atmosphere is friendly and casual.
Dual tees available for a full 18 hole round. The Palouse River borders the course.
Be straight off the tee as out of bounds borders nearly every hole on this course.

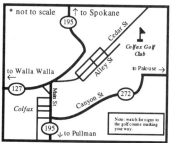

Directions: from Hwy 195 take the Cedar
Street exit and travel east bound to the golf
course. The golf course is located slightly
north of the city of Colfax, Washington.
Note: look for signs from the Highway
indicating your turn to the golf course.

Course Yardage & Par:

M-3010 yards, par 35.
W-2817 yards, par 36.
Dual tees for 18 holes:
M-5907 yards, par 70.
W-5556 yards, par 72.

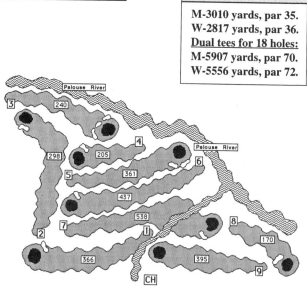

Columbia Park Golf Course (public)
Physical address: 2701 W. Columbia Drive; Kennewick, WA 99336
Mailing address: 505 S. Authur PL; Kennewick, WA 99336;(509) 585-4423
Pro: Dale Schoner, PGA. 18 hole executive course.
Rating/Slope: M 51.1/079; W 51.1/079. **Course record:** 47.
Green fees: W/D $8/$5; W/E $9/$5.50 Jr. & Sr. rates.
Power cart: not available. **Pull cart:** $2/$1.50. **Trail fee:** not allowed.
Reservation policy: yes, taken for weekends, 1 day in advance.
Winter condition: open weather permitting, course is dry. **Terrain:** very flat.
Tees: grass and mats. **Temporary greens:** no. **Services:** club rentals, driving
range, limited pro shop, lessons, snack bar, driving range. **Comments:** the course
is near the Columbia River which can be seen from nearly every tee. The golf
course is flat & easy to walk. Great course for seniors or to practice your iron play.

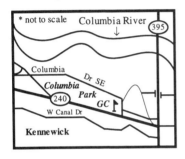

Directions: from Hwy 395 take the
Columbia Park exit. Go to Columbia
Drive and turn left. Proceed for 1 mile
to the course which will be on your left.
If you are coming from I-82 take the
Columbia Park exit and proceed to the
golf course. Look for signs marking your
way to the golf course.

Course Yardage & Par:
M-2682 yards, par 55.
W-2682 yards, par 55.

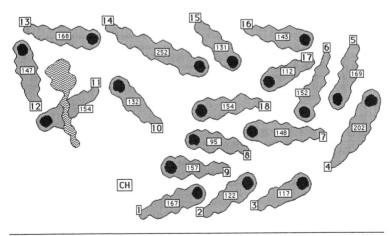

Colville Elks Golf Course (public)
1861 E Hawthorne; PO Box 367; Colville, WA 99114; (509) 684-5508
Pro: N/A. **9 hole course, dual tee for 18 holes.**
Rating/Slope: M 69.3/115; W 73.6/122. **Course record:** 62.
Green fees: $14/$11*; no credit cards. (* subject to change).
Power cart: $19/$11*. **Pull cart:** $2.50*. **Trail fee:** no charge.
Reservation policy: none. **Winter condition:** closed November 1st until thaw.
Terrain: flat, some hills, walkable. **Tees:** grass. **Temporary greens:** no.
Services: club rentals, lessons, snack bar, beer, restaurant, lounge, pro shop,
lockers, showers, driving range. **Comments:** This eastern Washington golf course
is well conditioned and plays much tougher than the yardage would indicate. The
golf course will be expanding to 18 holes in the future. Alternating tees.

Directions: from Spokane travel N on Hwy 395 through Chewelah to Colville. Go east on Hawthorne Avenue. While traveling on Hawthorne Avenue you will go up a hill then you will proceed to the golf course. Look for signs marking your way to the golf course.

Course Yardage & Par:

M-3125 yards, par 36.
W-2865 yards, par 36.
Dual tees for 18 holes:
M-6330 yards, par 72.
W-5990 yards, par 73.

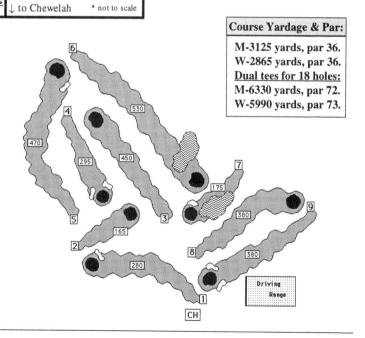

Course at Taylor Creek, The (public)

24206 SE 216th; Maple Valley, WA 98038; (206) 413-1900
Pro: none. General manager: Brad Habenicht. 9 hole course.
Rating/Slope: the golf course has not been rated. **Course record:** N/A.
Green fees: W/D $16.50/$10; W/E $18/$12; Jr. & Sr. rates.
Power cart: $10/$6 per person. **Pull cart:** $3/$2. **Trail fee:** $5.
Reservation policy: call in advance for a tee time. **Temporary greens:** N/A.
Winter condition: open, weather permitting. **Terrain:** rolling hills. **Tees:** grass.
Services: driving range. Other services to be determined. **Comments:** target
opening for this course is early spring of 1996. This new course has done alot of
mounding on many fairways. The golf course surrounds a historical landmark, a
mansion built in 1906 which is available for receptions and other like functions.

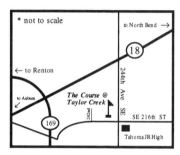

Directions: from Hwy 18 northbound
(toward North Bend) or southbound
(toward Auburn) turn eastbound on
244th Avenue SE. Proceed to the golf
course entrance that will be located on
your right hand side. Look for signs.

Course Yardage & Par:
C-2605 yards, par 35.
M-2410 yards, par 35.
W-2105 yards, par 35.

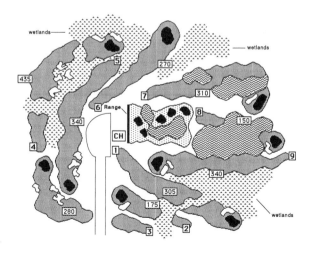

The Creek at Qualchan (public)

301 E Meadow Lane Road; Spokane, WA 99204; (509) 448-9317
Pro: Mark Gardner, PGA. 18 hole course. Course record: 66.
Rating/Slope: T 70.8/120; C 69.6/118; M 68.3/115; W 72.3/126.
Green fees: County resident, $16.50/$13; Others, $22/$16.50; Jr & Sr rates M-F.
Power cart: $22. **Pull cart:** $2. **Trail fee:** $8.75. **Reservation policy:** weekdays
call 1 day in advance, weekends 1 week in advance. **Winter condition:** closed
during winter. **Terrain:** hilly. **Tees:** grass. **Temporary greens:** not in use.
Services: club rentals, lessons, restaurant, beer, wine, pro shop, driving range.
Comments: the facility opened in spring of 1993. The golf course features
bunkers, 5 ponds, and a creek wandering through. Excellent newer golf course.

Directions: From I-90 E&W (#279)exit to
Hwy 195 and proceed southbound. Turn
eastbound on Meadow Lane RD. Follow
this to the golf course

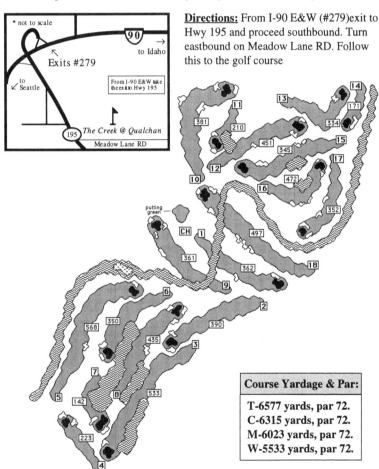

Course Yardage & Par:

T-6577 yards, par 72.
C-6315 yards, par 72.
M-6023 yards, par 72.
W-5533 yards, par 72.

Crescent Bar Resort (public)

8894 Crescent Bar Road NW; Suite 1; Quincy, WA 98848
(509) 787-1511 or call 1-800-824-7090.
Manager: Gil Stewart. 9 hole course, dual tees for 18 holes.
Rating/Slope: C 68.8/108; M 68.4/107; W 72.4/118. **Course record:** 67.
Green fees: $20/$15 all week long; Sr rates (Mondays only); VISA, M/C.
Power cart: $20/$15. **Pull cart:** $4/$3. **Trail fee:** $5; seasonal rates available.
Reservation policy: please call up to 1 week in advance for tee times.
Winter condition: the golf course is open all year long weather permitting.
Terrain: flat, easy walking. **Tees:** all grass. **Temporary greens:** not in use.
Services: club rentals, lessons, restaurant, cafe, lounge, store, pro shop, driving
range, tennis courts, marina, campground. **Comments:** well-designed course with
bunkers, water and rough. Accommodates both low and high handicappers. Good
eastern Washington golf course set on an island in the Columbia River.

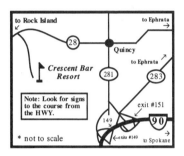

Directions: from I-90 E&W take exit
#149 to Hwy 281 to Quincy. When you
reach Hwy 28 turn left and go west on
Hwy 28. Proceed on Hwy 28 for 7.1
miles to Crescent Bar RD and turn left.
Note: look for the sign on the highway
marking your turn to the course.

Course Yardage & Par:
C-3034 yards, par 35.
M-2944 yards, par 35.
W-2844 yards, par 36.
Dual tees for 18 holes:
C-6068 yards, par 70.
M-5978 yards, par 70.
W-5788 yards, par 72.

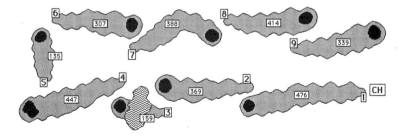

Crossroads Park Golf Course (public)
16000 NE 10th; Bellevue, WA 98008; (206) 453-4875.
Pro: none. Manager: not available. 9 hole par 3 course.
Rating/Slope: the golf course is not rated. **Course record:** 21.
Green fees: $5 all week long; Jr & Sr rates (weekdays only).
Power cart: not available. **Pull cart:** not available. **Trail fee:** not available.
Reservation policy: none needed, all times are on a first come first served basis.
Winter condition: the golf course is closed December 1st through February 1st.
Terrain: flat, some slight hills. **Tees:** all mats. **Temporary greens:** none.
Services: club rentals, lessons, snack machines, pop, putting green.
Comments: excellent course to take a young family member to learn the game of
golf. the atmoshpere is very casual with no pressure on having to play fast. Holes
range from 64 to 107 yards.

Directions: from I-405 N&S take the NE
8th exit eastbound. Follow NE 8th to 160th
Avenue NE and turn left. The pro shop is
located inside of the Community Center at
the end of 160th Avenue NE, just east of
the Crossroads Mall. Look for signs
indicating your turn to the golf course.

Course Yardage & Par:
M-837 yards, par 27.
W-837 yards, par 27.

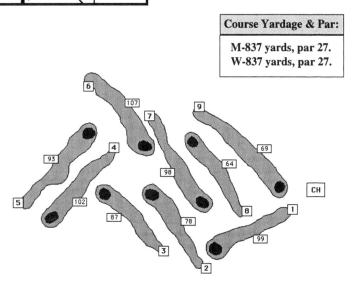

Dakota Creek Golf & Country Club (public)
3258 Haynie Road; Custer, WA 98240; (360) 366-3131
Owner: Pam Magee. 9 hole course, dual tees for 18 holes.
Rating/Slope: M 64./117; W 67.5/120. **Course record:** 31.
Green fees: W/D $11/$7; W/E $15/$9; M/C, VISA.
Power cart: $16/$8. **Pull cart:** $1.50. **Trail fee:** no charge.
Reservation policy: none. **Winter condition:** open, dry. **Terrain:** some hills.
Tees: grass. **Temporary greens:** seldom. **Services:** snack bar, pro shop,
chipping green. **Comments:** tough, challenging and fun, all holes different.
Most challenging nine holes under 5500 yards in the state. Excellent, well kept
golf course that is worth the trip, you will not be disappointed. Course now being
upgraded with new holes being phased in over a period of the next few years.

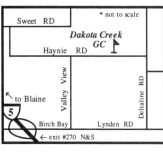

Directions: from I-5 N&S exit #270
to Birch Bay-Lynden RD turn right go
for 100' and turn left on Valley View.
Follow Valley View until you reach
Haynie Road. Turn right on Haynie
Road and proceed to the golf course.

Course Yardage & Par:
M-2379 yards, par 35.
W-2196 yards, par 35.
Dual tees for 18 holes:
M-4745 yards, par 69.
W-4392 yards, par 71.

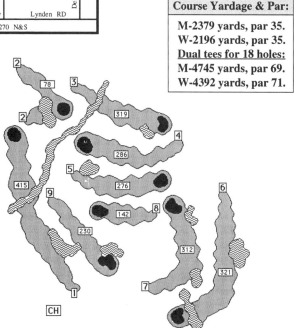

Deer Meadows Golf Course (public)
Route 1; Box 203; Davenport, WA 99122; (509) 725-8488
Manager: Charles Spencer. Superintendent: N/A. 9 hole course, range.
Rating/Slope: the golf course is to new to have been rated.
Green fees: W/D $13/$9; W/E $15/$10; call for special green fee rates.
Power cart: $10/$8. **Pull cart:** $3/$2. **Trail fee:** not allowed.
Reservation policy: please call up to 1 day in advance for tee times.
Winter Condition: the golf course is closed from November to March.
Terrain: flat, some hills (walkable). **Tees:** grass. **Temporary greens:** no.
Services: club rentals, pro shop, driving range. **Comments:** new 9 hole course
that opened the 1st 9 in April of 1995. The course offers the golfer modest length
and challenging terrain. Plans include an additional 9 holes (due to open some-
time in 1996) a clubhouse and other services in the future. Very friendly facility.

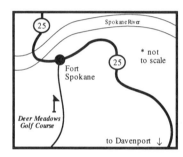

Directions: the golf course is located
south of Fort Spokane off of Hwy 25.
From Davenport follow Hwy 25 north
toward Fort Spokane. When in Fort
Spokane turn southboound on Miles
Creston Road. The course will be located
on your right hand side. Look for a sign
marking your turn to the golf course.

Course Yardage & Par:
M-3082 yards, par 36.
W-3000 yards, par 36.

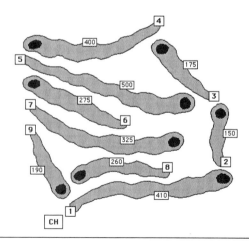

Deer Park Golf & Country Club (semi-private)
W 2658 Deer Park-Milan Road; Deer Park, WA 99006-9998
(509) 276-5912 or 1- 800-334-6443. 18 hole course, driving range.
Pro: Craig Schuh. Superintendent: N/A. Course record: N/A.
Rating/Slope: the golf course is to new to have been rated.
Green fees: W/D $18/$13; W/E $20/$15; call for special green fee rates.
Power cart: $20/$10. **Pull cart:** $2/$2. **Trail fee:** $5.
Reservation policy: call Sundays for the next W/E's. 1 day in advance for W/D's.
Winter Condition: golf course is closed from November to February or March.
Terrain: flat, some hills. **Tees:** grass. **Temporary greens:** no. **Services:** club
rentals, lessons, lounge, restuarant, snack bar, beer, wine, liquor, pro shop, putting
green, driving range. **Comments:** new desert design with 4 lakes, ponds and
streams. Waste bunkers and other traps are in play on nearly every hole. Very
scenic course that will be enjoyable for all. Great new track, worth a special trip.

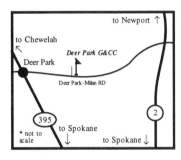

Directions: from I -90 take the exit for
Hwy 395 (Division Street) Proceed north
on Hwy 395 toward Deer Park. When you
get to Crawford turn east. Proceed to
Country Club Drive where you will turn
north to the course. Look for signs.

Course Yardage & Par:
C-6750 yards, par 72.
M-6340 yards, par 72.
W-5615 yards, par 72.

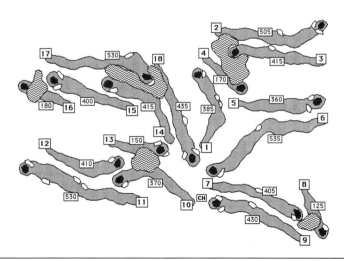

Delphi Golf Course (public)

6340 Neylon Drive SW; Olympia, WA 98512; (360) 357-6437
Manager: Rich Williams. 9 hole executive course.
Rating/Slope: M 61.4/102; W 61.8/102. **Course record:** 27 (9 holes).
Green fees: W/D $13.50/$9; W/E $15/$10; Jr/Sr, twlight rates; VISA, MC, AMX.
Power cart: $18/$12. **Pull cart:** $2.50. **Trail fee:** $5 for personal carts.
Reservation policy: yes reservation are taken, no time limit.
Winter Condition: the golf course is open all year long, damp at times.
Terrain: a few hills, but very walkable. **Tees:** grass. **Temporary greens:** no.
Services: club rentals, small pro shop. **Comments:** residential course. Beautiful
setting with narrow tree-lined fairways on every hole. This track is in excellent
condition throughout the season. The golf course is fun for golfers of all abilities.

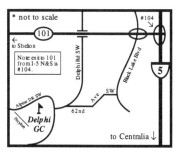

Directions: from I-5 N&S exit to Hwy
101 (exit #104) in Olympia. Follow 101
and exit at Black Lake Blvd. (which
becomes 62nd Ave. SW). Go south on
Black Lake Blvd to Delphi Road. Turn
left on Delphi Road to Alpine DR SW,
right to the golf course. Look for signs.

Course Yardage & Par:
M-1937 yards, par 32.
W-1789 yards, par 34.

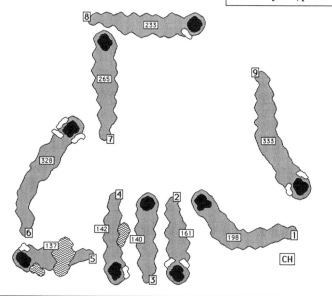

Desert Aire Golf Course (semi-private)

505 Clubhouse Way West; Desert Aire, WA 99349; (509) 932-4439
Pro: Brad Eakman, PGA. 18 hole course, driving range.
Rating/Slope: M 69.9/111; W 71.9/115. **Course record:** 65.
Green fees: W/D $16/$12; W/E $18/$14; memberships available.
Power cart: $16/$10.75. **Pull cart:** $1.35/$.81. **Trail fee:** $5.
Reservation policy: yes, please call 7 days in advance for times.
Winter condition: dry, golf course usually open during the winter. **Terrain:** flat, some hills. **Tees:** grass. **Temporary greens:** no. **Services:** club rentals, snack bar, pro shop, driving range, beer, wine, lessons, RV spots. **Comments:** the course is fairly wide open with a beautiful view of the Columbia River and surrounding countryside. The golf course can play very difficult if the wind picks up. Good eastern Washington track.

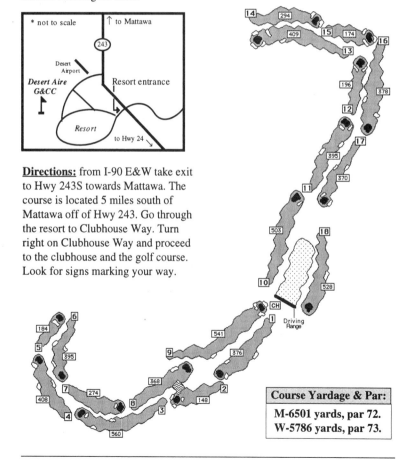

Directions: from I-90 E&W take exit to Hwy 243S towards Mattawa. The course is located 5 miles south of Mattawa off of Hwy 243. Go through the resort to Clubhouse Way. Turn right on Clubhouse Way and proceed to the clubhouse and the golf course. Look for signs marking your way.

Course Yardage & Par:
M-6501 yards, par 72.
W-5786 yards, par 73.

Desert Canyon Golf Resort (public, resort)

114 Brays Road; Orondo, WA 98843; (509) 784-1111; 1-800-258-4173
Director of Golf: Jack Frei. Head Pro: Brad Dally, PGA. 18 hole course.
Rating/Slope: T 74.0/127; C 72.4/121; M 68.2/108; W 67.5/104. **Record:** 66.
Green fees: $65 June 16th-September 30th; lower rates rest of year; M/C, VISA.
Power cart: included in green fee. **Pull cart:** not needed. **Trail fee:** not allowed.
Reservation policy: yes, please call 7 days in advance. **Winter condition:** open,
weather permitting. **Terrain:** rolling hills. **Tees:** grass. **Services:** club rentals, full
service resort facilities, driving range, pro shop. **Comments:** This is a desert style,
links course with spectacular views of the Columbia River. This course is going
to be regarded, if not already, as one of the best courses in the state of Washington.

Directions: the golf course is located on
the east side of the Columbia River off
of Hwy 97 (not Alt. 97 on the westside).
From Hwy 97 E&W turn eastbound on
Brays Road. Proceed for 3/4 of a mile to
the entrance. Look for signs at your turn.

Putting Course Yardage & Par:
2571 feet, par 70.
Course fees: $5, 18 holes.

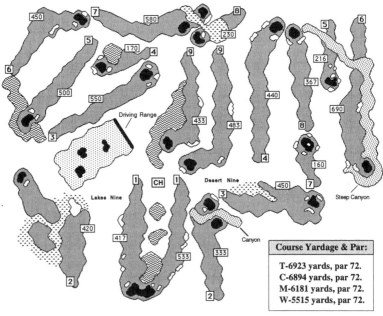

Course Yardage & Par:
T-6923 yards, par 72.
C-6894 yards, par 72.
M-6181 yards, par 72.
W-5515 yards, par 72.

Downriver Golf Course (public)

3225 Columbia Circle; Spokane, WA 99205; (509) 327-5269
Pro: Steve Conner, PGA. 18 hole course, driving range.
Rating/Slope: M 68.8/115; W 72.8/118. **Course record:** 66.
Green fees: county resident $14/$11; others $18/$13; Jr/Sr rates W/D's
and after 3pm weekends; VISA, M/C on merchandise only. **Power cart:** $20.
Pull cart: $2. **Trail fee:** $5. **Reservation policy:** weekdays call ahead 1 day
in advance, weekends-previous Sat. **Winter condition:** closed. **Terrain:** flat,
some hills. **Tees:** grass. **Temporary greens:** no. **Services:** club rentals, lessons,
restaurant, snack bar, beer, wine, pro shop, lockers, showers, driving range.
Comments: tree-lined fairways are a challenge on this course. If you are looking
for a good public golf course at a very affordable price try Downriver.

Directions: from I-90 eastbound take
exit #280 (westbound #280A) to
Walnut St. Go north on Walnut until
you reach Northwest Blvd. Turn left on
Northwest Blvd. and follow to Euclid
St. From this point there will be signs
to the golf course that you can follow.

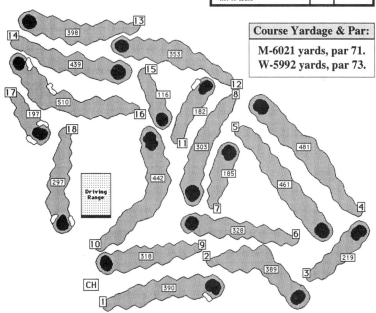

Course Yardage & Par:

M-6021 yards, par 71.
W-5992 yards, par 73.

Dungeness Golf & Country Club (public)

1965 Woodcock Road: Sequim, WA 98382; (360) 683-6344; 1-800-447-6826
Pro: John Hughes, PGA. Superintendent: N/A. 18 hole course, range.
Rating/Slope: C 70.1/123; M 68.5/120; W 70.3/119. **Course record:** 63.
Green fees: M-Thur. $20/$14; Fri.-Sun. $24/$16; winter rates; M/C, VISA.
Power cart: $21/$13.50. **Pull cart:** $3/$2. **Trail fee:** $11/$6 (all prices + tax).
Reservation policy: yes, call in advance. Tournaments welcome anytime.
Winter condition: very dry. **Terrain:** flat, some hills. **Tees:** grass. **Services:** pro
shop, driving range, club rentals, lessons, restaurant and lounge, beer, wine, liquor,
showers. **Comments:** has an excellent golf package with the Red Ranch Inn. One
of the finest and friendliest golf courses in Washington. Worth a special trip.

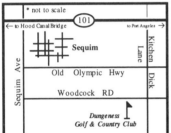

Directions: from Seattle take the Edmonds
or Winslow ferry. Follow signs to the Hood
Canal Bridge and Hwy 104. From Hwy
104 follow to Hwy 101. Proceed on Hwy
101 to Sequim. At the first light (Sequim
Ave.) turn right. Go for 3 miles to Woodcock Road. Turn left on Woodcock Road.
Proceed for 3 miles, the course will be on
your right. Note signs marking your turn.

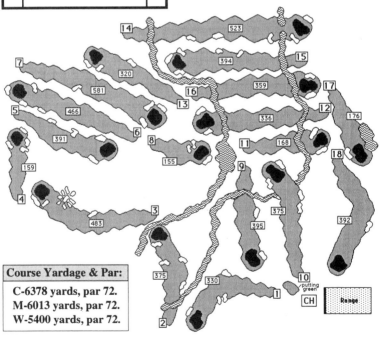

Course Yardage & Par:
C-6378 yards, par 72.
M-6013 yards, par 72.
W-5400 yards, par 72.

Eaglemont (semi-private)

4127 Eaglemont DR; Mt. Vernon, WA 98273; (360) 424-0800; 1-800-368-8876
Pro: Mike O'Laughlin, PGA. Supt.: Charles Fisher. 18 hole course, range.
Rating/Slope: T 73.4/134; C 71.6/129; M 70.5/126; M 69.4/124; W 70.7/124.
Green fees: W/D $35; W/E $45; includes cart; twilight rates; M/C, VISA.
Power cart: included in green fee. **Pull cart:** not available. **Trail fee:** not allowed.
Reservation policy: yes, call in advance for reservations. **Winter condition:** dry.
Terrain: very hilly. **Tees:** grass. **Services:** the golf course will offer a full service
clubhouse and pro shop. **Comments:** This John Steidel designed golf course is of
championship caliber, featuring ponds, tree lined fairways and bunkers galore.
Excellent newer course that will eventually expand to 27 holes in 1997 or 1998.

Directions: From I-5 N&S take exit #227
(College Way). Proceed eastbound on College
Way until you reach Waugh RD. Turn right on
Waugh RD. Go Waugh RD to Eaglemont DR
where you will turn left to the golf course.

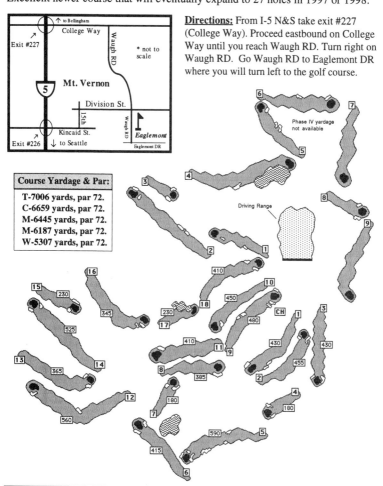

Course Yardage & Par:

T-7006 yards, par 72.
C-6659 yards, par 72.
M-6445 yards, par 72.
M-6187 yards, par 72.
W-5307 yards, par 72.

Echo Falls Country Club (semi-private)

20414 121st Ave. SE; Snohomish, WA 98290; (800) 377-2420; (360) 668-3030
Dir. of Golf: Scot Solomonson, PGA. **Supt.:** Mike Hilsenkopf. **18 hole course.**
Rating/Slope: C 67.6/124; M 65.6/119; W 69.5/122. **Course record:** 61.
Green fees: Mon. to Thur. $27.50; Frid. to Sun. $37; winter rates; VISA, M/C.
Power cart: $11 per person. **Pull cart:** $3. **Trail fee:** personal carts not allowed.
Reservation policy: accepted 5 days in advance. **Winter condition:** open, good
winter drainage. **Terrain:** relatively hilly. **Tees:** grass. **Temporary greens:** for
frost. **Services:** the golf course offers a full service pro shop and clubhouse, range.
Comments:18th hole is an island green that is spectacular. The staff at Echo Falls
wants you to feel that this facility is "The Public's Country Club". Excellent track.

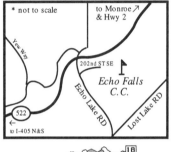

Directions: If traveling on I-405 N&S
exit to Hwy 522 eastbound. Proceed for
5.1 miles to Echo Lake Road. Turn right
on Echo Lake Road. Proceed to your first
left (202nd Ave SE) and turn left. Proceed
for 1/4 of a mile to the course entrance on
your right hand side. Look for signs to
mark your way to the golf course.

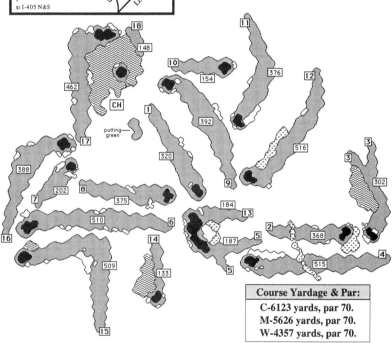

Course Yardage & Par:
C-6123 yards, par 70.
M-5626 yards, par 70.
W-4357 yards, par 70.

Elk Run Golf Course (public)

22500 SE 275th Place; Maple Valley, WA 98038; (206) 432-8800
Pro: Steve Dubsky, PGA. Superintendent: Tony Bubenas. 18 holes, range.
Rating/Slope: M 63.4/108; W 65.0/106. **Course record:** N/A.
Green fees: W/D $22/$15; W/E $25./$17; special rates; M/C, VISA.
Power cart: $18/$12. **Pull cart:** $3/$2. **Trail fee:** $7 for personal carts.
Reservation policy: yes, please call 7 days in advance. **Winter condition:** open,
very dry. **Terrain:** flat, some slight hills. **Tees:** grass. **Temporary greens:** no.
Services: club rentals, lessons, restaurant, coffee shop, pro shop, lighted driving
range, call for seasonal hours. **Comments:** one of the driest golf courses in
the Northwest. The new 9 is a real challenge with fairways that are narrow and
tree-lined. Numerous sand traps and ponds guard tricky undulating greens. If you
are looking for great course for your company tournament give Elk Run a try.

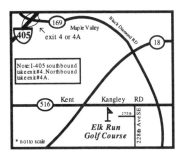

Directions: from I-405 N&S take exit #4
(southbound) #4A (northbound) to Hwy
169 (Maple Valley-Black Diamond Road).
Proceed to the Kent-Kangley RD and turn
right. Proceed for 1 mile to 228th SE.
Turn left on 228th SE and follow to the
golf course. Look for signs marking your
turn to the course the way is well marked.

Course Yardage & Par:
M-4747 yards, par 71.
W-4400 yards, par 71.

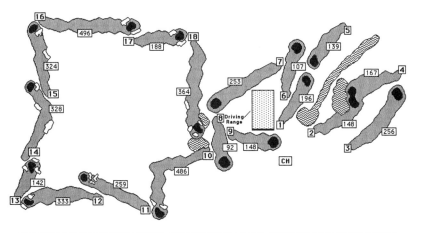

Ellensburg Golf Club (semi-private)

3231Thorp Road South; Ellensburg, WA 98926; (509) 962-2984
Pro: Rich Farrell, PGA. 9 hole course, dual tees for 18 holes.
Rating/Slope: M 69.9/109; W 72.3/120. **Course record:** 29/62.
Green fees: W/D $16/$9; W/E $17/$10; no credit cards.
Power cart: $17/$8.50. **Pull cart:** $1.50. **Trail fee:** no charge.
Reservation policy: you may call ahead to make a tee time.
Winter condition: golf course is closed mid November to March. **Terrain:** flat.
Tees: grass. **Temporary greens:** no. **Services:** club rentals, lessons, restaurant,
snack bar, lounge, beer, wine, liquor, pro shop, lockers, showers, driving range.
Comments: sand traps and water make this 9 hole course a real challenge. Dual
tees available for 18 hole play. Course does limit outside play at certain times so
be sure call ahead for your tee time.

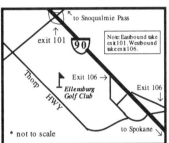

Directions: from I-90 eastbound take
Thorp Hwy exit #101 and go for 2 miles
to the golf course. From westbound I-90
take exit #106 the West Interchange by
the KOA campground. Cross the bridge
over the Yakima River onto Thorp Road
and proceed for 2 miles to the golf course.

Course Yardage & Par:
M-2988 yards, par 35.
W-2807 yards, par 36.
Dual tees for 18 holes:
M-5974 yards, par 70.
W-5597 yards, par 73.

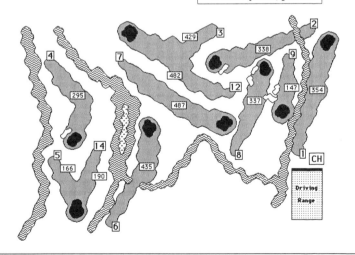

Enumclaw Golf Course (public)

45220 288th SE; Enumclaw, WA 98002; (360) 825-2827
Pro: John McGregor, PGA. Superintendent: Chad Chevalier 18 hole course.
Rating/Slope: M 66.0/106; W 68.8/110. **Course record:** 62.
Greens fee: $17/$12; Jr. & Sr. rates (Monday thru Friday only); no credit cards.
Power cart: $20/$10. **Pull cart:** $3. **Trail fee:** no charge.
Reservation policy: yes, call up to one week in advance.
Winter condition: wet. **Terrain:** relatively hilly. **Tees:** grass & mats.
Temporary greens: no. **Services:** club rentals, lessons, snack bar, restaurant,
beer, wine, lockers, chipping & putting greens. **Comments:** The golf course has
beautiful views of the surrounding countryside. Boise Creek winds through the
golf course and is a factor on many of the holes. The course itself can play much
longer than the yardage would indicate.

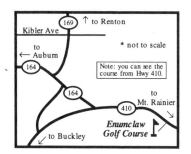

Directions: from I-5 N&S take exit 142
to Hwy 18E. East to Auburn Way S/Hwy
164E exit. Go east on Hwy 164 for 13.8
miles to Hwy 410 (SE 448th). Proceed
eastbound for 1 mile to the golf course.
Note: You can see the golf course when
driving on Hwy 410. Look for signs
indicating your turn to the golf course.

Course Yardage & Par:
M-5561 yards, par 70.
W-5211 yards, par 71.

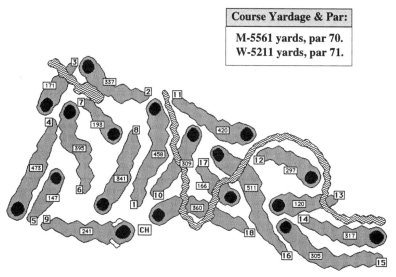

Esmeralda Golf Course (public)

E 3933 Courtland; Spokane, WA 99207; (509) 487-6291
Pro: Bill Warner, PGA. 18 hole course, driving range.
Rating/Slope: C 69.2/114; M 68.2/112; W 70.1/112. **Course record:** 62.
Green fees: County resident $14/$11; others $18/$13; no credit cards.
Power cart: $20/$10. **Pull cart:** $2. **Trail fee:** $7 for personal carts.
Reservation policy: yes, up to 1 day-weekdays, 1 week for the weekends.
Winter condition: course open weathering permitting. **Terrain:** flat, some hills.
Tees: grass. **Temporary greens:** in winter only. **Services:** club rentals, lessons,
restaurant, beer, wine, pro shop, driving range, putting green. **Comments:** large,
quick greens and fairly flat terrain make for a pleasant round. Excellent public
golf course with tree lined fairways and few hazards. Beverage cart in summer.

Directions: from I-90 E&W take the
Freya/Thor exit #283B. Go northbound
for 3 miles to Euclid Avenue. Go right on
Euclid Avenue for 3 blocks to Freya. Turn
left on Freya to the golf course. Look for
signs indicating your turn to the course.

Course Yardage & Par:
C-6249 yards, par 70.
M-6015 yards, par 70.
W-5594 yards, par 72.

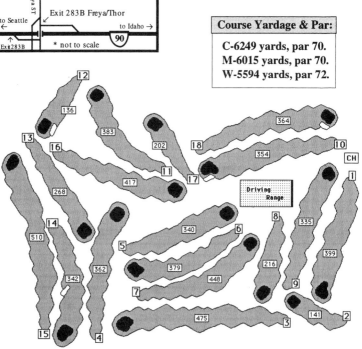

Everett Golf & Country Club (private)
1500 52nd Street; PO Box 2300; Everett, WA 98203; (206) 259-1214
Pro: Bob Borup, PGA. Superintendent: Randy White. 18 hole course.
Rating/Slope: C 70.0/126; M 69.2/124; W 73.1/126. Course record: 62.
Green fees: private course, members & guests only; reciprocates.
Power cart: private club. **Pull cart:** private club. **Trail fee:** not allowed.
Reservation policy: private club, members only. **Winter condition:** dry.
Terrain: flat, some hills. **Tees:** grass. **Temporary greens:** occasionally.
Services: lessons, lounge, restaurant, beer, wine, liquor, lockers, showers,
pro shop, driving range. **Comments:** the golf course is fairly flat with tree lined
fairways with small well bunkered greens. This private track was built in 1912
and gives the golfer many outstanding views of the surrounding countryside.

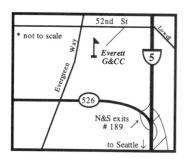

Directions: from I-5 N&S take exit #189
to Hwy 526E for .5 miles to Evergreen
Way. Turn right (north) on Evergreen
Way and proceed for 2 miles to 52nd
Street. Turn right (east) on 52nd Street.
Proceed to the golf course.

Course Yardage & Par:

C-6087 yards, par 72.
M-6073 yards, par 72.
W-5731 yards, par 72.

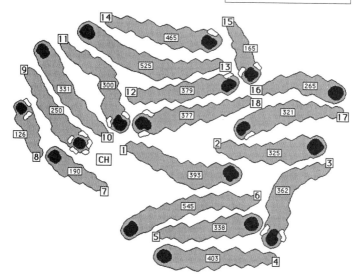

Evergreen Golf Course (public)

P.O. Box 156; 413 E Main Street; Everson, WA 98247; (360) 966-5417
Owner: Jerry McBeth. 9 hole executive course.
Rating/Slope: the golf course is not rated. **Course record:** 28, 9 holes.
Green fees: W/D $9/$6; W/E $11/$7.50; no credit cards.
Power cart: none available for use. **Pull cart:** $2. **Trail fee:** no charge.
Reservation policy: none. **Winter condition:** the golf course is closed during
the winter months. **Terrain:** flat, some slight hills. **Tees:** grass, no mats.
Temporary greens: not in use. **Services:** club rentals, snack bar, beer, wine,
limited pro shop. **Comments:** family owned executive course with narrow tree
lined fairways. A creek which wanders throughout the course comes into play on
a number of holes. Fairly rustic course that is very friendly.

Directions: from I-5 N&S take exit #256
to Guide Meridian St. Go northbound on
Meridian (Hwy 539) for 7.7 miles to Hwy
544E. Turn eastbound on Hwy 544 for 8.4
miles to the golf course. Look for signs
marking your way to the entrance of the
golf course.

Course Yardage & Par:
M-2145 yards, par 31.
W-2145 yards, par 31.

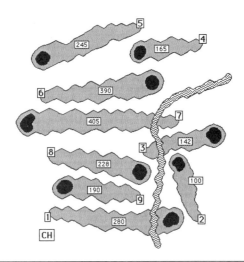

Fairway Village Golf Course (public)

15503 SE Fernwood Drive; Vancouver, WA 98684; (360) 254-9325
Manager: Russ Dixon. 9 hole course, dual tees for 18 holes.
Rating/Slope: M 64.3/106; W 67.1/106. **Course record:** 29.
Green fees: W/D $17/$10; W/E $18/$11; Sr. rates weekdays; M/C, VISA.
Power cart: $17/$11. **Pull cart:** $1. **Trail fee:** personal carts not allowed.
Reservation policy: yes, up to 1 week in advance. **Winter condition:** open, dry.
Terrain: flat, some hills. **Tees:** grass. **Temporary greens:** no, not in use.
Services: lessons, pro shop, vending machines. **Comments:** this well bunkered short and narrow golf course was dedicated by Sam Snead. If you want to play early in the morning try the Early Bird Special Saturday & Sunday before 9am. Greens and fairways are kept in excellent condition. Great golf course.

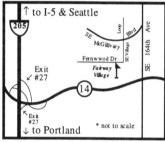

Directions: from I-5 N&S exit to I-205 N&S. Exit from I-205 to Hwy 14 going eastbound. Proceed east to exit #8 (SE 164th). Turn left on SE 164th and proceed for 1 mile to SE McGillivary (2nd light). Turn left for .2 miles to SE Village Loop. At SE Village Loop turn left and then follow this to the golf course.

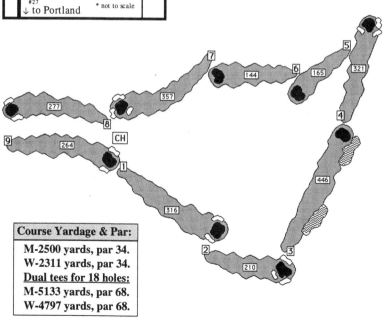

Course Yardage & Par:
M-2500 yards, par 34.
W-2311 yards, par 34.
Dual tees for 18 holes:
M-5133 yards, par 68.
W-4797 yards, par 68.

Fairways at West Terrace, The (public)

W 9810 Melville Road; Cheney, WA 99004; (509) 747-8418
Pro: Jerry Zink, PGA. 18 hole course, driving range.
Rating/Slope: C 69.2/114; M 67.7/111; W 63.6/102. **Course record:** 61.
Green fees: W/D $15/$11; W/E $18/$13; Jr & Sr rates $13; M/C, VISA.
Power cart: $20/$10. **Pull cart:** $2. **Trail fee:** $8. **Reservation policy:** yes, up
to 1 week in advance. **Winter condition:** dry, open until snow. **Terrain:** flat,
some hills. **Tees:** grass. **Temporary greens:** no. **Services:** club rentals, lessons,
snack bar, restaurant, beer, wine, liquor, driving range, pro shop, putting green.
Comments: home of the "Lilac City Invitational." The course has numerous sand
traps and 6 ponds which come in to play. Great golf course that can play tough.

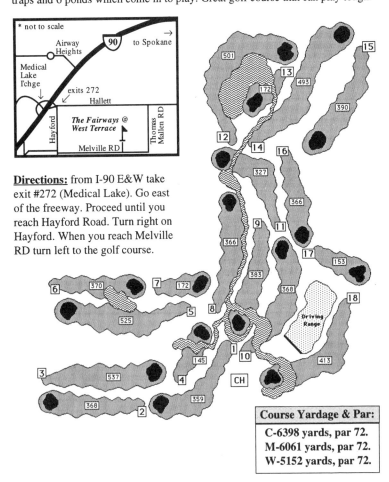

Directions: from I-90 E&W take
exit #272 (Medical Lake). Go east
of the freeway. Proceed until you
reach Hayford Road. Turn right on
Hayford. When you reach Melville
RD turn left to the golf course.

Course Yardage & Par:

C-6398 yards, par 72.
M-6061 yards, par 72.
W-5152 yards, par 72.

Fairwood Golf & Country Club (private)
17070 140th SE; Renton, WA 98055; (206) 226-7890
Pro: Ron Hanson, PGA. Superintendent: Greg Hall. 18 hole course.
Rating/Slope: C 70.8/126; M 69.2/122; W 71.8/125. **Course record:** 63.
Green fees: private club, members and guests only, limited reciprocation.
Power cart: private club. **Pull cart:** private club. **Trail fee:** not allowed.
Reservation policy: yes, call on Thursday for the following week.
Winter condition: dry. **Terrain:** relatively hilly. **Tees:** grass.
Temporary greens: occasionally. **Services:** lessons, lounge, beer, wine, liquor,
lockers, showers, sauna, pro shop, driving range, chipping & putting green.
Comments: OB on both sides of each hole. Undulating greens, bunkers and
length make this golf course difficult. Excellent private facility built in 1972.

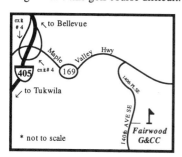

Directions: from I-5 N&S exit to
I-405 N&S. From I-405 N&S take exit
#4 to Hwy 169S. Proceed on Hwy 169
until you reach 140th PL SE. Turn
right on 140th PL SE. Travel up the
hill until 140th PL SE turns into 140th
St SE. The golf course will be on your
left. Note the clubhouse is beyond
the main entrance. Do not turn into the
main entrance.

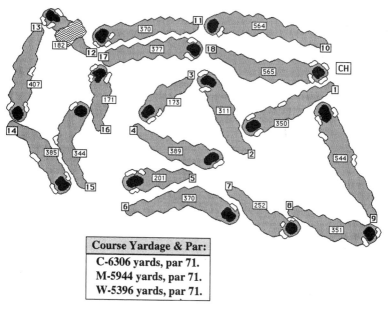

Course Yardage & Par:
C-6306 yards, par 71.
M-5944 yards, par 71.
W-5396 yards, par 71.

Fircrest Golf Club (private)

6520 Regents Boulevard; Tacoma, WA 98466; (206) 564-5792; 564-6756
Pro: Glenn Malm, PGA. Superintendent: Mike Etchemendy 18 hole course.
Rating/Slope: C 72.0/129; M 71.2/125; W 74.8/129. **Course record:** 62.
Green fees: private, members only; very limited reciprocation; no credit cards.
Power cart: private club. **Pull cart:** private club. **Trail fee:** not allowed.
Reservation policy: none. **Winter condition:** dry. **Terrain:** relatively hilly.
Tees: grass. **Temporary greens:** no. **Services:** lessons, snack bar, lounge,
restaurant, beer, wine, liquor, lockers, showers, pro shop, practice range, club
memberships, dress code. **Comments:** Established in 1923, this course's
fairways are surrounded by trees. Greens are fast and well bunkered. Great course.

Directions: from I-5 N&S exit to Hwy 16
(Gig Harbor/Bremerton). Proceed on Hwy
16 to the Union Avenue exit. Exit to Union
and proceed south for .2 miles to Center
Street. Go westbound on Center Street.
which becomes Regents Blvd. Proceed
on Regents Boulevard for 2.1 miles to the
golf course.

Course Yardage & Par:
C-6605 yards, par 71.
M-6400 yards, par 71.
W-5995 yards, par 75.

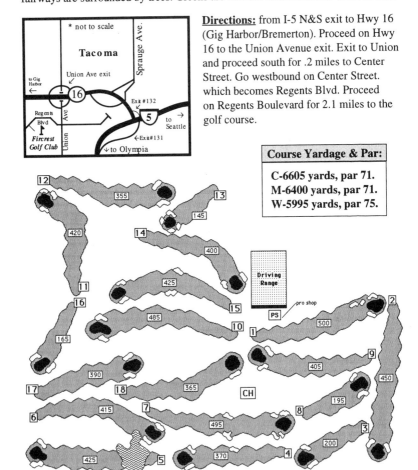

Fisher Park Golf Course (public)

2301 Fruitvale Boulevard; Yakima, WA 98901; (509) 575-6075
Manager: Doty Hodgson. Teaching Pro: Bob Hoag. 9 hole par 3 course.
Rating/Slope: the golf course has not been rated. **Course record:** 23.
Green fees: W/D $9/$6; W/E & Holidays $9/$6; Jr & Sr rates.
Power cart: none available. **Pull cart:** $2. **Trail fee:** no personal carts allowed.
Reservation policy: first come first served. **Winter condition:** the golf course
is closed from November 15th to February 15th. **Terrain:** flat, some slight hills.
Tees: grass. **Temporary greens:** no. **Services:** club rentals, lessons, snack bar,
putting green. **Comments:** Economical course golf course run by the City of
Yakima Parks Department. This par 3 golf course can play long at times with
holes ranging from 118 to 191 yards. You will use every iron in your bag.

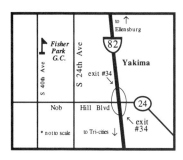

Directions: From I-82 take the Nob Hill
exit #34 and proceed westbound. At 40th
Avenue turn right and proceed to the golf
course. The golf course will be located on
your right hand side. Look for signs.

Course Yardage & Par:
M-1354 yards, par 27.
W-1354 yards, par 27.

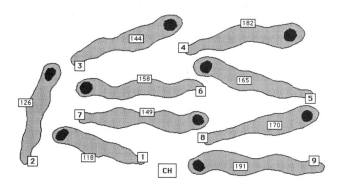

Flowing Lake Golf Course (public)

5001 Weber Road; Snohomish, WA 98290; (360) 568-2753
Managers: Stan & Gary Laz. 18 hole course.
Rating/Slope: the golf course has not been rated. **Course record:** N/A.
Green fees: W/D $15/$10; W/E $18/$12. **Power cart:** $20/$10.
Pull cart: $3/$1.50. **Trail fee:** $5. **Reservation policy:** yes, call in advance for a
tee time. **Winter condition:** course closed from November 15th to February 15th.
Terrain: flat, some hills (very walkable). **Tees:** grass. **Temporary greens:** no.
Services: club rentals, snack bar, beer, lessons, driving range, putting green,
chipping green, pro shop. **Comments:** newer family run golf course that can play
very tight in spots. This is a beautiful country course with spectacular views of the
Cascades from many of the tees and fairways. Water a factor on many holes.

Directions: from Hwy 2 exit at 100th St
SE (which is east of Snohomish). Follow
to Spada Road. Right on Spada. Proceed
to Storm Lake Road. Right on Storm Lake
Road to Weber Road where you will turn
left. The golf course entrance is located
ahead on your right. Look for signs.

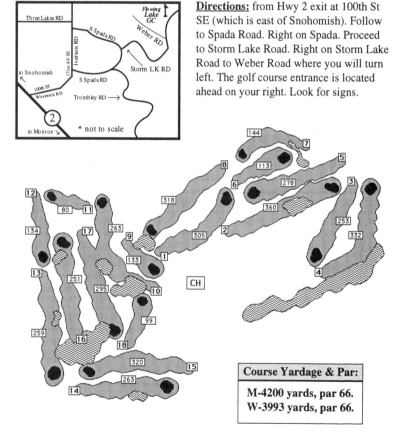

Course Yardage & Par:

M-4200 yards, par 66.
W-3993 yards, par 66.

Fort Lewis Golf Course (military-private)

PO Box 33175; Fort Lewis Army Base; Fort Lewis, WA 98433; (206) 967-6522
Pro: James Barnhouse. **Superintendent:** John Ford. **27 hole course.**
Course record: 64. **Rating/Slope:** Red/Blue C 73.4/130; M 71.3/124; W 73.1/127.
Green fees: military & guests only, sliding scale based on rank, accompanied
civilian guest fee. **Power cart:** private. **Pull cart:** private. **Trail fee:** private.
Reservation policy: call and ask for policy. **Winter condition:** dry.
Terrain: relatively hilly. **Tees:** grass & mats. **Temporary greens:** yes.
Services: club rentals, lessons, snack bar, beer, lockers, showers, two driving
ranges, pro shop, putting green. **Comments:** Mature trees, ponds and sand traps
make this 27 hole layout a very difficult course to score on. Excellent military
facility that provides good drainage for winter play.

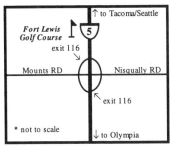

Directions: from I-5 N&S take exit
#116 (Mounts RD-Nisqually). Proceed
west for .1 miles to the golf course.
Note: the golf course is adjacent to I-5.

Course Yardage & Par:
Red/Blue: C-6855 yards, par 72.
Red/Blue: M-6388 yards, par 72.
Red/Blue: W-5822 yards, par 74.

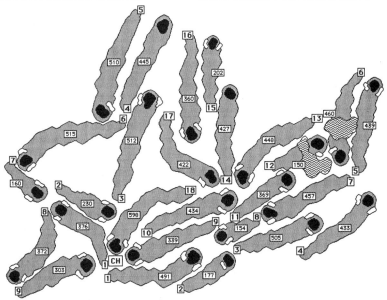

Fort Steilacoom Golf Course (public)

Box 97325; 8202 87th SW; Tacoma, WA 98498; (206) 588-0613
Pro: Jim Osborn, PGA. Superintendent: Scott Tyson. 9 holes, dual tees.
Rating/Slope: M 62.8/098; W 66.8/105. **Course record:** 55.
Green fees: $15/$9.75 all week long; Jr & Sr rates available; M/C, VISA.
Power cart: $14/$8. **Pull cart:** $3. **Trail fee:** $5 for personal carts.
Reservation policy: yes, call in advance for tee times. **Winter condition:** golf
course is open, dry. **Terrain:** flat. **Tees:** grass & mats. **Temporary greens:** yes.
Services: club rentals, lessons, pro shop, vending machines, hot & cold
sandwiches, snacks, putting & chipping green. **Comments:** golf course is not
overly long so its an excellent course to practice your short irons on. Dual tees
are available for an 18 hole round. Fairways are tree lined and fairly wide.

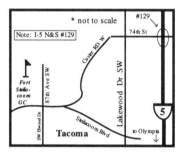

Directions: from I-5 N&S take exit 129 to
S 74th. Turn west on S 74th and proceed
2.2 miles to Custer Road W. Go south for
1 mile to Steilacoom Blvd. Turn west on
Steilacoom Blvd. for 1.1 miles to 87th
Ave. SW. Turn north on 87th Ave. SW for
.2 miles to the golf course driveway. Look
for signs marking your turn to the golf
course.

Course Yardage & Par:
M-2518 yards, par 34.
W-2410 yards, par 34.
<u>Dual tees for 18 holes:</u>
M-4928 yards, par 68.
W-4928 yards, par 68.

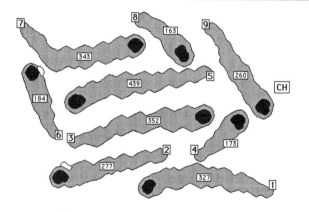

Foster Golf Links (public)

13500 Interurban Avenue; Tukwila, WA 98168; (206) 242-4221
Pro: Marty O'Brien, PGA. Supt.: Chuck Morris. 18 hole course.
Rating/Slope: M 62.3/94; W 66.6/101. **Course record:** 60.
Green fees: $17/$13; Jr & Sr rates (weekdays) $13.50/$11; VISA, MC.
Power cart: $18/$11. **Pull cart:** $2/$1. **Trail fee:** $5 for personal carts.
Reservation policy: yes, up to 1 week in advance. **Winter condition:** dry.
Terrain: flat, some hills. **Tees:** grass & mats. **Temporary greens:** not in use.
Services: club rentals, snack bar, restaurant, beer, wine, pop, liquor, pro shop.
Comments: the course is easy to walk and a favorite of seniors. This track has
been undergooing changes the last two years to enhance its playability. If you are
looking for a change of pace from the 6000+ yards golf course, give Foster a try.

Directions: from I-5 N&S take exit
#156 (Tukwila) to Interurban South.
Proceed south for .4 miles to the golf
course which will be on your left hand
side. Look for a sign indicating your
turn into the parking lot.

Course Yardage & Par:
M-4930 yards, par 69.
W-4665 yards, par 70.

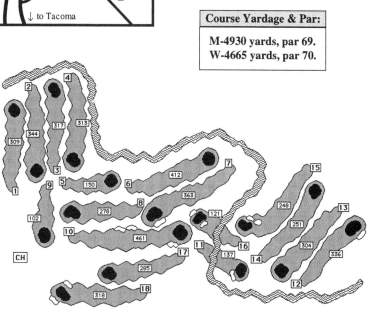

Gallery Golf Course (military & authorized guests)

MWR Golf; NAS Whidbey Island; Oak Harbor, WA 98278; (360) 257-2178
Manager/Superintendent: Christopher M. Braun. 18 hole course, range.
Rating/Slope: C 70.4/129; M 69.4/126; W 70.7/123. **Course record:** 66.
Green fees: W/D $20/$15; W/E $22/$16; sliding scale military fees; VISA, M/C.
Power cart: $18/$9. **Pull cart:** $3. **Trail fee:** $10. **Reservation policy:** yes,
call in advance. **Winter condition:** dry. **Terrain:** flat, some hills (walkable).
Tees: grass. **Temporary greens:** no. **Services:** club rentals, lessons, restaurant,
lounge, beer, wine, liquor, lockers, pro shop, driving range, short practice chipping
green, putting green. **Comments:** a very scenic and demanding layout located at
the Whidbey Island Naval Air Station. Military golf course that features well
bunkered greens and fairways. Course open for the military and guests only.

Directions: from I-5 N&S take exit 230
to Hwy 20 W. Travel west to Whidbey
Island and exit at Ault Field Road.
Continue beyond NAS to Clover Valley
Road to the golf course. **Note:** the golf
course is located right outside the military
base. Look for signs indicating your way
to the base.

Course Yardage & Par:
C-6351 yards, par 72.
M-6101 yards, par 72.
W-5454 yards, par 74.

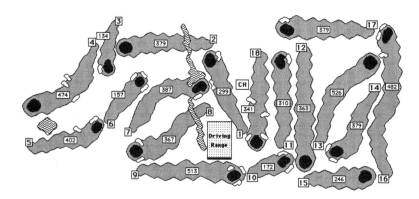

Gateway Golf Course (public)

839 Fruitdale Road; Sedro Woolley, WA 98284; (360) 856-0315
Pro: Wellington Lee. 9 hole course, putting green.
Rating/Slope: C 68.8/122; M 68.2/120; W 68.0/115. **Course record:** 31.
Green fees: W/D $13/$9; W/E & Hol. $16/$13; Sr. rates M-F; no credit cards.
Power cart: $15/$10. **Pull cart:** $3/$2. **Trail fee:** $1 per 9 holes.
Reservation policy: no, play happens on a first come first serve basis.
Winter condition: open weather permitting, damp. **Terrain:** relatively hilly.
Tees: grass (mats in winter). **Temporary greens:** occasionally in winter.
Services: club rentals, lessons, snack bar, beer, pro shop, chipping area, club
memberships. **Comments:** ditches, ponds and creeks come into play throughout
the course. Peek a boo view of the Cascades from several tees and fairways.

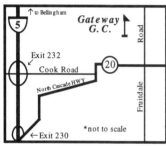

Directions: from I-5 N&S take exit #232
to Cook Road. Travel east for 4.4 miles
to Hwy 20 E. Turn east for .7 miles to
Fruitdale Road. Proceed on Fruitdale Road
to the golf course. Look for signs locating
your turn to the golf course.

Course Yardage & Par:
C-3050 yards, par 36.
M-2914 yards, par 36.
W-2500 yards, par 36.

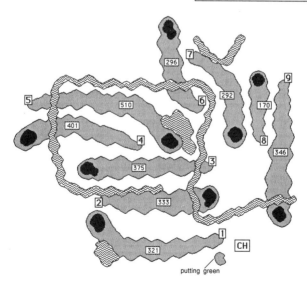

Gig Harbor Golf & Country Club (semi-private)

6909 Artondale Drive. NW; Gig Harbor, WA 98335; (206) 851-2378
Pro: Jeff Mehlert. **Supt.:** Russell Price. **9 hole course, dual flags & tees.**
Rating/Slope: M 65.6/109; W 68.8/114. **Course record:** 64.
Green fees: $18/$13 all week long; Jr. & Sr. & twilite rates; M/C, VISA.
Power cart: $18/$12. **Pull cart:** $3. **Trail fee:** $10 for personal carts.
Reservation policy: please call in advance for tee times. **Winter condition:** the
course is open, dry. **Terrain:** relatively hilly. **Tees:** grass. **Temporary greens:** no.
Services: club rentals, lessons, snack bar, beer, wine, lounge (members only),
lockers, pro shop, driving range. **Comments:** beautiful views of Mount Rainier
and the surrounding countryside from many holes. A friendly staff and some of
the best greens in the Northwest can be found at Gig Harbor Golf & C. C.

Directions: from I-5 N&S take exit #132 to Highway 16 West. Proceed on Highway 16 West to the Gig Harbor City Center exit. Turn south off exit onto Pioneer Way. Proceed for 2 miles to Artondale RD where you will turn right. Proceed for .3 miles to the golf course located on your right hand side.

Course Yardage & Par:
M-2702 yards, par 35.
W-2614 yards, par 35.
<u>Dual tees for 18 holes:</u>
M-5420 yards, par 70.
W-5095 yards, par 70.

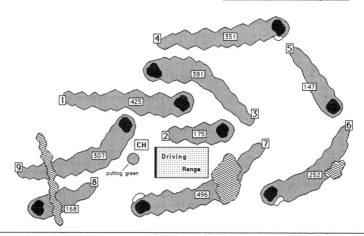

Glen Acres Golf & Country Club (private)

1000 S 112th; Seattle, WA 98168; (206) 244-3786
Pro: Bart Turchin, PGA. Supt.: Daniel Kukla. 9 hole course, dual tees.
Rating/Slope: M 69.5/122; W 73.2/127. Course record: 61.
Green fees: private club, members only, no credit cards; limited reciprocation.
Power cart: private club. **Pull cart:** private club. **Trail fee:** private club.
Reservation policy: yes, call up to 1 week in advance. **Winter condition:** wet.
Terrain: flat to hilly terrain. **Tees:** grass. **Temporary greens:** not in use.
Services: club rentals, lessons, snack bar, lounge, restaurant, beer, wine, liquor, pro shop, lockers, showers, club memberships, driving range, putting green.
Comments: the fairways are narrow and tree lined. All greens are well bunkered, elevated and are tough to putt on due to undulations. Good older private club that is kept in very good condition throughout the golfing year.

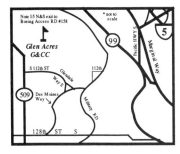

Directions: from I-5 N&S take exit 158B. Go west on Boeing Access Road for .4 miles to Pacific Hwy S. Travel south for 1.2 miles to S 128th. West for 1 mile to Des Moines Way. Go north for .5 miles and veer left to Glendale Way S. Proceed north for .7 miles to the golf course.

Course Yardage & Par:
M-3060 yards, par 36.
W-2829 yards, par 36.
Dual tees for 18 holes:
M-6088 yards, par 72.
W-5652 yards, par 72.

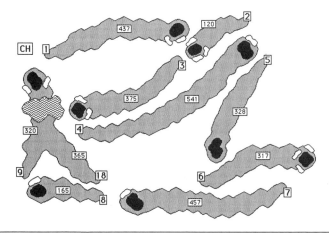

Glendale Golf & Country Club (private)

13440 Main; Bellevue, WA 98005; (206) 746-7377
Pro: Stan Hyatt, PGA. Superintendent: Stephen Kealy. 18 hole course.
Rating/Slope: C 71.5/135; M 70.2/132; W 73.1/131. **Course record:** 65.
Green fees: private club, members only; limited reciprocation; no credit cards.
Power cart: private club. **Pull cart:** private club. **Trail fee:** not allowed.
Reservation policy: yes, up to 1 week in advance, weekends only.
Winter condition: open, dry (drains well). **Terrain:** relatively hilly. **Tees:** grass.
Temporary greens: no. **Services:** lessons, snack bar, lounge, restaurant, beer,
wine, liquor, pro shop, lockers, showers, club memberships, driving range.
Comments: tough, well-trapped, woodsy layout that has fast greens and trouble
off the tees. This private facility has hosted the Washington State Open
Championship. A well maintained track that will challenge any level of golfer.

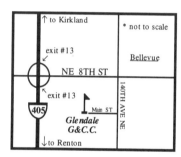

Directions: from I-405 N&S take exit
#13 to NE 8th St eastbound. Travel east
for 1.6 miles to 140th Ave. Turn south
(right) and proceed for 1 mile to Main
St. When you reach Main St. turn west
(right) on Main St. and proceed to the
golf course. **Note:** small sign just before
the entrance to the facility.

Course Yardage & Par:
C-6568 yards, par 72.
M-6274 yards, par 72.
W-5706 yards, par 72.

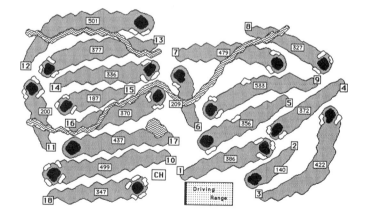

Gleneagle Golf Course (public)

7619 Country Club Drive; Arlington, WA 98223; (360) 435-6713
Pro: Bob Garza, PGA. Supt.: Tom Brower. 18 hole course, driving range.
Rating/Slope: C 69.0/128; M 66.8/119; W 67.6/121. **Course record:** 66.
Green fees: $27/$22; twilight rates. **Power cart:** $12 per person. **Pull cart:** $2.
Trail fee: $10. **Reservation policy:** call 7 days in advance for tee times.
Winter condition: open, weather permitting. **Terrain:** flat, some hills.
Tees: grass. **Temporary greens:** no. **Services:** club rentals, pro shop, driving
range, snack bar, full service clubhouse with restaurant. **Comments:** The course
features tree lined fairways, ponds and well bunkered greens. The 1st 9 holes
have been open for play since 1993. The driving range and full service clubhouse
with restaurant and bar are now open. Great golf course that plays tight in places.

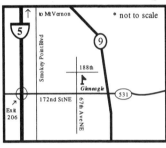

Directions: From I-5 N&S take exit #206
and proceed eastbound on 172nd ST NE until
you reach 67th Ave. NE. At 67th Ave. proceed
straight through up the hill to Gleneagle DR
where you will turn left. Proceed on Gleneagle
DR to the course. Look for signs along the way.

Course Yardage & Par:
C-6003 yards, par 70.
M-5480 yards, par 70.
W-4697 yards, par 70.

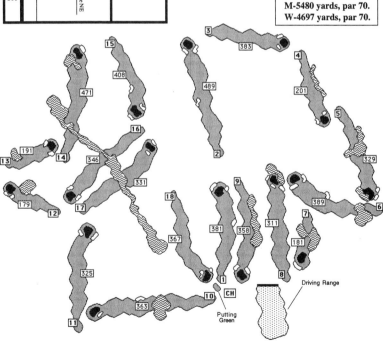

Gold Mountain Golf Course (public)
Physical address: 7263 West Belfair Valley Road; Gorst, WA 98337
Mailing address: P.O. Box 4130; Bremerton, WA 98312
Phone numbers: (360) 674-2363; or call toll free 1-800-249-2363
36 hole course, driving range, putting & chipping greens.
Pro: Scott Alexander, PGA. Superintendent: John Alexander.
Rating/Slope: C 71.6/120; M 68.6/116; W 69.9/116. Course record: 63.
Green fees: W/D $19/$13; W/E $23/$16; Jr/Sr rates (M-F) M/C, VISA.
Power cart: $20/$12. Pull cart: $3. Trail fee: $12 for personal carts.
Reservation policy: please call 1 week in advance at 11am for your tee-times.
Winter condition: the golf course is open all year long. Dry conditions.
Terrain: flat, some steep hills. **Tees:** all grass. **Temporary greens:** yes (winter).
Services: club rentals, lessons, snack bar, lounge, restaurant, beer, wine, pop,
lockers, well stocked pro shop, driving range, putting & chipping greens.
Comments: the course is well manicured, bunkered and long. The complex is
planning to open an additional 18 holes sometime in September of 1996. The new
course will feature extensive mounding, varied terrain and tree-lined fairways.
Water will come into play on some holes leaving the golfer many challenges from
the fairway. Gold Mountain is one of the finest public golf courses in the state of
Washington. If you get a chance to play this facility do not pass it up. The course
also has a well stocked pro shop for all your golfing needs.

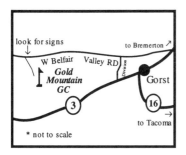

Directions: from I-5 N&S take exit 132
to Hwy 16W. Travel west to Hwy 3S. Go
straight ahead on Sam Christopherson Ave.
to W. Belfair Valley Road. Turn left and
follow for 2.3 miles to the course on your
left. From the Bremerton Ferry veer left
to 1st for 1 block to Burwell (Hwy 304W).
Follow signs to Shelton to Hwy 3S. Turn
south on 3S to Sam Christopherson Ave.
Turn right to W. Belfair Valley Rd. Turn
left and go 2.3 miles. **Note:** look for signs
to the course the way is well marked.

Old Course
Course Yardage & Par:
C-6708 yards, par 71. M-6059 yards, par 71. W-5306 yards, par 74.

New Course
Course Yardage & Par:
T-6912 yards, par 72. C-6404 yards, par 72. M-5936 yards, par 72. W-5371 yards, par 72.

New Golf Course

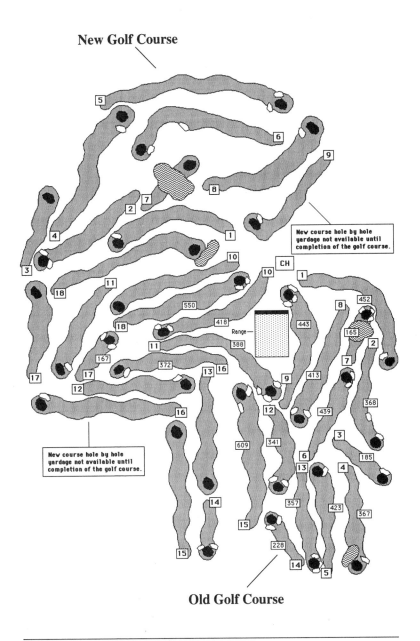

New course hole by hole yardage not available until completion of the golf course.

New course hole by hole yardage not available until completion of the golf course.

Old Golf Course

Goldendale Country Club (semi-private)

1901 N Columbus; P.O. Box 1026; Goldendale, WA 98620; (509) 773-4705
Pro: Joel Crocker, PGA. 9 hole course, dual tees for 18 holes.
Rating/Slope: M 66.2/107; W 69.4/114. **Course record:** 67.
Green fees: W/D $16/$11; W/E $19/$11; winter rates; no credit cards.
Power cart: $20/$12. **Pull cart:** $2. **Trail fee:** $3 for personal carts.
Reservation policy: none needed. Times are on a first come first served basis.
Winter condition: the course is sometimes closed in December and February.
Terrain: flat, some hills. **Tees:** separate grass tees. **Temporary greens:** no.
Services: club rentals, lessons, pro shop, putting green, chipping area.
Comments: the course is open to men only after 1 pm on Wednesday. This track
offers dual tees for those wanting to play a full 18 hole round. Beautiful mountain
and territorial views abound from this golf course. A creek comes into play on two
holes with sand bunkers doting some fairways. Good 9 hole course.

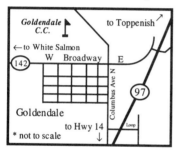

Directions: from Hwy 97 N&S follow
to city center to Columbus St. (flashing
light). Turn right and travel 1.5 miles to
the golf course. **Note:** the golf course is
located on the north edge of the city.
Look for signs indicating your turn.

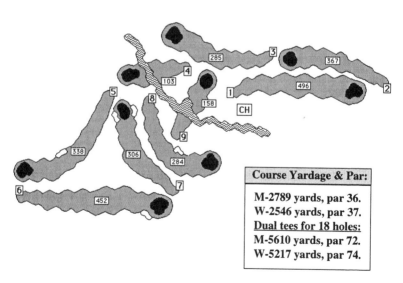

Course Yardage & Par:
M-2789 yards, par 36.
W-2546 yards, par 37.
Dual tees for 18 holes:
M-5610 yards, par 72.
W-5217 yards, par 74.

Golfgreen Golf Center (public)

Box 1123; 561 7th Avenue; Longview, WA 98632; (360) 425-0450
Manager: Skip Manke. 9 hole par 3 course.
Rating/Slope: the golf course is not rated. **Course record:** 21.
Green fees: W/D $9/$4.75; W/E $9.50/$5; no credit cards.
Power cart: not available. **Pull cart:** $2.00. **Trail fee:** private carts not allowed.
Reservation policy: none, tee times are on a first come first served basis.
Winter condition: sometimes closed in bad weather. **Terrain:** flat, very
walkable. **Tees:** grass. **Temporary greens:** not in use. **Services:** club rentals $2,
coffee shop, full service pro shop, miniature golf. **Comments:** good hole
variation. Yardage ranges from 55 yards to almost 200. A great course to practice
your short and long iron game on. Good golf course for family golf or the first
time golfer. Very easy course to walk so it is great for the senior golfer.

Directions: From I-5 N&S take exit #36
(Hwy 423) and travel westbound on Hwy
432 for .7 mile. Turn left at your first
available left at 9th Avenue to the golf
course. Look for signs indicating your
turn to the golf course. (The course is
located across from the drive in theater).

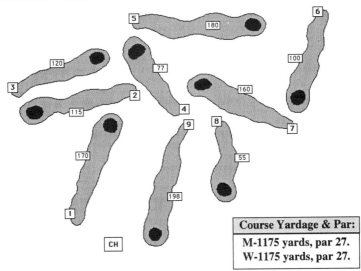

Course Yardage & Par:
M-1175 yards, par 27.
W-1175 yards, par 27.

Grandview Golf Course (public)

7738 Portal Way; Custer, WA 98240; (360) 366-3947
Manager: Kai Aihara. 18 hole course, putting green.
Rating/Slope: C 70.8/118; M 69.4/114; W 71.2/120. **Course record:** 67.
Green fees: W/D $18/$14; W/E $20/$16; Jr & Sr rates (M-F); VISA, M/C.
Power cart: $22/$16. **Pull cart:** $3. **Trail fee:** $8. **Reservation policy:** yes, call
7 days in advance for a tee time. **Winter condition:** open, dry. **Terrain:** flat.
Tees: grass. **Temporary greens:** no. **Services:** club rentals, snack bar, beer, wine,
pro shop, lockers. **Comments:** a very flat easy to walk course where water comes
into play on numerous holes. Bunkers guard medium size greens on many of your
approach shots. The golf course is fast becoming a top rate facility with adding
upgrades to enhance its playability. The golf course has great freeway access.

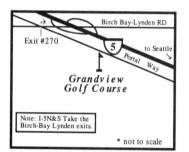

Directions: from I-5 N&S take exit 270
(Lynden-Birch Bay) to the west. Travel
west for .2 miles to Portal Way. Turn
south for 1.4 miles to the golf course.
Note: the golf course can be seen from
Interstate 5. Look for signs marking your
way to the golf course.

Course Yardage & Par:
C-6497 yards, par 72.
M-6203 yards, par 72.
W-5656 yards, par 72.
F-5101 yards, par 72.

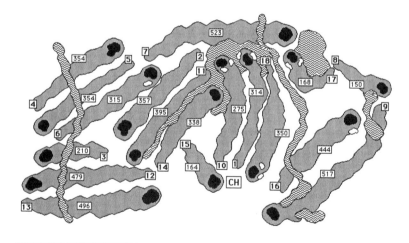

Grays Harbor Country Club (private)

5300 Central Park Drive; Aberdeen, WA 98520; (360) 532-1931
Pro: Keith Liedes, PGA. Superintendent: Don Scott. 9 hole course, dual tees.
Rating/Slope: M 67.1/111; W 71.6/119. **Course record:** 62.
Green fees: private club, members & guest only; reciprocates.
Power cart: private club. **Pull cart:** private club. **Trail fee:** private club.
Reservation policy: yes, minimum call 1 day in advance. **Winter condition:** the
golf course is open, dry (drains well). **Terrain:** flat, some hills. **Tees:** grass.
Temporary greens: occasionally. **Services:** club rentals, lessons, snack bar,
lounge, restaurant, beer, wine, liquor, lockers, pro shop, showers, club memberships, driving range, putting green. **Comments:** a variety of shots are required
on this course. Greens are medium to large in size. Challenging holes abound from
this 9 holer. Great course that plays and is much harder than it looks.

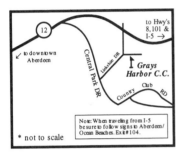

Directions: from I-5 N&S take exit
#104 (Ocean Beaches) to Hwy 12 to
Aberdeen/Hoquiam. Exit (left) in
Central Park on Central Park Drive.
Travel .75 miles to the golf course.

Course Yardage & Par:
M-2915 yards, par 35.
W-2884 yards, par 36.
Dual tees for 18 holes:
M-5779 yards, par 70.
W-5644 yards, par 72.

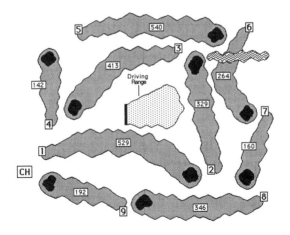

Green Lake Golf Course (public)

5701 W Greenlake Way N; Seattle, WA 98103; (206) 632-2280.
Manager: Marlene Taitch. Pro: none. 9 hole par 3 course.
Rating/Slope: the golf course is not rated. **Course record:** 22.
Green fees: $4/$2 additional 9 holes (all week long); Jr. & Sr. rates.
Power cart: none. **Pull cart:** $1. **Trail fee:** no personal carts allowed .
Reservation policy: tee times are on a first come first served basis.
Winter condition: the golf course is closed. **Terrain:** very, flat. **Tees:** mats.
Temporary greens: not in use. **Services:** club rentals, lessons, vending machines,
small pro shop. **Comments:** the course is located at Green Lake in north Seattle.
Excellent for practice on your short iron play. If you are looking for a course for
the first time golfer Green Lake is sure to fit the bill.

Directions: From I-5 N&S take exit 159
to NE 50th. Go westbound for 1.3 miles to
Green Lake Way N. North for .8 miles to
the golf course (located at the southern tip
of Greenlake).

Course Yardage & Par:
M-705 yards, par 27.
W-705 yards, par 27.

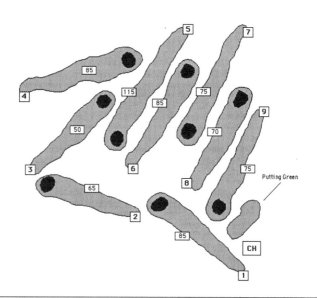

Hangman Valley Golf Club (public)

2210 E Hangman Valley Road; Spokane, WA 99203; (509) 448-1212
Pro: Steve Nelke, PGA. 18 hole course, driving range.
Rating/Slope: C 71.9/126; M 69.7/122; W 72.2/124. **Course record:** 64.
Green fees: $14/$10 residents, $18/$13.50 non-residents; Jr. & Sr. rates;
M/C, VISA for carts and merchandise only. **Power cart:** $20/$10. **Pull cart:** $2.
Trail fee: $5. **Reservation policy:** call ahead up to 1 week in advance for times.
Winter condition: the golf course is closed from November until mid March.
Terrain: relatively hilly. **Tees:** grass. **Temporary greens:** yes (at times).
Services: club rentals, lessons, restaurant, snack bar, beer, wine, pro shop, driving
range, putting green, chipping green. **Comments:** a challenging course featuring
elevated tees, many trees, and well bunkered greens. Hangman Creek comes into
play on four holes and is a major factor. Excellent public golf course.

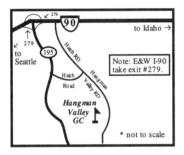

Directions: from I-90 east and west, take
the exit for Hwy 195 S. Proceed for 4.5
miles to the Hatch Road exit. Turn left
on Hatch Road for .2 miles to Hangman
Valley Road. Turn right on Hangman
Valley Road. The golf course will be
located five miles ahead. Look for signs.

Course Yardage & Par:
C-6551 yards, par 71.
M-6109 yards, par 71.
W-5603 yards, par 71.

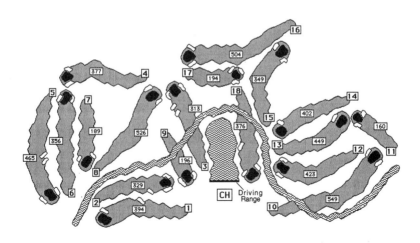

Harbour Pointe Golf Club (public)

11817 Harbour Pt. Blvd; Mukilteo, WA 98275; 800-233-3128, (206) 355-6060
Pro: Mark Rhodes, PGA. Supt.: Sean Cracraft. 18 hole course, range.
Rating/Slope: T 72.8/135; C 71.6/130; M 69.7/122; W 64.1/119. **Record:** 62.
Green fees: Mon.-Thurs. $40/$22; Fri.- Sun. $45/$25; twilight rates; M/C, VISA.
Power cart: $26/$15. **Pull cart:** $3/$2. **Trail fee:** personal carts not allowed.
Reservation policy: yes, call 5 days in advance for times. **Winter condition:** dry.
Terrain: flat, some hills. **Tees:** grass. **Temporary greens:** no. **Services:** club
rentals, lessons, restaurant, lounge, beer, wine, liquor, pro shop, driving range,
practice area. **Comments:** outstanding layout with water and sand coming into
play on nearly every hole. This track is challenging and demanding. Breathtaking
view of Puget Sound from the 11th hole. The course is worth the trip if in the area.

Directions: from I-5 or I-405 exit onto
Mukilteo to Hwy 99. Turn right on Hwy
99. At the first stop light turn left onto the
Mukilteo Speedway. Once on the Mukilteo
Speedway go to the second light and turn
left onto Harbour Pointe Blvd. Proceed to
the golf course on your right hand side.
I-5 southbound should exit at 164th St. and
prooceed to 99 northbound and proceed to
the Mukilteo Speedway. Follow above
directions.

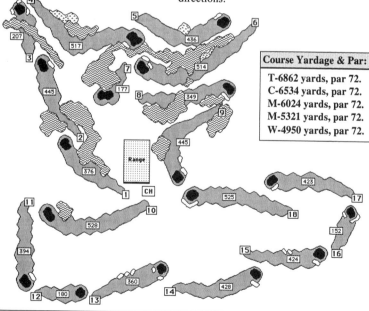

Course Yardage & Par:
T-6862 yards, par 72.
C-6534 yards, par 72.
M-6024 yards, par 72.
M-5321 yards, par 72.
W-4950 yards, par 72.

Harrington Golf & Country Club (semi-private)
700 South 2nd; PO Box 191; Harrington, WA 99134; (509) 253-4308
Pro: George Winn, PGA. 9 hole course, dual tees for 18 holes.
Rating/Slope: M 70.1/119; W 74.6/126. **Course record:** 66.
Green fees: W/D $14/$10; W/E $16/$11; Sr rates (weekdays); M/C, VISA.
Power cart: $20/$12. **Pull cart:** $3.00. **Trail fee:** $6/$4.
Reservation policy: please call for starting times. **Winter condition:** the golf
course is open, if playable. **Terrain:** moderate to relatively hilly. **Tees:** grass.
Temporary greens: no. **Services:** club rentals, restaurant, snack bar, lounge
(members and guests), beer, wine, liquor, pro shop, driving range, putting green.
Comments: the course is one of the finest 9 holers in the state. This course is
situated in the midst of rolling, beautiful wheat fields. Excellent golf course that
has wide open fairways and large, well bunkered greens.

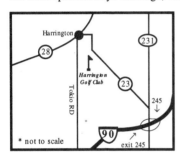

Directions: from I-90 east & west exit
to Hwy 231, #245 and head northbound.
Hwy 231 will intersect with Hwy 23.
Follow Hwy 23 to Harrington. When in
Harrington exit to Hwy 28. From Hwy 28
exit on Main Street and proceed south to
the golf course.

Course Yardage & Par:
M-3166 yards, par 36.
W-2983 yards, par 36.
Dual tees for 18 holes:
M-6348 yards, par 72.
W-5988 yards, par 72.

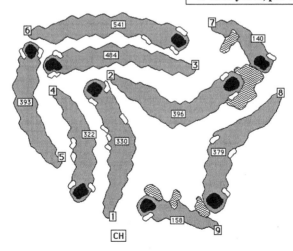

Hat Island Golf Course (private)

1016A 14th St. Everett, WA; 98201; (206) 339-8485
Manager: Ray Carnevali. 9 hole course, dual tees for 18 holes.
Rating/Slope: golf course is not rated. **Course record:** 32.
Green fees: private club, property owners and their guests $10/$5.
Power cart: private club. **Pull cart:** private club. **Trail fee:** private club.
Reservation policy: private club, members & guests only.
Winter condition: the golf course is open for play open, weather permitting.
Terrain: flat, easy walking course. **Tees:** grass. **Temporary greens:** no.
Services: private club, members and guests only. **Comments:** the golf course is
very flat and easy to walk. Holes are very narrow with many trees surrounding
fairways and greens. Tight golf course.

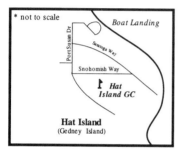

Directions: Hat Island golf course is
located in Puget Sound just west of
Everett and southeast of Camano Island.

Course Yardage & Par:
M-2335 yards, par 35.
W-2335 yards, par 35.
<u>**Dual tees for 18 holes:**</u>
M-4805 yards, par 70.
W-4805 yards, par 70.

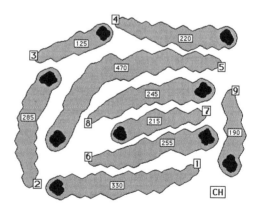

High Cedars Golf Club (public)

14604 149th Ct E; Box 490; Orting, WA 98360; (360) 893-3171, (206) 845-1853
Pro: Ryan Wilson, PGA. **Supt.:** Darin Thompson. **18 hole, 9 hole exec. course.**
Rating/Slope: C 70.2/116; M 68.7/113; W 72.0/118. **Course record:** 64.
Executive course Rating/Slope: M 53.8/78; W 56.4/83. **Power cart:** $21.50/$15.
Green fees: W/D $21.50/$16.25; W/E $30/$22; M/C, VISA. **Pull cart:** $4/$2.50.
Trail fee: $15. **Reservation policy:** call ahead up to 1 week in advance for times.
Winter condition: dry. **Terrain:** flat. **Tees** grass. **Temporary greens:** yes. **Services:** club rentals, lessons, snack bar, beer, pro shop, large driving range, outdoor barbecue. **Comments:** towering cedar trees, great restaurant, and beautiful flowers make for a fantastic day of golf. This one is a favorite with the locals. The facility has just added an 18 hole all grass putting course, fees are $6.00. Great complex.

<u>**Directions:**</u> From I-5 S exit to I-405 N to Hwy 167S. Proceed southbound on Hwy 167 and exit at Hwy 410E. Proceed east on Hwy 410E to the Orting exit (Hwy 162). Turn right on Hwy 162 and proceed for 5 miles to the golf course. From I-5 N take exit #127 to Hwy 512E. Travel east to the Pioneer Ave exit. Turn right on Hwy 162 and travel 4 miles to the golf course. **Note:** Sign on Hwy 410 for your turn off of the Highway.

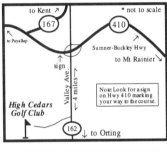

Executive Course Yardage & Par:
C-1566 yards, par 28.
M-1538 yards, par 28.
W-1326 yards, par 28.

Course Yardage & Par:
C-6303 yards, par 71.
M-5971 yards, par 72.
W-5503 yards, par 72.

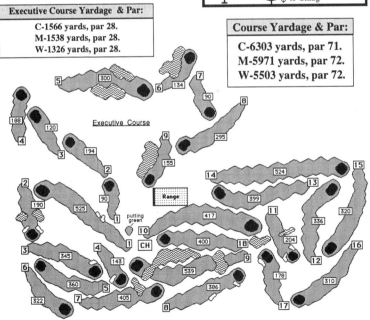

High Valley Golf Course (private)

633 Cannon Road, Box 427; Packwood, WA 98361; (360) 494-8431
Manager: Mike Christiansen. Supt.: Michael Gibbons. 9 hole course.
Rating/Slope: M 56.4/88; W 59.1/95. **Course record:** 29.
Green fees: W/D $8 all day rate; W/E $10 all day rate.
Power cart: limited. **Pull cart:** limited. **Trail fee:** available.
Reservation policy: none. **Winter condition:** closed from November to February.
depending on the weather. **Terrain:** flat. **Tees:** grass. **Temporary greens:** no.
Services: club rentals, limited pro shop, vending machines, pool, putting green.
Comments: a very scenic private club near Mount Rainier and right on the
Cowlitz River. Fairways are tree lined with few other hazards coming into play.
The course can play tough if the wind begins to blow.

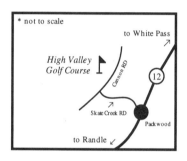

Directions: from Hwy 12 exit on Skate
Creek Road (north in Packwood). Travel
east, just over the river (.5 miles). Turn
right on Cannon Road. Proceed 2 miles
to the golf course.

Course Yardage & Par:
M-1782 yards, par 31.
W-1782 yards, par 33.

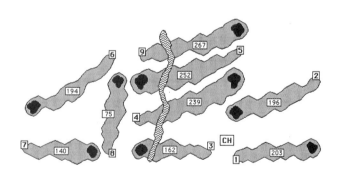

Highland Golf Course (public)
300 Yard Drive; P.O. Box 542; Cosmopolis, WA 98537; (360) 533-2455
Pro: Joe Golia, PGA. Superintendent: Joseph Strada. 18 hole course.
Rating/Slope: C 68.1/111; M 66.5/106: W 63.8/100. **Course record: 62.**
Green fees: W/D $15/$9; W/E & Hol. $17/$12; credit cards accepted.
Power cart: $20/$10. **Pull cart:** $3. **Trail fee:** $5. **Reservation policy:** call in
advance for tee times. **Winter condition:** dry. **Terrain:** relatively hilly.
Tees: grass and mats. **Temporary greens:** yes. **Services:** club rentals, lessons,
snack bar, beer, wine, pro shop, driving range. **Comments:** established in 1929
this course has many mature trees with which one must contend to score well.
The golf course has been expanded to 18 holes in June of 1994. Worth a trip.

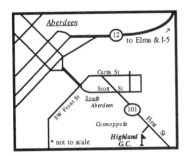

Directions: from I-5 north & south take
exit #104 and follow Hwy 12 to Aberdeen
Proceed to Hwy 101. The golf course is
located 2 miles south of the Aberdeen city
limits. Turn westbound to the golf course.
Look for signs marking your way to the
golf course.

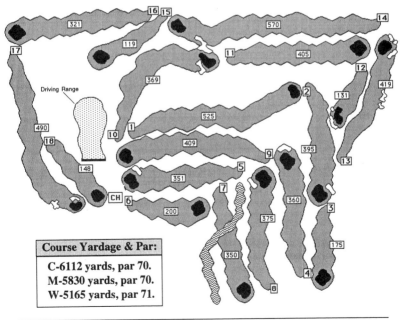

Course Yardage & Par:
C-6112 yards, par 70.
M-5830 yards, par 70.
W-5165 yards, par 71.

Highlands Golf & Racquet Club (public)

1400 Highlands Parkway N; Tacoma, WA 98406; (206) 759-3622
Manager: George Greco. Supt.: Clyde Stramper. 9 hole executive course.
Rating/Slope: golf course is not rated. **Course record:** 9 holes 23, 18 holes 52.
Green fees: $12/$7.50; Jr /Sr rates $10/$6.50; punch cards available; credit cards.
Power cart: not allowed. **Pull cart:** $2. **Trail fee:** not allowed.
Reservation policy: tee times are on a first come first serve d basis.
Winter condition: the golf course is open all year long, dry, excellent drainage.
Terrain: flat, some hills. **Tees:** grass. **Temporary greens:** not in use.
Services: club rentals, pro shop, club memberships, putting & chipping greens.
Comments: kept in good condition, two water holes, lots of bunkers, tennis courts
available. Excellent executive length golf course that will be worth the trip if you.
are looking for a change of pace. Chipping and putting greens to practice on.

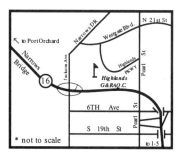

Directions: from I-5 N&S take exit #132
to Hwy 16W. From Hwy 16W exit at 6th
Avenue. Go westbound for .1 mile to
Pearl Street. Go northbound for 1 mile to
Westgate Blvd. Turn west for .5 miles to
Highlands Parkway N. Left for one block
to the clubhouse. Note: You can see the
golf course from Hwy 16. Look for signs.

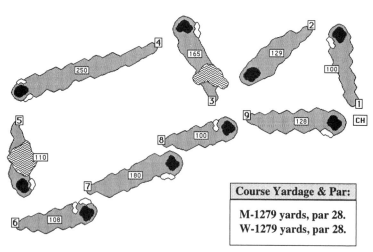

Course Yardage & Par:
M-1279 yards, par 28.
W-1279 yards, par 28.

Holmes Harbor Golf Club (public)
5023 Harbor Hills Drive; Freeland, WA 98249; (360) 331-2363
Pro: N/A. **18 hole course, 9-hole natural grass putting course.**
Rating/Slope: C 61.9/104; M 60.9/102; W 62.3/100. **Course record:** 63.
Green fees: Monday-Thursday $18/$13; Friday-Sunday $24/$19; Jr. & Sr. rates.
Power cart: $9 per player. **Pull cart:** $2. **Trail fee:** $12. **Reservation policy:** call
up to 5 days in advance (7 days for members). **Winter condition:** open, dry.
Terrain: flat, some hills. **Tees:** grass. **Temporary greens:** no. **Services:** club
rentals, lessons, lounge, restaurant, snack bar, beer, wine, liquor, pro shop.
Comments: very scenic newer course with views of the Cascades, Olympics, and
Holmes Harbor from many tees and greens. Excellent well managed golf course.

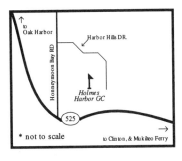

Directions: take the Mukilteo ferry to
Clinton. Travel 10.1 miles on Hwy 525.
Turn right on Honeymoon Bay Road.
Travel 1.3 miles. Turn right on Harbor
Hills Dr. and follow directly to the parking
lot of the golf course (this is where the
road ends).

Course Yardage & Par:
C-4371 yards, par 64.
M-4035 yards, par 64.
W-3565 yards, par 64.

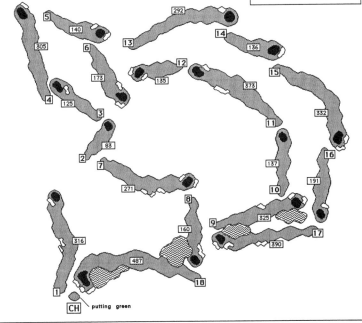

Homestead Golf & Country Club (semi-private)

115 Homestead Blvd.; Lynden, WA 98264; 1-800-354-1196
Pro: Wayne Clark, PGA. 18 hole course, range. Course record: N/A.
Rating/Slope: T 73.6/129; C 71.9/125; M 69.9/117; W 72.9/123.
Green fees: W/D $32/$20; W/E $36/$24; Jr. & Sr. rates all week long.
Power cart: $22/$12. **Pull cart:** $3/$2. **Trail fee:** not allowed.
Reservation policy: 1 week in advance. **Winter condition:** dry. **Terrain:** flat,
some hills. **Tees:** grass. **Services:** club rentals, lessons, driving range, full service
clubhouse with restaurant, beer, wine, pro shop. **Comments:** this Bill Overdorf
design promises to be a challenge to all golfers. All 18 holes opened in the spring
of 1995. Signature hole is the par 5 eighteenth hole that will test your nerve.

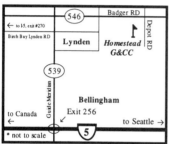

Directions: from I-5 northbound take exit
#256, Hwy 539 (Guide Meridian) to
Lynden (10 miles). Turn eastbound on Hwy
546 for 1.5 miles to Depot RD. Turn south
on Depot RD for 1/4 mile to the course.
From I-5 southbound exit off of I-5 at Birch
Bay-Lynden #270 and follow to Lynden.
Turn northbound on Hwy 539 and follow
the above directions to the golf course.

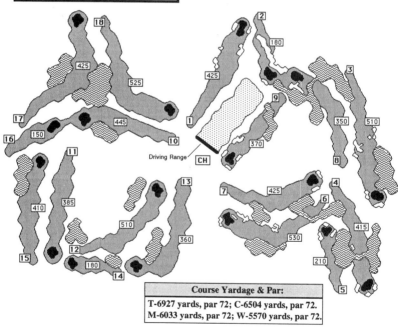

Course Yardage & Par:
T-6927 yards, par 72; C-6504 yards, par 72.
M-6033 yards, par 72; W-5570 yards, par 72.

Horn Rapids Golf & Country Club (public)

2800 SR 240; PO Box 840; Richland, WA 98352; (509) 375-4714
Pro: Matt Mandel, PGA. 18 hole course, driving range.
Rating/Slope: T N/A; C 73.6/130; M 71.0/122; W 70.4/117. **Course record:** 67.
Green fees: W/D $15/$10; W/E $20/$15; Jr. & Sr., twilight rates.
Power cart: $20/$12. **Pull cart:** $4. **Trail fee:** $10. **Reservation policy:** you may
call 1 week in advance for tee times. **Winter condition:** dry, course open weather
permitting. **Terrain:** flat, some rolling hills. **Tees:** grass. **Temporary greens:** no.
Services: club rentals, lessons, snack bar, beer, wine, pro shop, driving range.
Comments: the golf course is a desert style track emphasizing shot placement
(target golf). If you are looking for change and want a challenge try Horn Rapids.

Directions: the golf course is located on
Highway 240 2 miles west of Richland
Washington (the Vantage Highway). From
I-182/Hwy12 in Richalnd, WA take exit #4
and proceed northbound to the golf course
which is located 2.3 miles north. Look for
signs indicating your turn to the course.

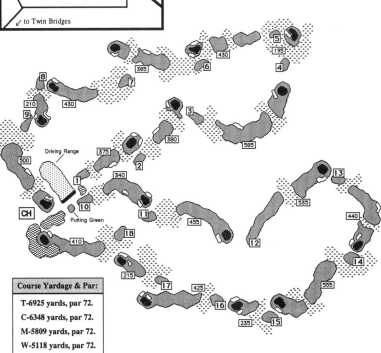

Course Yardage & Par:
T-6925 yards, par 72.
C-6348 yards, par 72.
M-5809 yards, par 72.
W-5118 yards, par 72.

Horseshoe Lake Golf Course (public)

15932 Sidney RD SW; Port Orchard, WA 98366; 1-800-843-1564, (206) 857-3326
Pro: Craig Wilcox, PGA. Superintendent: Scott Brooke. 18 hole course.
Rating/Slope: C 68.0/115; M 66.0/108; W 68.0/112. **Course record:** 57.
Green fees: W/D $25*/$13; W/E 29*/$17 (*includes power cart rental on back 9).
Jr. & Sr. rates. **Power cart:** 9 hole rental fee $5 per person. **Pull cart:** $3.
Trail fee: not allowed. **Reservation policy:** call up to 7 days in advance.
Winter condition: very dry. **Terrain:** front 9, flat; back 9 very hilly. **Tees:** grass.
Services: club rentals, driving range, full service clubhouse, restaurant, lessons.
Comments: this excellent on course restaurant, and challenging golf course is
worth a special trip. You will have fantastic views of the countryside and the
Olympic Mountains from nearly every tee. Challenging course that can be tough.

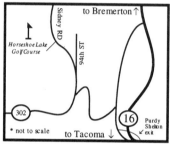

Directions: from Hwy 16 take the Purdy
exit. Proceed over the Purdy Bridge. At
94th Street turn right (this will become
Sidney Road). The golf course is located
3.5 miles from the Purdy exit. Look for
signs marking your way to the course.

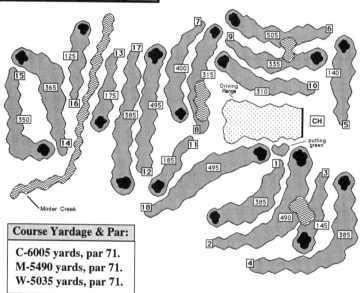

Course Yardage & Par:

C-6005 yards, par 71.
M-5490 yards, par 71.
W-5035 yards, par 71.

Hot Springs Golf Course (public)

Saint Martin Road; PO Box 370; Carson, WA 98610; (509) 427-5150
Managers: John Broughten, Bob Leonard. 18 hole course.
Rating/Slope: C 72.1/125; M 70.4/122; W 68.9/116. **Course record:** 73.
Green fees: W/D $16/$9; W/E $19/$11; Sr. & winter rates.
Power cart: $20/$10. **Pull cart:** $3.50/$2.50. **Trail fee:** no charge.
Reservation policy: yes, accepted for weekend tee-times, please call ahead.
Winter condition: dry, closed during ice or snow. **Terrain:** flat, some hills.
Tees: grass. **Temporary greens:** no. **Services:** snacks, beer, pro shop, driving
range. **Comments:** Gentle rolling terrain and wind that roles through the tree lined
fairwys characterize this golf course. Bunkered fairways along with water come
into play off the tee and approach shots. Greens are medium in size and are usually
well bunkered. Course plays much longer than the yardage would indicate.

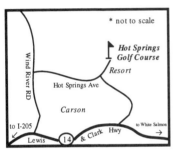

Directions: the golf course is located 1
mile north of Hwy 14 on the east side of
Carson. From Hwy 14 turn northbound
toward Carson, Washington. Turn right
on Hot Springs Avenue to the golf course.
Look for signs marking your way.

Course Yardage & Par:
C-6559 yards, par 73.
M-6150 yards, par 73.
W-5365 yards, par 73.

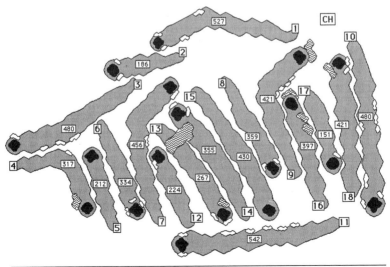

Husum Hills Golf Course (public)

820 Hwy 141, White Salmon, WA 98672; (509) 493-1211 or 1-800-487-4537
Pro: Craig Holland, PGA. 9 hole course.
Rating/Slope: 63.7/96; W 67.6/104. **Course record:** 31.
Green fees: $15/$8 all week long; credit cards are accepted.
Power cart: $17/$9. **Pull cart:** $4/$2. **Trail fee:** $5.
Reservation policy: yes, up to seven days in advance they are taken but not
necessary. **Winter condition:** golf course is open when playable. Closed Mondays
& Tuesdays from November to February. **Terrain:** flat to very hilly. **Tees:** grass
and mats. **Temporary greens:** no. **Services:** club rentals, restaurant, pro shop,
wine, beer, putting and chipping green. **Comments:** The course is well treed,
with beautiful views of Mount Adams. Grass bunkers abound which create some
difficult lies. Good nine hole track that can challenge any level of golfer. Course
is adding new hazards as well as rebuilding some tees to lengthen some holes.

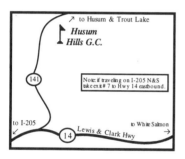

Directions: from I-5S take exit #7 to
I-205S. Travel southbound to exit #27 to
Hwy14E. Proceed eastbound to Hwy 141
and exit at Hwy 141. Go northbound on
Hwy 141 for 5.5 miles to the golf course.
Look for signs that are posted marking
your turn to the golf course.

Course Yardage & Par:
C-2631 yards, par 35.
M-2458 yards, par 35.
W-2390 yards, par 35.

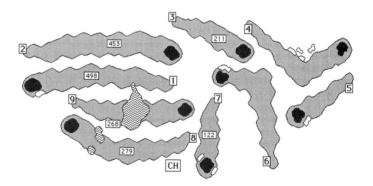

Indian Canyon Golf Course (public)

West 4304 West Drive; Spokane, WA 99204; (509) 747-5353
Pro: Gary Lindeblad, PGA. 18 hole course, driving range.
Rating/Slope: C 70.7/126; M 69.3/123; W 73.9/132. **Course record:** 62.
Green fees: county resident $16.75/$13; others $22/$17; Jr. & Sr. rates;
no credit cards except for merchandise. **Power cart:** $22. **Pull cart:** $3.
Trail fee: $9. **Reservation policy:** yes, weekdays -1 day, weekends -1 week
in advance. **Winter condition:** closed. **Terrain:** very hilly. **Tees:** grass.
Services: club rentals, lessons, restaurant, snack bar, beer, wine, pro shop,
driving range. **Comments:** consistently rated in the top 75 public courses by
Golf Digest. Greens are large and well bunkered. This golf course is extremely
well maintained and is worth a special trip if you are in the Spokane area.

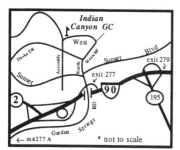

Directions: from I-90 eastbound &
westbound take the Garden Springs exit.
#277 or #277A. Proceed north on Rustle
Street to the Sunset Hwy where you will
turn left. Proceed to Assembly Street and
turn right. Follow this to the golf course.
Look for signs marking your way.

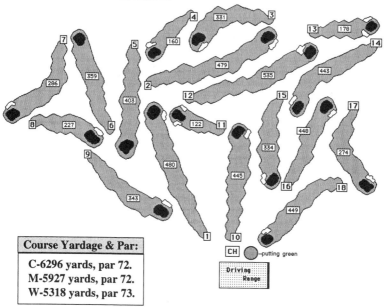

Course Yardage & Par:

C-6296 yards, par 72.
M-5927 yards, par 72.
W-5318 yards, par 73.

Indian Summer Golf & Country Club (private)

5900 Troon Lane SE; Olympia, WA 98501; (360) 459-3772
Pro: Kevin Bishop, PGA. Supt.: Thomas McCarthy. 18 hole course, range.
Rating/Slope: T 74.5/133; C 72.5/128; M 70.8/124; W 70.4/123. **Record:** 65.
Green fees: private club, members only. **Power cart:** $25. **Pull cart:** yes.
Trail fee: no. **Reservation policy:** have your golf pro call for recprocity.
Winter condition: dry. **Terrain:** flat, some hills. **Tees:** grass. **Services:** full
service clubhouse, restaurant, snack bar, lounge, pro shop, lockers, driving range.
Comments: championship caliber course. The back 9 winds through Pacific NW
old growth timber stands and bordering wetlands. The front 9 features wide open,
rolling terrain and water on 7 holes. Home of the Pacific NW PGA offices.

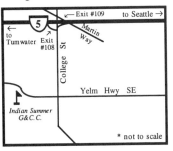

Directions: from I-5S exit #108 College
St. Proceed to College St. and turn right.
Follow College St. for 3.4 miles to the
Yelm Hwy. Turn right and follow for 1/2
mile to the golf course which will be on
your left. From I-5N take exit #109. Take
left on College St. and follow the same
directions. Look for signs at your turn.

Course Yardage & Par:

T-7216 yards, par 72.
C-6786 yards, par 72.
M-6374 yards, par 72.
F-5766 yards, par 72.
W-5199 yards, par 72.

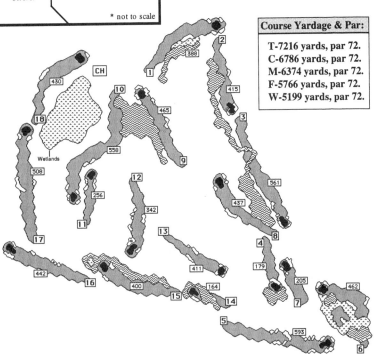

Inglewood Golf & Country Club (private)

6505 Inglewood RD NE; PO Box 70; Kenmore, WA 98011; (206) 488-7000
Pro: Rick Adell, PGA. Supt.: Tom Christy. 18 hole course, driving range.
Course record: 63. Competitive course record 64.
Rating/Slope: T 72.9/131; C 71.7/128; M 69.0/122; W 70.2/121.
Green fees: private club members & guests only; reciprocates; no credit cards.
Power cart: private club members & guests only. **Pull cart:** private club.
Trail fee: not allowed. **Reservation policy:** accepted. **Winter condition:** damp.
Terrain: very hilly. **Tees:** grass. **Services:** club rentals, lessons, snack bar,
restaurant, lounge, beer, wine, liquor, shower, lockers, pro shop, driving range.
Comments: past home of the Senior PGA event the "GTE Northwest Classic".
Hilly terrain gives a wide variety of fairway lies. Excellent, well stocked pro shop.

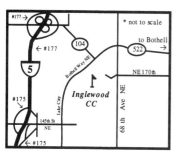

Directions: from I-5S take exit 177 to Hwy 104E (Forest Park Drive). Travel east 2.5 miles to Hwy 522 E (Bothell Way). Turn east fir 1.3 miles to 68th NE-Juanita Dr. Turn south for .4 miles to NE 170th. Turn west to the golf course. From I-5N take exit 175 to NE 145th. Travel east for 1.5 miles to Bothell Way NE. Turn left and travel 3.1 miles to 68th-Juanita Dr. Turn right. Proceed .4 miles to NE 170th. Turn right to the golf course.

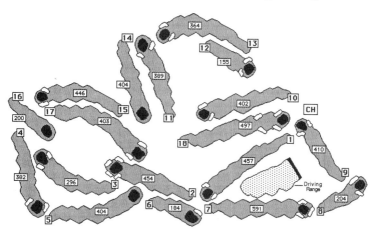

Course Yardage & Par:		
T-6731 yards, par 73; C-6460 yards, par 73.		
M-6075 yards, par 73; W-5163 yards, par 73.		

Ironwood Green Public Golf Course (public)
8138 U.S. Hwy 12; Glenoma, WA 98336; (360) 498-5425
Owners: Jim & Alice Redmon. 9 hole executive course.
Rating/Slope: the golf course is not rated. **Course record:** 28.
Green fees: $7.50/$5.50; Sr. rates $6.50 all week long; VISA M/C.
Power cart: $15/$8. **Pull cart:** $2. **Trail fee:** $7.50.
Reservation policy: no. **Winter condition:** open, dry. **Terrain:** flat.
Tees: grass. **Temporary greens:** no. **Services:** club rentals, lessons, pro shop,
convenience store, RV park. **Comments:** Nestled in the foothills of the Cascade
Mountains this tree lined executive course is an excellent test for your iron skills.
A friendly family owned golf course. Flat and only 1500 yards it is very walker
and senior friendly. Small bentgrass greens are a challenge for all who play. For
those traveling in an RV there is an RV park along the 9th fairway.

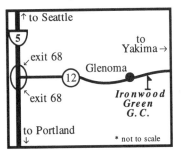

Directions: from I-5 N&S take exit #68
onto Hwy 12. Proceed eastbound to 47
miles to Glenoma. The golf course is
located just off Hwy 12 on the right.

Course Yardage & Par:
M-1500 yards, par 30.
W-1500 yards, par 31.

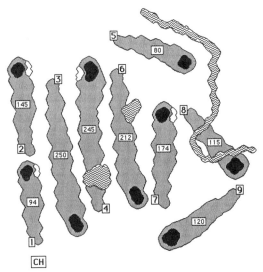

Island Greens (public)

3890 E French Road; Clinton, WA 98236; (360) 579-6042
Owners: Dave & Karen Anderson. 9 hole par 3 course.
Rating/Slope: the golf course is not rated. **Course record:** 25.
Green fees: W/D $10/$5; W/E $10/$5 (honor system @ times); no credit cards.
Power cart: not available. **Pull cart:** $1. **Trail fee:** no private carts.
Reservation policy: no policy, tee times are on a first come first serve basis.
Winter condition: the golf course is open all year long, damp.
Terrain: gently rolling terrain that is very walkable. **Tees:** grass & mats.
Services: club rentals, vending machines. **Comments:** this challenging par 3
course features rolling terrain, tree lined fairways and well manicured greens.
With three ponds, bunkered greens and a good variety of hole lengths Island
Greens can be a handful. Excellent par 3 course that is worth a trip during April
to June when the Rhodys are in bloom.

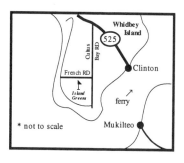

Directions: take the Mukilteo-Clinton
ferry to Clinton. Follow Hwy 525 2 miles
to Cultus Bay Road. Left on Cultus Bay
for 2 miles to French Road. Right on
French Road, course is .5 miles ahead.
Look for signs marking your way.

Course Yardage & Par:
C-1355 yards, par 27.
M-1135 yards, par 27.
W-859 yards, par 27.

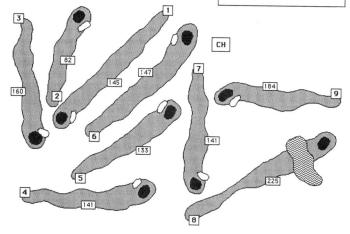

Jackson Park Golf Course (public)

1000 NE 135th; Seattle, WA 98125; (206) 363-4747; Tee-Times: 301-0472
Pro: Mark Granberg, PGA. Superintendent: Don Hellstrom. Record: 61.
Rating/Slope: C 68.6/113; M 67.4/111; W 71.8/118. **18 hole course, 9 hole par 3.**
Green fees: $15* all week long; M/C, VISA. (*all prices are subject to change).
Power cart: $18/$13*. **Pull cart:** $3/$2*. **Trail fee:** $4* for personal carts.
Reservation policy: yes, call up to 1 week in advance. **Winter condition:** damp.
Terrain: very hilly. **Tees:** grass. **Temporary greens:** yes (in winter).
Services: club rentals, lessons, snack bar, lounge, restaurant, beer, wine,
lockers, pro shop. **Comments:** few hazards, wide open. Very busy during the
peak golfing season. Good public golf course run by Municipal Golf of Seattle.
The course has a well stocked pro shop for all your golfing needs.

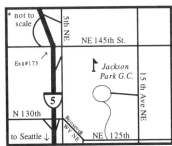

Directions: from I-5 N&S take exit #175
to NE 145th. Travel east for .5 miles to
15th Ave NE. Turn southbound on 15th
Ave NE and proceed for .5 miles to NE
135th. Turn west on 135th and go up
the hill to the entrance to the golf course
which will be on your right. Look for
signs marking your turn into Jackson Park.

Course Yardage & Par:
C-6212 yards, par 71.
M-5893 yards, par 71.
W-5636 yards, par 74.

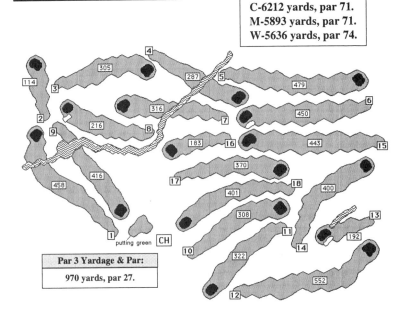

Par 3 Yardage & Par:
970 yards, par 27.

Jade Greens Golf Course & Driving Range (public)

18330 SE Lake Holm Road; Auburn, WA 98092; (206) 931-8562
Pro: Doug MacDonald, PGA. Manager: Jim Hawk Jr.
9 hole course (dual tees for 18 holes). Superintendent: Joseph Bauman.
Rating/Slope: C 65.9/113; M 65.0/110; W 62.1/103 . **Course record:** 61.
Green fees: W/D $16/$11; W/E $18/$13. Jr./Sr. rates $11/$7 (M-F); M/C VISA.
Power cart: $18/$13. **Pull cart:** $4/$2. **Trail fee:** $5/$2.50.
Reservation policy: yes, call up to 1 week in advance. **Winter condition:** dry.
Terrain: flat, some hills. **Tees:** grass. **Temporary greens:** no, not in use.
Services: club rentals, lessons, deli, beer, wine, pro shop, lighted driving range.
Comments: course surrounds natural wetlands. Excellent drainage for winter play.
Golf course has a 25 stall covered & lighted driving range. Great golf course.

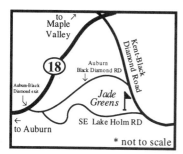

Directions: from I-5 take exit exit #142 (Hwy 18). Proceed eastbound on Hwy 18 to Auburn. Proceed just past the city limits on Hwy 18 where you will exit on the Auburn Black Diamond Road. Proceed for .5 miles to SE Lake Holm RD where you will turn right to the and proceed for 3.2 miles to the golf course.

Course Yardage & Par:
C-2656 yards, par 34.
M-2531 yards, par 34.
W-2232 yards, par 35.
Dual tees for 18 holes:
C-5348 yards, par 69.
M-5099 yards, par 69.
W-4501 yards, par 71.

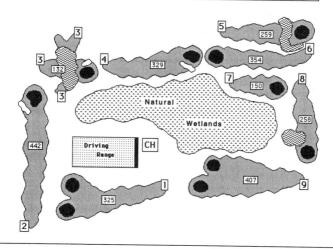

Jefferson Park Golf Course (public)

4101 Beacon Ave. S; Seattle, WA 98108; (206) 762-4513; Tee-Times: 301-0472
Pro: Pete Guzzo, PGA. Superintendent: James Weir.
18 hole regulation course, 9 hole par 3 course, covered, lighted driving range.
Rating/Slope: C 68.3/112; M 67.0/110; W 70.2/116. **Course record:** 62.
Green fees: $15* all week long; M/C, VISA; (*all prices subject to change).
Power cart: $18/$13*. **Pull cart:** $3*. **Trail fee:** $4*. **Winter condition:** damp.
Reservation policy: yes, up to 1 week in advance. **Terrain:** relatively hilly.
Tees: grass, mats. **Temporary greens:** yes. **Services:** club rentals, lessons, snack
bar, restaurant, beer, wine, lockers, pro shop, lighted and covered driving range.
Comments: a very busy golf course. Jefferson has a flat front nine and a relatively hilly back nine. Greens are large with a few greenside bunkers coming into
play on your approach shots. Many lovely views of the Seattle skyline can be seen
from several holes. Well stocked pro shop, and great lesson center.

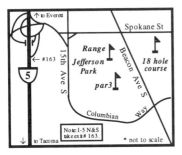

Directions: from I-5 N&S take exit #163
to Columbia Way. Turn left at the light
and travel .3 miles to Beacon Avenue S.
Turn southbound for .2 miles to the golf
course on your left hand side. The pro
shop will be located on your right hand
side next to the driving range.

Course Yardage & Par:
C-6093 yards, par 70.
M-5852 yards, par 70.
W-5490 yards, par 73.

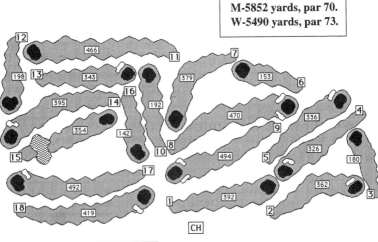

Par 3 Yardage & Par:
1225 yards, par 28.

Kahler Glen Golf Course (public)

20890 Kahler DR; Leavenworth, WA 98826; (509) 763-4025
Pro: Ed Paine. 18 hole course, putting green. Course record: 63.
Rating/Slope: M 68.3/129; W 71.4/132 (the golf course will be rerated).
Green fees: Monday thru Thursday $20/$12; Friday thru Sunday $25/$15.
Power cart: $22/$11. **Pull cart:** $3/$2. **Trail fee:** $10 for personal carts.
Reservation policy: yes, please call up to 3 weeks ahead for a tee time.
Winter condition: the golf course closed durinmg the winter months.
Terrain: flat, some hills. **Tees:** all grass. **Temporary greens:** not in use.
Services: club rentals, lessons, snack bar, pro shop, driving range, putting green.
Comments: located in Lake Wenatchee State Park this course is surrounded by
trees and sports very narrow fairways. The greens are medium to large giving the
golfer ample room to manoeuvre the ball. This definitely is a shot makers course.

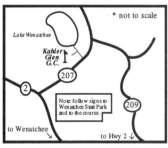

Directions: on Hwy 2 the course is
located 15 miles west of Leavenworth.
Turn in at Lake Wenatchee State Park
where the golf course is located. Make
sure you look for signs along the way.
A brown and white golf sign is on Hwy
2 marking your turn off of the Hwy.

Course Yardage & Par:

C-6105 yards, par 70.
M-5682 yards, par 70.
W-4994 yards, par 70.

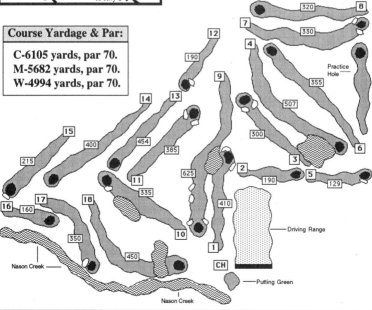

Kayak Point Golf Course (public)

15711 Marine Drive; Stanwood, WA 98292; (360) 652-9676; 1-800-562-3094
Director of Golf: Elwin Fanning, PGA. Pro: Doug Fair.
18 hole course, driving range, putting green. Supt.: Randy Vander Vaate
Rating/Slope: C 72.7/133; M 71.4/128; W 72.8/129. **Course record:** 67.
Green fees: Mon.-Fri. $23/$14, Sat.-Sun. & Hol. $27/$16; Jr./Sr. & winter rates
(M-F); M/C VISA. **Power cart:** $25/$12.50. **Pull cart:** $3. **Trail fee:** $12.50.
Reservation policy: yes, up to 1 week in advance for weekday tee times. Call 5
days in advance for weekend tee times. **Winter condition:** open, dry, golf course
has excellent drainage for winter play. **Terrain:** very hilly (consider a cart).
Tees: grass. **Temporary greens:** no. **Services:** club rentals, lessons, snack bar,
restaurant, liquor, lounge, beer, wine, pro shop, driving range. **Comments:** one
of the NW's most beautiful and difficult golf courses. Tree-lined fairways demand
accuracy off the tee. Greens are medium to large and well bunkered. Excellent
winter course that drains well. Course is worth a special trip if you are in the area.

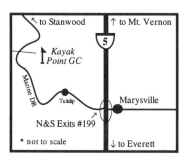

Directions: from I-5 N&S take exit
199 (Marysville-Tulalip) to Hwy 528W.
Travel west on Hwy 528W for approximately 14 miles to the golf course
entrance which will be on your right.
Follow the road up the hill to the golf
course. **Note:** Look for a sign on the Hwy
marking your turn to the golf course.

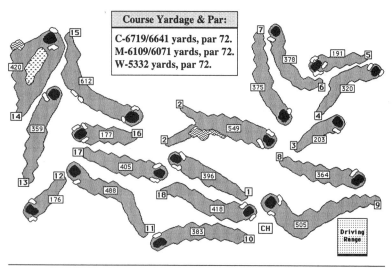

Course Yardage & Par:
C-6719/6641 yards, par 72.
M-6109/6071 yards, par 72.
W-5332 yards, par 72.

Kenwanda Golf Course (public)

14030 Kenwanda Drive; Snohomish, WA 98290; (360) 668-1166
Manager: Curtis Creighton. **18 hole course, putting green.**
Rating/Slope: M 65.3/119; W 70.4/126. **Course record:** 63.
Green fees: $18/$11; $25 all day rate; VISA, M/C.
Power cart: none. **Pull cart:** $2.50. **Trail fee:** no charge, weather restrictions.
Reservation policy: yes, call 7 days a week, up to 1 week in advance.
Winter condition: course is open, dry. **Terrain:** relatively hilly. **Tees:** grass.
Temporary greens: no. **Services:** club rentals, snack bar, restaurant, coffee shop, beer, wine, pro shop.**Comments:** atop a hill, Kenwanda boasts beautiful views of Mt. Baker, Mt. Rainier, and the Cascades. The course has very small greens, wide sloping fairways lined by trees. Accuracy is a must at Kenwanda.

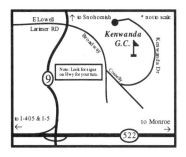

Directions: from Hwy 9 turn right on Broadway/131st Street. Follow approximately 1/2 mile to Connelly St. and turn left. Go .2 miles to Kenwanda Dr. Turn left. The clubhouse is at the top of the hill and will be on your left hand side. From I-405 take exit #23 to Hwy 522. Follow Hwy 522 to Hwy 9 and follow the above directions. **Note:** Look for a sign on Hwy 9 marking your way to the golf course.

Course Yardage & Par:

M-5336 yards, par 69.
W-5336 yards, par 72.

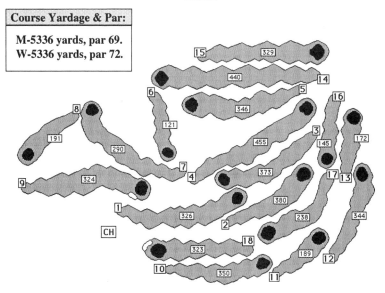

Kitsap Golf & Country Club (private)

3885 NW Golf Club Hill Road; Bremerton, WA 98312; (360) 373-5101
Pro: Mark Sivara, PGA. Superintendent: Scott Westwood. 18 hole course.
Rating/Slope: C 70.7/121; M 70.0/120; W 72.0/124. **Course record:** 64.
Green fees: private club members and guests only; reciprocates.
Power cart: private club. **Pull cart:** private club. **Trail fee:** private club.
Reservation policy: yes, up to 1 week in advance. **Winter condition:** open, dry.
Terrain: relatively hilly. **Tees:** grass. **Temporary greens:** yes. **Services:** coffee
shop, dining room, ballroom, lounge, pro shop, driving range, lessons, putting &
chipping green, club memberships available. **Comments:** very demanding layout
with tricky doglegs and well bunkered, fast greens. Fairways are tree lined and can
be very narrow in spots. This private track is always in excellent condition.

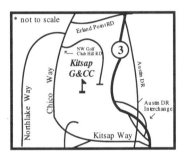

Directions: from Hwy 3 take the exit for
Austin-Kitsap Lake. Turn right on Austin
Road and proceed for 1.1 miles to Erland
Point Road. Turn left and proceed for .5
miles to Chico Way. Turn Left and proceed
for .3 miles to NW Golf Club Hill Road.
Proceed to the golf course on NW Golf
Club Hill Road. Look for a small sign
marking your turn to the golf course.

Course Yardage & Par:
C-6329 yards, par 71.
M-6153 yards, par 71.
W-5590 yards, par 73.

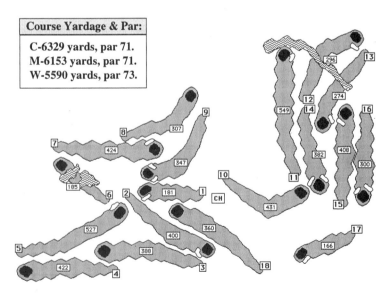

Lake Chelan Golf Course (public)

1501 Golf Course Drive; PO Box 1669; Chelan, WA 98816; (509) 682-5421
Pro: Jim Oscarson, PGA. Supt.: Don Hensley. 18 hole course, range.
Rating/Slope: C 70.3/119; M 68.7/116; W 71.1/122. **Course record:** 65.
Green fees: $24/$15 all week long; VISA, M/C.
Power cart: $20/$12. **Pull cart:** $3/$2. **Trail fee:** $10.
Reservation policy: yes, up to 1 week in advance. **Winter condition:** the golf
course is closed during the winter November to March. **Terrain:** flat, some hills.
Tees: grass. **Temporary greens:** not in use. **Services:** lessons, club rentals, snack
bar, beer, wine, pro shop, driving range, putting green. **Comments:** this is a
beautiful course situated in a favorite summer spot of weekend vacationers.
This golf course is set atop a hill over looking Lake Chelan and the surrounding
landscape. Greens are medium to large in size but can become very firm and fast
in the summer months. Great course for the summer golfer. The golf course has
improved many of the teeing area's in the last few months.

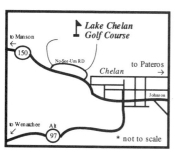

Directions: follow Hwy 150 through
Chelan toward Manson. About 1/4 mile
beyond the City Trailer Park take the right
fork of the No-See-Um Road to the golf
course. Look for signs to the golf course
on the Manson Hwy marking your turn.

Course Yardage & Par:
C-6440 yards, par 72.
M-6152 yards, par 72.
W-5501yards, par 73.

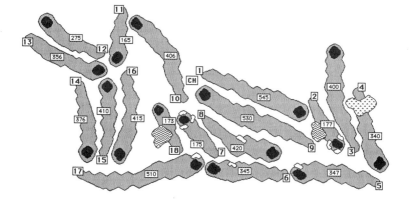

Lake Cushman Golf Course (public)

North 210 W Fairway Drive; Hoodsport, WA 98548; (360) 877-5505
Manager: Brad Brush. 9 hole course, dual tees for 18 holes.
Rating/Slope: M 68.0/117; W 71.5/122. **Course record:** 62.
Green fees: W/D $16/$11; W/E & Holidays $19/$15; tightwad Tuesday $12/$6.
Power cart: $20/$12. **Pull cart:** $2.50. **Trail fee:** $5 for personal carts.
Reservation policy: yes, you may call ahead 14 days for tee-time reservations.
(advised in summer). **Winter condition:** damp, open depending on the weather.
Terrain: flat, some hills. **Tees:** grass. **Temporary greens:** no, not in use.
Services: club rentals, snack bar, small pro shop, practice range, putting green,
club memberships. **Comments:** a very challenging 9 hole course set in the beautiful Olympic Mountains. Fairways are tree-lined with few hazards coming into play
around the greens. Excellent on course driving range so plan to practice.

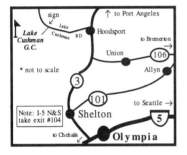

Directions: from I-5 N&S take exit 104 to
Hwy 101. Exit Hwy 101N to Shelton-Port
Angeles. Follow to Hoodsport. At the
north end of Hoodsport turn left to the
Lake Cushman Resort. Follow for 2.8
miles to Fairway Village. Left, then right
to the golf course. Look for signs.

Course Yardage & Par:
C-2848 yards, par 35.
M-2957 yards, par 35.
W-2674 yards, par 35.
Dual tees for 18 holes:
C-5696 yards, par 70.
M-5914 yards, par 70.
W-5348 yards, par 70.

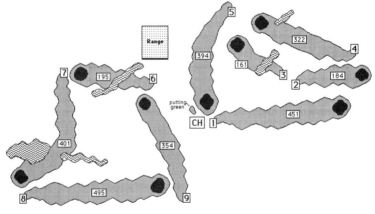

Lake Limerick Country Club (semi-private)
E 790 Saint Andrews Drive; Shelton, WA 98584; (360) 426-6290
Pro: Terry O'Hara. 9 hole course, dual tees for 18 holes.
Rating/Slope: M 67.2/114; W 70.9/120. **Course record:** 67.
Green fees: W/D $15/$10; W/E $18/$13; M/C, VISA, AMEX.
Power cart: $21/$13. **Pull cart:** $3/$2. **Trail fee:** $5 for personal carts.
Reservation policy: yes, call up to one week in advance for tee times.
Winter condition: open, damp. **Terrain:** flat, some hills. **Tees:** grass.
Temporary greens: no. **Services:** club rentals, restaurant, beer, wine, snack bar,
pro shop. **Comments:** narrow tree lined fairways and tricky greens makes this
course a real test of golf. Greens are medium in size and fairly flat. Perfect golf
course for a quick 9 holes on a weekend to the Olympic Peninsula. Do not let the
lack of yardage fool you this course plays very tough in spots.

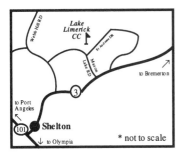

Directions: on Hwy 3 go 5 miles north of
Shelton to Mason Lake Road. Turn left
on Mason Lake Road and travel approximately 3 miles to the Lake Limerick
entrance. Turn left on St. Andrews Drive
and follow for 1 mile to the golf course.
Look for signs marking your way to the
golf course.

Course Yardage & Par:
M-2898 yards, par 36. **W-2658 yards, par 36.** **<u>Dual tees for 18 holes:</u>** **M-5779 yards, par 72.** **W-5424 yards, par 72.**

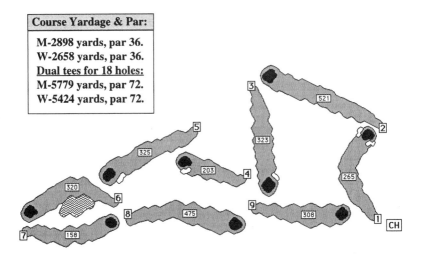

Lake Padden Golf Course (public)

4882 Samish Way; Bellingham, WA 98226; (360) 676-6989
Pro: Kene Bensel, PGA. Superintendent: James Howes. 18 hole course.
Rating/Slope: C 72.0/124; M 69.9/120; W 71.9/122. **Course record:** N/A.
Green fees: Whatcom County residents $15/$12, non residents $22/$17;
Jr. & Sr. rates; VISA, M/C. **Power cart:** $22/$13. **Pull cart:** $3. **Trail fee:** $5.
Reservation policy: yes, up to 1 week in advance. Advised during the summer.
Winter condition: damp. **Terrain:** relatively hilly. **Tees:** grass & mats.
Temporary greens: yes. **Services:** club rentals, lessons, snack bar, beer, driving
range, pro shop. **Comments:** Lake Padden's primary difficulty lies in the towering
evergreens surrounding every fairway. Popular golf course in a recreational area.

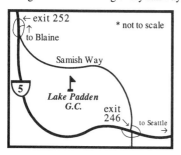

Directions: from I-5 southbound take exit
#252 to Samish Way. Travel east for 2.4
miles to the golf course which will be on
your right. If traveling on I-5 northbound
take exit #246 to Samish Way and proceed
2.5 miles to the golf course. The golf
course will be on your left hand side.

Course Yardage & Par:
C-6575 yards, par 72.
M-6133 yards, par 72.
W-5496 yards, par 72.

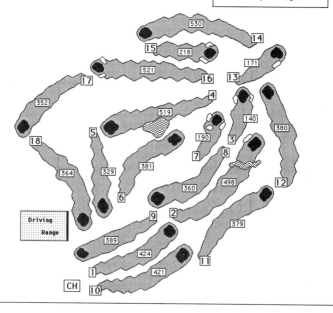

Lake Spanaway Golf Course (public)

15602 Pacific Avenue; Tacoma, WA 98444; (206) 531-3660
Pro: Keith Johnson. Superintendent: Andy Soden. 18 hole course.
Rating/Slope: C 71.8/121; M 70.0/118; W 73.4/123. **Course record:** 64.
Green fees: Pierce Co. residents $19/$12.25; non residents $24.50; M/C, VISA.
Power cart: $20/$12. **Pull cart:** $3. **Trail fee:** $5. **Reservation policy:** public
call up to 5 days in advance. **Winter condition:** dry, excellent drainage.
Terrain: flat, some hills. **Tees:** grass. **Temporary greens:** no, not in use.
Services: club rentals, lessons, snack bar, restaurant, beer, wine, pro shop, putting
green, covered driving range. **Comments:** the course is kept in excellent condition
all year long. The length, many bunkers, ponds, and trees will challenge you at
every turn. Shot placement off the tee is very important. Great public track.

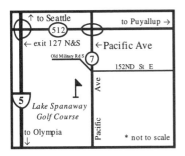

Directions: from I-5 N&S take exit #127
to Hwy 512 eastbound. Proceed east on
512 to Hwy 7 S. Exit to Hwy 7 southbound. Proceed south on Hwy 7 for 2.8
miles to the golf course which will be on
your right hand side. Look for signs.

Course Yardage & Par:
C-6810 yards, par 72.
M-6405 yards, par 72.
W-5935 yards, par 74.

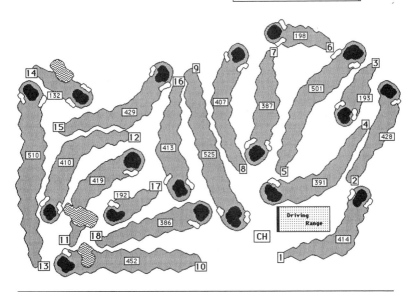

Lake Wilderness Golf Course (public)

25400 Witte Road SE; Maple Valley, WA 98038; (206) 432-9405
Manager: Russell Lee. Superintendent: Tim Sherer. 18 hole course.
Rating/Slope: C 66.1/118; M 64.7/116; W 66.6/117. **Course record: 65.**
Green fees: W/D $18/$12; W/E $22; Jr & Sr rates; twi-lite rates; VISA, M/C.
Power cart: $20/$12. Pull cart: $4. Trail fee: $7.50 for personal carts.
Reservation policy: yes, up to 1 week in advance. **Winter condition:** open, dry.
Terrain: relatively hilly, but walkable. **Tees:** grass. **Temporary greens:** no.
Services: club rentals, lessons, snack bar, lounge, restaurant, beer, wine, liquor,
club memberships, pro shop. **Comments:** new layout is not long but yet is very
demanding. Out of bounds comes into play on every hole. Tough golf course.

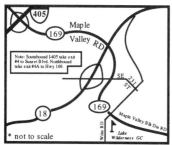

Directions: from I-5 N&S take exit 149
to Hwy 516E. Travel east for 3.4 miles to
S. Central Avenue. Turn north and go .6
miles to James St. Turn east on James (it
becomes SE 240th) for 8.7 miles to Hwy
169 S. Turn south for .2 miles to Witte
Road SE. Proceed south for 1 mile to the
golf course. Look for signs marking your
way to the facility.

Course Yardage & Par:
C-5494 yards, par 70.
M-5146 yards, par 70.
W-4767 yards, par 70.

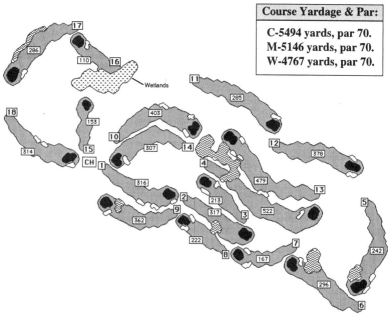

Lake Woods Golf Course (public)

240 State Park Road; PO Box 427; Bridgeport, WA 98813; (509) 686-5721
Manager: Sue Vranjes. 9 hole course, dual tees for 18 holes.
Rating/Slope: M 66.7/115; W 67.8/115. **Course record:** 63.
Green fees: W/D $14/$9; W/E $15/$10; Jr. & Sr. rates; VISA, M/C.
Power cart: $18/$11. **Pull cart:** $2.50. **Trail fee:** not allowed.
Reservation policy: advance tee-time reservations are not required.
Winter condition: the course is closed from October to March, depending on
the weather. **Terrain:** flat, some hills. **Tees:** grass. **Temporary greens:** no.
Services: club rentals, restaurant, beer, pro shop, putting green, driving range.
Comments: the course runs partially along the Columbia River although it does
not come into play. Small, sloping well bunkered greens make approach shots very
difficult. Campground near the golf course for those wanting to spend the night.

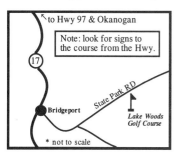

Directions: the golf course is located off
Hwy 17 by Bridgeport State Park, south
of Bridgeport. Watch for the sign on the
highway directing you to the golf course.
You will turn on State Park Road to the
golf course. From Hwy 97 turn east on
Hwy 17 for 8.1 miles to the Bridgeport
State Park Road. Proceed to the golf
course.

Course Yardage & Par:

M-2845 yards, par 35.
W-2543 yards, par 35.
Dual tees for 18 holes:
M-5646 yards, par 70.
W-5091 yards, par 70.

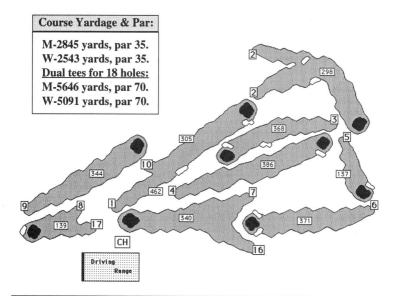

LakeLand Village Golf & Country Club (semi-private)
E 200 Old Ranch Road; PO Box 670; Allyn, WA 98524; (360) 275-6100
Pro: Randy Jensen, PGA. Superintendent: Steve Anderson. 18 hole course.
Rating/Slope: C 68.5/117; M 67.7/114; W 69.6/119. **Course record:** 62.
Green fees: W/D $18/$13; W/E $22/$15; Sr. rates Mondays only; no credit cards.
Power cart: $21. **Pull cart:** $3. **Trail fee:** personal carts are not allowed.
Reservation policy: yes, call ahead, no time limit. **Winter condition:** damp.
Terrain: flat, some hills. **Tees:** all grass. **Temporary greens:** not in use.
Services: club rentals, lessons, snack bar, restaurant, beer, wine, liquor, pro shop,
club memberships, driving range (irons only). **Comments:** well maintained, this
beautiful layout sports 14 water hazards to challenge any golfer. Look for the
facility to be adding an additional 9 holes in the near future. Great golf course.

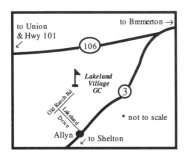

Directions: from the Bremerton ferry
veer left to 1st St. for 1 block to Pacific.
Turn right. Travel 1 block to Burwell
(Hwy 304 W). Turn left and follow signs
to Shelton to Hwy 3 S. Turn south on
Hwy 3 S to Allyn. Turn right on Lakeland Drive and proceed to the golf course.
The golf course is located just off of Hwy
3 toward Shelton or Bremerton. Look for
signs marking your turns to the course.

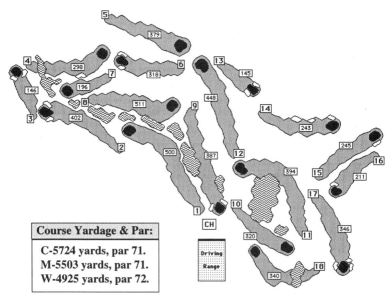

Course Yardage & Par:
C-5724 yards, par 71.
M-5503 yards, par 71.
W-4925 yards, par 72.

Lakeview Golf Challenge (public)

2425 NW 69th Street; Vancouver, WA 98665; (360) 693-9116
Manager: Charley Greene. 9 hole par 3 course.
Rating/Slope: the golf course is not rated. **Course record:** 56 for 18 holes.
Green fees: $11/$6 all week long; Sr. rates $9/$5; no credit cards.
Power cart: not available. **Pull cart:** $1. **Trail fee:** personal carts are not allowed.
Reservation policy: reservations are not required. **Winter condition:** damp,
open depending on the weather. **Terrain:** very flat. **Tees:** grass & mats.
Temporary greens: no. **Services:** club rentals, small pro shop, putting green.
Comments: difficult golf course that will challenge you at every turn. The course
sports sloping well bunkered greens. Water comes into play on several holes and
is a major factor. If you are looking for change of pace try Lakeview.

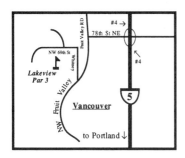

Directions: I-5 N&S take exit for 78th St.
Travel west to the end of the road. Turn
left (on Fruit Valley Road) and travel .7
miles. Turn right (sharp) Whitney Road
which becomes 69th St. Proceed on 69th
Street to the golf course. Look for signs
marking your turn to the facility.

Course Yardage & Par:
M-833 yards, par 27.
W-833 yards, par 27.
Dual tees for 18 holes:
M-1836 yards, par 54.
W-1836 yards, par 54.

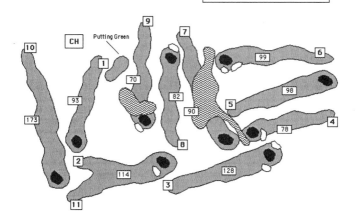

Lakeview Golf & Country Club (private)

52 Golf Club Road; Soap Lake, WA 98851; (509) 246-0336
Pro: Don Tracy, PGA. **18 hole course, driving range.**
Rating/Slope: C 70.9/114; M 69.5/111; W 72.4/117. **Course record:** 62.
Green fees: private club; members only; reciprocates; no credit cards.
Power cart: private club. **Pull cart:** private club. **Trail fee:** private club.
Reservation policy: private club members only. **Winter condition:** open, dry.
Terrain: flat. **Tees:** grass. **Temporary greens:** no. **Services:** club rentals,
lessons, restaurant, snack bar, lounge, beer, wine, liquor, pro shop, showers,
lockers, putting green, driving range. **Comments:** the course is unique in as much
as there are no adjoining fairways. Greens are medium to large in size and fast.

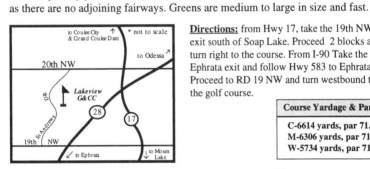

Directions: from Hwy 17, take the 19th NW
exit south of Soap Lake. Proceed 2 blocks and
turn right to the course. From I-90 Take the
Ephrata exit and follow Hwy 583 to Ephrata.
Proceed to RD 19 NW and turn westbound to
the golf course.

Course Yardage & Par:
C-6614 yards, par 71.
M-6306 yards, par 71.
W-5734 yards, par 71.

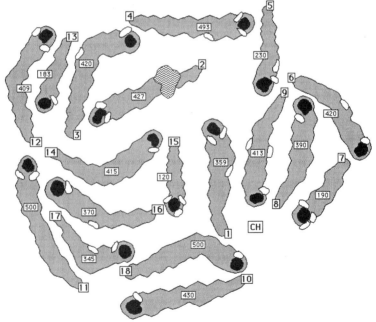

Lams Golf Links (public)

585 W Ducken Road; Whidbey Island, WA 98277; (360) 675-3412
Manager: Bill Lam. 9 hole executive course.
Rating/Slope: the golf course is not rated. **Course record:** 26.
Green fees: W/D $8/$5; W/E $9/$6; Sr. rates; no credit cards.
Power cart: none available. **Pull cart:** $3. **Trail fee:** not allowed.
Reservation policy: reservations are not needed, first come first served.
Winter condition: the golf course is closed from December through March.
Terrain: flat (easy to walk). **Tees:** grass. **Temporary greens:** no, not in use.
Services: very limited services, vending machines. **Comments:** executive length
golf course located on scenic Whidbey Island just south of the Deception Pass
Bridge. Golf course has an honor box for green fees if the clubhouse is not open.
Very easy to just walk on for a quick 9 holes.

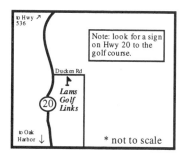

Directions: the course is located 1 mile
south of Deception Pass off Hwy 20.
Turn left on Ducken Road to the golf
course. **Note:** Look for a sign on Hwy 20
marking the turn to the golf course.

Course Yardage & Par:
M-1347 yards, par 28.
W-1347 yards, par 28.

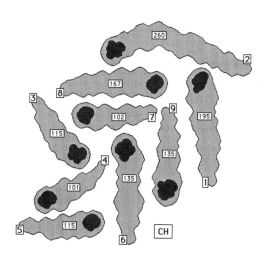

Leavenworth Golf Club (semi-private)
9101 Icicle Road; P.O. Box 247; Leavenworth, WA 98826; (509) 548-7267
Pro: Jim Van Tuyl, PGA. **18 hole course, putting green.**
Rating/Slope: M 67.0/116; W 69.6/119. **Course record:** 61.
Green fees: W/D $18/$12; W/E $18/$12; M/C, VISA.
Power cart: $20. **Pull cart:** $2. **Trail fee:** $5 for personal carts.
Reservation policy: call Monday to book the coming week (Monday to Monday).
Winter condition: the golf course is closed from mid November to March.
Terrain: flat, some slight hills. **Tees:** grass. **Temporary greens:** no, not in use.
Services: snack bar, beer, wine, lessons, pro shop. **Comments:** a beautiful setting
in the heart of the Cascade Mountains. Many trees, sand traps, and the Wenatchee
River come into play on a number of holes. The town of Leavenworth and the
Bavarian Village alone are worth the trip. Some restricted tee times, Sunday AM
men members only; Wednesday AM women members only.

Directions: golf course located 1 mile west
of Leavenworth. From Hwy 2 go south on
Icicle Road for 0.6 miles to the golf course
which will be on your left hand side.
Note: Look for a sign on the Hwy marking
your turn to the golf course.

Course Yardage & Par:
M-5711 yards, par 71.
W-5343 yards, par 71.

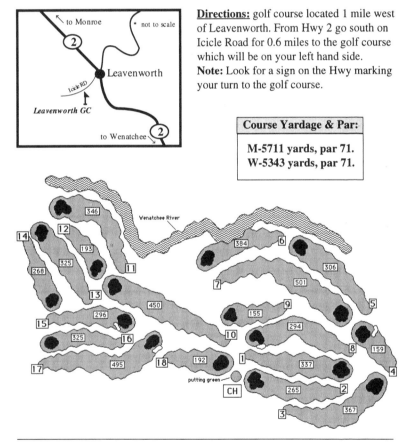

Legion Memorial Golf Course (public)

144 W Marine View Drive; Everett, WA 98201; (206) 259-4653
Pro: Bob Whisman, PGA. 18 hole course. Superintendent: Edward Phelps.
Rating/Slope: C 69.4/113; M 68.6/111; W 71.5/113. **Course record:** 62.
Green fees: Everett resident $12.50/$9.75; non-resident $17/$14.25; Jr. & Sr.
rates; no credit cards. **Power cart:** $20/$10. **Pull cart:** $3. **Trail fee:** N/A.
Reservation policy: W/D 1 week in advance, W/E Mon. prior to the W/E @ 9am.
Winter condition: damp, open. **Terrain:** flat, some hills. **Tees:** grass & mats.
Temporary greens: yes. **Services:** club rentals, lessons, snack bar, beer, wine,
practice range, pro shop, lockers, showers. **Comments:** nice public course that is
wide open with good drainage and few hazards. Nice practice area available, so
bring your shag bag. The greens are generally in excellent condition.

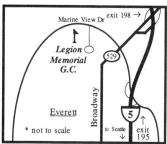

Directions: from I-5 N take exit 195.
Turn left on Marine View Drive and
follow for 2.1 miles to the golf course.
From I-5 S take exit 194. Go west for .1
mi to Walnut. Go north for 1.2 miles to
Marine View Drive and turn west for
1.3 miles to golf course. Look for signs.

Course Yardage & Par:
C-6406 yards, par 72.
M-6298 yards, par 72.
W-5681 yards, par 73.

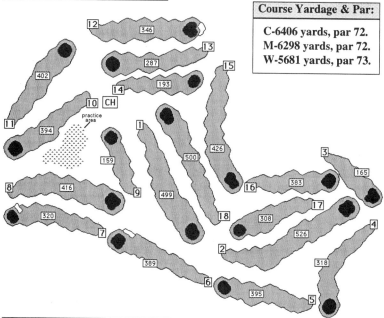

Lewis River Golf Course (public)

3209 Lewis River Road; Woodland, WA 98674; (360) 225-8254
Pro: Dick Smith, PGA. 18 hole course, driving range.
Rating/Slope: C 69.7/121; M 67.9/116; W 68.9/118. **Course record:** 62.
Green fees: Monday-Thursday $22/$12; Friday $23/$12; Sat.-Sunday $27/$15;
Sr rates $16/$8 (M-F); M/C, VISA. **Power cart:** $22/$11. **Pull cart:** $2.
Trail fee: $8. **Reservation policy:** yes, up to 1 week in advance. No 9 hole tee
times for weekends and holidays. **Winter condition:** very dry. **Terrain:** flat,
some hills. **Tees:** grass. **Temporary greens:** no. **Services:** club rentals, lessons,
snack bar, lounge, restaurant, beer, wine, liquor, driving range, pro shop, club
memberships. **Comments:** Lewis River sports the longest golf hole in Washington, a 649 yard par 5. Great winter & summer course. Course can play very tough
with water and sand coming into play on several holes. Excellent course that is
worth a special trip. Play golf and take in Mount St. Helens in the same day.

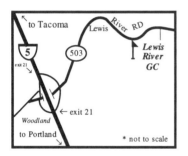

Directions: the golf course is located east
of Woodland. From I-5 N&S take exit #21.
Travel east for 4.7 miles to the golf course
which will be located on your right hand
side of the road. This golf course has great
freeway access.

Course Yardage & Par:
C-6338 yards, par 72.
M-5900 yards, par 72.
W-5240 yards, par 73.

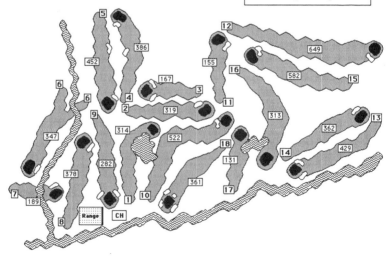

Liberty Lake Golf Course (public)
24403 E Sprague Avenue; Liberty Lake, WA 99019; (509) 255-6233
Pro: Bob Scott, PGA. 18 hole course, driving range.
Rating/Slope: C 69.8/121; M 68.7/118; W 72.6/125. **Course record:** 61.
Green fees: resident $14.50/$11; non $19.50/$14.50; Jr/Sr rates; VISA, M/C.
Power cart: $20/$10. **Pull cart:** $2. **Trail fee:** $5.50 (seasonal rate available).
Reservation policy: yes, call Tuesday. **Winter condition:** dry, course is closed during incliment weather. **Terrain:** flat, some slight hills on the back nine.
Tees: grass. **Temporary greens:** yes. **Services:** club rentals, lessons, restaurant, snack bar, beer, wine, pro shop, driving range, putting green. **Comments:** the golf course is easy to walk with many well-trapped greens. Liberty Lake can play much tougher than the layout indicates. Shot placement from the tee is a must. This is one of the finest public courses in the state. Worth a trip if in the Spokane area.

Directions: the golf course is located east of Spokane. From I-90 eastbound and westbound take exit #296 and go south to Sprague Avenue. Turn left on Sprague Avenue and continue to the golf course. Look for signs marking your turn to the golf complex.

Course Yardage & Par:
C-6398 yards, par 70.
M-6153 yards, par 70.
W-5886 yards, par 74.

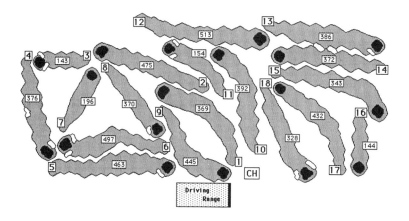

Linden Golf & Country Club (private)

2519 Main Avenue E; Puyallup, WA 98371; (206) 845-2056
Pro: David Leon Jr, PGA. Supt.: Dean Hanson. 9 hole course, dual tees.
Rating/Slope: M 69.4/120; W 74.1/123. **Course record:** 62.
Green fees: private club members & guests only; no credit cards.
Power cart: private club. **Pull cart:** private club. **Trail fee:** private club.
Reservation policy: private club members only. **Winter condition:** open, dry.
Terrain: flat, some hills. **Tees:** grass. **Temporary greens:** rarely in use.
Services: lessons, pro shop, lockers, showers, club memberships, putting green.
Comments: private 9 hole course with separate tee boxes for 18 hole play.
Rolling terrain small greens and bunkers enhance this interesting course design.
The course is well kept with water coming into play on two holes.

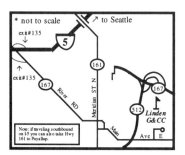

Directions: from I-5 N&S take exit
135 to Hwy 167 N. Turn north and
travel 5.3 miles to Meridian Street N.
Turn south for .4 miles to Main Avenue
E. Proceed east for 1.5 miles to the golf
course on your left hand side.

Course Yardage & Par:
M-3120 yards, par 36.
W-3110 yards, par 37.
<u>Dual tees for 18 holes:</u>
M-6112 yards, par 72.
W-6017 yards, par 73.

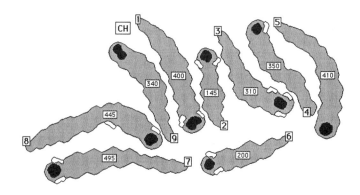

Lipoma Firs Golf Course (27 hole course, public)
18615 110th Ave. E; Puyallup, WA 98374; (206) 841-4396; 1-800-649-4396
Dir. of Golf: Gerry Mehlert, PGA. Pro: Jim Cayton. Supt.: Rod Ragsdale.
Rating/Slope: Gold/Green C 72.1/122; M 69.7/117; M 66.3/109; W 70.4/117.
Green fees: W/D $17/$10; W/E $22/$15; Jr. & Sr., twilight rates; M/C, VISA.
Power cart: $18/$12. **Pull cart:** $3. **Trail fee:** $6. **Course record:** 68.
Reservation policy: yes, call up to 1 week in advance. **Winter condition:** dry.
Terrain: flat, some hills, **Tees:** grass. **Temporary greens:** yes, rarely.
Services: club rentals, lessons, snack bar, beer, wine, pro shop, grass tee driving range, 2 practice greens, practice bunkers. **Comments:** the course is always in good condition, excellent drainage provides good winter play. Great golf course.

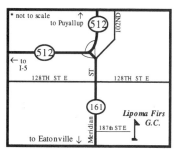

Directions: from I-5 N&S take the exit for Hwy 512E. Travel 8 miles to Hwy 161S. Proceed 6 miles to 187th. The course will located on your left hand side of the road.

* note: check course scorecard for additional ratings.

Course Yardage & Par:	
Green Course	Gold Course
C-3302 yards, par 36.	C-3420 yards, par 36.
M-3123 yards, par 36.	M-3094 yards, par 36.
W-2716 yards, par 36.	W-2760 yards, par 36.

Course Yardage & Par:
Blue Course
C-3385 yards, par 36.
M-3051 yards, par 36.
W-2757 yards, par 36.

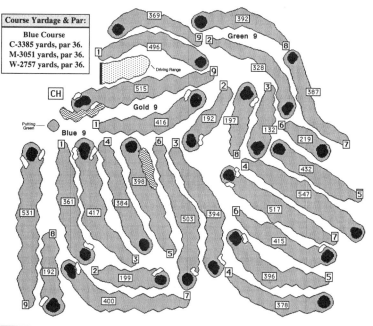

Lobo Country Club (public)
12015 84th Street SE; Snohomish, WA 98290; (360) 568-1638
Owners: Gordon & Fedora Loth. 9 hole par 3 course
Rating/Slope: the golf course is not rated. **Course record:** 25.
Green fees: $10/$6 all week long; Sr. rates $9/$5 (weekdays); no credit cards.
Power Cart: $12/$8. **Pull Cart:** $2. **Trail fee:** not available.
Reservation policy: advance tee times are not required. **Winter condition:** dry,
course open all year long. **Terrain:** flat, some hills, easy walking golf course.
Tees: grass. **Temporary greens:** not in use. **Services:** club rentals, clubhouse,
vending machines, chipping and putting greens. **Comments:** friendly family
owned course, surrounded by a beautiful country setting. If you are looking for a
place to take the first time golfer try Lobo C.C. it will not disappoint.

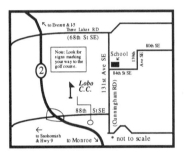

Directions: from Hwy 2 exit at the
Snohomish 88th Street exit eastbound.
Proceed on 88th Street to 121st Avenue
SE turn north to the course. Look for signs
marking your turn to the golf course.

Course Yardage & Par:
M-1005 yards, par 27.
W-1005 yards, par 27.

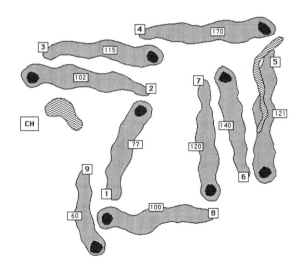

Longview Golf & Country Club (private)
41 Country Club Drive; Longview, WA 98632; (360) 425-3132
Pro: Jeff Bartleson, PGA. **18 hole course, driving range.**
Rating/Slope: M 68.2/120; W 71.6/117. **Course record:** 62.
Green fees: private club, members only; reciprocates; VISA, M/C.
Power cart: private club, members only. **Pull cart:** private club.
Trail fee: private club. **Reservation policy:** private club, members only.
Winter Condition: open, damp. **Terrain:** relatively hilly. **Tees:** grass.
Temporary greens: no. **Services:** club rentals, lessons, snack bar, restaurant,
beer, wine, liquor, pro shop, lockers, showers, club memberships, practice range.
Comments: course has newly redesigned three holes that are now in excellent
condition. Challenging, well maintained greens are this course's trademark.

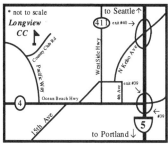

Directions: from I-5 take exit # 39
and follow to the Ocean Beach Hwy,
continuing to Pacific Hwy. Travel north
on Pacific Hwy to Country Club Road.
Turn right on Country Club Road to the
golf course.

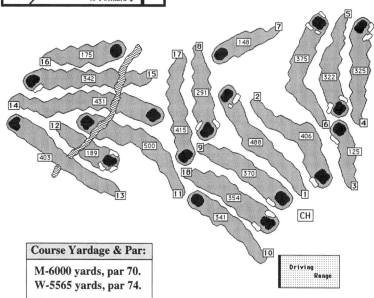

Course Yardage & Par:
M-6000 yards, par 70.
W-5565 yards, par 74.

Loomis Trail Golf Club (private)

4342 Loomis Trail Road; Blaine, WA 98230; (360) 332-1608
Pro: Jerry Palumbo, PGA. 18 hole course, driving range. Course record: 69.
Rating/Slope: T 74.9/139; C 72.3/133; 69.4/125; W 72.4/129.
Green fees: private club. For membership information call (206) 682-8714.
Power cart: members only. **Pull cart:** members only. **Trail fee:** not allowed.
Reservation policy: private club, members only. **Winter condition:** dry, excellent
drainage. **Terrain:** flat, some hills. **Tees:** grass. **Services:** pro shop, restaurant,
lodging for members and their guests, memberships. **Comments:** Open since 1993,
the course was rated 3rd best new private course by *"Golf Digest"*. This 18 hole
layout was also ranked #3 best course in the Washington State. This tough track
sports numerous bunkers, ponds and tree lined fairways. Excellent private facility.

Directions: from I-5 N&S take exit #270
(Birch Bay - Lynden RD). Travel W on Birch
Bay-Lynden RD for 2.1 miles to Kickerville
RD. Turn N on Kickerville RD for .8 mile to
Loomis Trail RD. Turn W on Loomis Trail RD
and proceed to course.

Course Yardage & Par:		
T-7137 yards, par 72; C-6611 yards, par 72.		
M-6167 yards, par 72; W-5475 yards, par 72.		

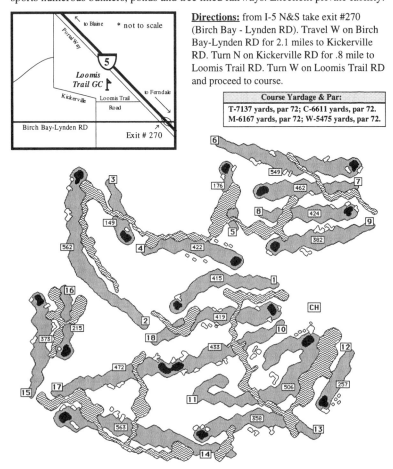

Lopez Island Golf Course (public)

Airport Road; Box 124; Lopez Island, WA 98261; (360) 468-2679
Pro Shop Manager: L. Holmes. 9 hole course, putting green.
Rating/Slope: C 65.2/110; M 62.8/105; W 67.0/114. **Course record:** 30.
Green fees: $18/$12 all week long; Jr rates; no credit cards.
Power cart: power carts are not available. **Pull cart:** $1. **Trail fee:** no charge.
Reservation policy: advance tee times are not required. **Winter condition:** damp.
Terrain: relatively hilly, but walkable. **Tees:** grass. **Temporary greens:** no.
Services: club rentals, pro shop. **Comments:** situated in the scenic San Juan Islands this course is easy to walk with few hazards. Good course in a very beautiful part of Washington. If in the islands make sure to bring your clubs along.

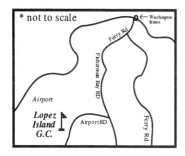

Directions: from I-5 N&S take exit # 230 to Hwy 20W to Anacortes and the San Juan ferry terminal. Board the ferry for Lopez Island. From the Lopez ferry landing proceed south on Ferry Road on to Fisherman Bay Road. Turn right on Airport Road. Proceed for .5 miles and turn left to the golf course which will be on your right hand side. Look for signs that will be posted indicating your turn.

Course Yardage & Par:
M-2711 yards, par 35.
W-2427 yards, par 35.

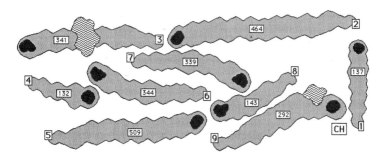

Lower Valley Golf Club (public)

31 Ray Road; Sunnyside, WA 98944; (509) 837-5340
Pro: Craig Thomas, PGA. 18 hole course, driving range, putting green.
Rating/Slope: C 70.2/112; M 68.4/108; W 70.6/111. **Course record:** N/A.
Green fees: $16/$11 all week long; M/C, VISA.
Power cart: $20/$10. **Pull cart:** $2. **Trail fee:** $4.
Reservation policy: you may call ahead 1 week in adavance for tee times.
Winter condition: dry, open weather permitting. **Terrain:** flat. **Tees:** grass.
Temporary greens: yes. **Services:** club rentals, Henry-Griffits club fitting,
lessons, pro shop, driving range, vending machines, coffee shop, putting green.
Comments: this course is an excellent facility which added a new nine in spring
of 1995. This track is a challenging golf course that is easy to walk and demanding.
Water comes into play on 10 holes and the greens are of varing sizes.

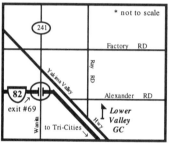

Directions: from I-82 eastbound take
exit # 69 (Sunnyside). Travel north on
Wanita to the Yakima Valley Hwy. Turn
eastbound. Proceed 1.5 miles to Ray Road
and the golf course. Look for signs.

Course Yardage & Par:
C-6664 yards, par 72.
W-6271 yards, par 72.
W-5618 yards, par 72.

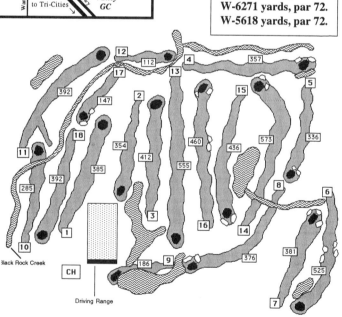

Lynnwood Municipal Golf Course (public)

20200 68th Avenue W; PO Box 5008; Lynnwood, WA 98036; (206) 672-4653
Pro: Dan Smith, PGA. Supt.: Gary Stormo. 18 hole executive course, range.
Rating/Slope: M 62.9/107; W 63.5/105. **Course record:** M 59; W 65.
Green fees: $18/$13; Jr. & Sr. rates Monday thru Friday $2 discount.
Power cart: $20/$10. **Pull cart:** $3. **Trail fee:** not allowed.
Reservation policy: Seven days in advance for Monday thru Friday. Five days
in advance for Saturday & Sunday. **Winter condition:** open all year long, dry.
Terrain: flat, some hills. **Tees:** grass. **Services:** club rentals, lessons, restaurant,
pro shop, driving range, lessons, putting green. **Comments:** Excellent, short length
golf course that is very demanding off the tee. Tree lined fairways, bunkers and
ponds make this track a challenge. If you are looking for a change of pace from the
standard 6000+ yard golf course, try Lynnwood Municipal it will not disappoint.

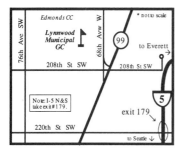

Directions: from I-5 N&S take exit # 179
and travel west on 220th St. SW. Proceed
to Hwy 99 and turn right (north). Follow
to 208th St. SW and turn left. Then take
the immediate right on 68th Ave. W. The
entrance to the golf course is on 68th and
204th. The golf course is located adjacent
to the Edmonds Community College
campus. Look for signs indicating your
turn to the golf course.

Course Yardage & Par:
M-4741 yards, par 65.
W-4094 yards, par 65.

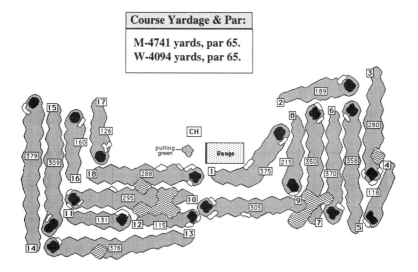

M A 8+1 Golf (public)

455 Wapato Lake Road; Manson, WA 98831; (509) 687-6338
Manager/Pro: N/A. 9 hole course, driving range.
Rating/Slope: the golf course is not rated. **Course record:** 30.
Green fees: $18/$10 all week long; Jr. rates (Monday-Friday); no credit cards.
Power cart: none available. **Pull cart:** $3. **Trail fee:** personal carts not allowed.
Reservation policy: yes, please call 3 days in advance for all tee times.
Winter condition: the golf course is closed in the winter months Nov. to March.
Terrain: flat, some hills. **Tees:** grass. **Temporary greens:** no. **Services:** club
rentals, snack bar, driving range. **Comments:** the course is fairly flat and easy to
walk. Although not overly long the course can play tough if the wind blows. This
track has large greens with few traps that hold shots well.Those vacationing in the
Chelan area might want to take a chance and play a course off the beaten path.

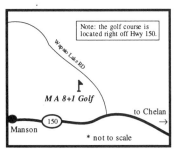

Directions: the golf course is located
near the Manson Hwy. From Lake
Chelan on Hwy 150 proceed westbound
for 6 miles. Turn right on Wapato Lake
Road and proceed to clubhouse. The golf
course is located right next to the Hwy.

Course Yardage & Par:
M-1881 yards, par 30.
W-1881 yards, par 30.

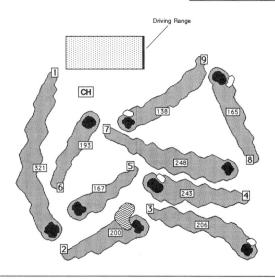

Madrona Links Golf Course (public)

3604 22nd Avenue NW; Gig Harbor, WA 98335; (206) 851-5193
Pro: Rob Edwards, PGA. Supt.: Chad Niedermeier. 18 hole course.
Rating/Slope: C 66.8/116; M 65.2/113; W 67.4/119. **Course record:** 59.
Green fees: W/D $20/$14; W/E $20/$15; Jr & Sr rates; VISA, M/C.
Power cart: $20/$12. **Pull cart:** $2.50. **Trail fee:** $6.
Reservation policy: yes, up to 1 week in advance. **Winter condition:** dry.
Terrain: flat, some hills. **Tees:** grass. **Temporary greens:** occasionally.
Services: club rentals, lessons, snack bar, lounge, restaurant, beer, wine, liquor, pro shop, club memberships. **Comments:** friendly, well kept, heavily wooded course. Great golf course that is worth a special trip. If you are looking for a quality course that is excellent for tournaments and company outings try Madrona.

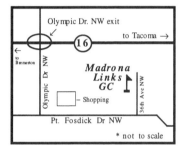

Directions: from Hwy 16 take the exit for Olympic Dr. Follow Olympic Dr. to Pt. Fosdick Dr. NW and turn left. Travel .9 miles to 36th Avenue NW. Turn left (it is not well marked). The golf course is located .4 miles ahead on your left.

Course Yardage & Par:
C-5602 yards, par 71.
M-5193 yards, par 71.
W-4737 yards, par 73.

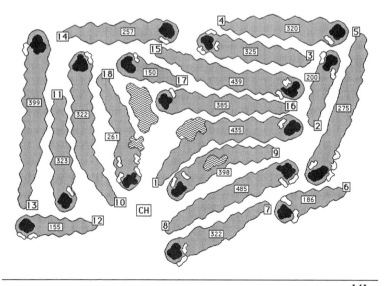

Manito Golf & Country Club (private)
4502 Hatch Road; Spokane, WA 99203; (509) 448-5829
Pro: Steve Prugh, PGA. 18 hole course, driving range.
Rating/Slope: C 70.0/123; M 69.2/120; W 72.3/125; W 69.2/118. **Record:** 60.
Green fees: private club members & guests only; reciprocates; VISA, M/C.
Power cart: private club members & guests only. **Pull cart:** private club.
Trail fee: not allowed. **Reservation policy:** private club members & guests only.
Winter condition: closed during winter months. **Terrain:** flat. **Tees:** grass.
Temporary greens: no. **Services:** club rentals, lessons, restaurant, snack bar,
lounge, beer, wine, liquor, showers, pro shop, driving range, putting green.
Comments: premium put on accuracy due to many sand traps, well bunkered
greens and tight tree-lined fairways. Holes 9 and 18 on an island and are very
demanding. Excellent private facility that is very hard to score on.

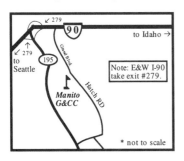

Directions: from I-90 E&W take the exit
for Hwy 195S southbound #279. Travel
for approximately 4.5 miles to the Hatch
Road exit. Proceed eastbound for 2 miles
to the golf course on your left hand side.

Course Yardage & Par:
C-6378 yards, par 70.
M-6153 yards, par 71.
W-5678 yards, par 72.
W-5401 yards, par 72.

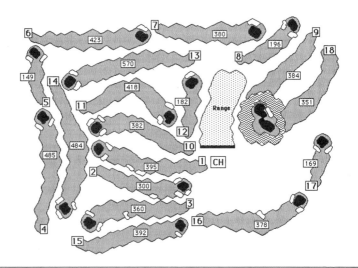

Maple Grove Golf (public)

Hwy 12 & Cispus Road; PO Box 205; Randle, WA 98377; (360) 497-2741
Owner: Roy McCain. Pro: none. 9 hole executive course, putting green.
Rating/Slope: M 53.7/72; W55.2/76. Course record: 26.
Green fees: $9.75/$7.50; all day $12; Jr. & Sr. rates (weekdays); M/C, VISA.
Power cart: none available. **Pull cart:** $2. **Trail fee:** no charge.
Reservation policy: for tournaments only. **Winter condition:** dry.
Terrain: flat, some hills. **Tees:** grass. **Temporary greens:** no.
Services: club rentals, snack bar, beer, wine, pro shop, driving range, RV
parking and hook-ups. **Comments:** course situated in Maple Grove Park. Short
course that has medium sized greens with few hazards. The course is wide open
with few hazards. Easy walking course for the senior or first time golfer.

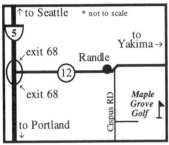

Directions: from I-5 N&S cut-off eastbound on Highway 12 exit #68 toward
Randle, Washington. Turn right on Cispus
Road. Proceed to the golf course which
will be located on your left hand side.
Look for signs marking your way to the
golf course.

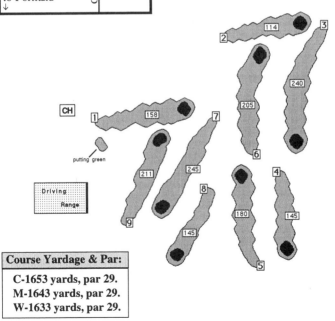

Course Yardage & Par:

C-1653 yards, par 29.
M-1643 yards, par 29.
W-1633 yards, par 29.

Maplewood Golf Course (public)

4000 SE Maple Valley Highway; Renton, WA 98055; (206) 277-4444
Pro: Gordy Graybeal, PGA. Superintendent: Brad Barnes. 18 hole course.
Rating/Slope: C 67.9/113; M 67.4/112; W 69.5/116. **Course record:** 61.
Green fees: $18/13; Sr rates (Monday thru Friday only $13/$10); no credit cards.
Power cart: $18/$10. **Pull cart:** $3/$2. **Trail fee:** $6 for personal carts.
Reservation policy: yes, call up to 1 week in advance for weekdays, call Monday
for the following weekend. **Winter condition:** the golf course is open, damp.
Terrain: flat, some hills. **Tees:** grass (mats in winter). **Temporary greens:** yes.
Services: club rentals, lessons, restaurant, lounge, beer, wine, liquor, pro shop,
club memberships. **Comments:** a very popular course, it has recently been
renovated to enhance play with four new holes. The greens are medium to large
in size and have few undualations in them. The restaurant is also very good.

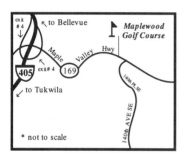

Directions: from I-405 N&S take exit 4
to Hwy 169 southbound. Travel south
for 1.7 miles to the golf course entrance
which will be located on your left hand
side. If you are coming from I-5 N&S,
exit to I-405 and follow the above directions to the golf course. Look for a sign on
Hwy 169 indicating your turn into the golf
course.

Course Yardage & Par:
C-5846 yards, par 72.
M-5723 yards, par 72.
W-5399 yards, par 73.

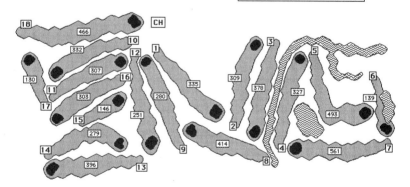

McCormick Woods Golf Club (public)

5155 SW McCormick Woods Drive; Port Orchard, WA 98366
(360) 895-0130 or 1-800-323-0130. Superintendent: Howard Sisson.
Pro: Ernie Taylor, PGA. 18 hole course, driving range. Course record: 64.
Rating/Slope: T 74.1/135; C 72.3/129; M 70.0/124; W 73.6/127; E 71.1/122.
Green fees: Monday thru Thursday $38/$22; Friday thru Sun. & Holidays. $52;
Sr. rates $27 (Monday thru Wednesday); Twilite rates; VISA, M/C, Discover.
Power cart: $22/$123. **Pull cart:** $3/$2. **Trail fee:** personal carts not allowed.
Reservation policy: recommended, call up to 5 days in advance for tee times.
Winter condition: dry, excellent drainage. **Terrain:** flat, some hills. **Tees:** grass.
Temporary greens: no. **Services:** club rentals, lessons, snack bar, beer, wine,
restuarant, lounge, pro shop, driving range. **Comments:** ranked in the top 50 public
golf courses by *Golf Digest Magazine. Golfweek* voted McCormick Woods the #1
course in Washington State. Championship caliber track. Well bunkered by grass
and sand bunkers. Great golf course that is worth a special trip. You will often see
deer walking down your fairway so if you are in the area don't miss this course.

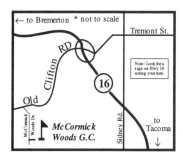

Directions: from I-5 N&S take the exit
for Hwy 16 westbound. Follow Hwy 16
to the Old Clifton/Tremont exit. Turn left
and proceed 1.8 miles to the golf course
entrance which will be located on your
left hand side. **Note:** look for signs on Hwy
16 that you can follow to the golf course.

Course Yardage & Par:
T-7040 yards, par 72.
C-6658 yards, par 72.
M-6165 yards, par 72.
W-5758 yards, par 72.
Exc-5299 yards, par 72.

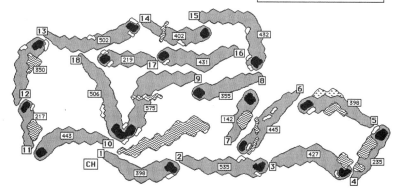

Meadow Park Golf Course (public)

7108 Lakewood Drive W; Lakewood, WA 98467; (206) 473-3033
Pro: Lynn Rautio, PGA. 18 hole regulation and 9 hole par 3.
Rating/Slope: C 69.0/114; M 67.3/111; W 70.3/118. **Course record:** N/A.
Green fees: W/D $20/$14; W/E $23/$15; Jr./Sr. rates (M-Thur.); VISA, M/C.
Green fees for par 3 course: $12/$8 all week long; Jr. & Sr. rates (M-Thur.).
Power cart: W/D $18/$10; W/E $20/$12. **Pull cart:** $2.50. **Trail fee:** $6.
Reservation policy: yes, up to 1 week in advance. **Winter condition:** dry.
Terrain: flat, some hills. **Tees:** grass. **Temporary greens:** yes.
Services: club rentals, lessons, snack bar, lounge, restaurant, pro shop, lockers,
club memberships, driving range. **Comments:** the golf course has been comp-
letely revamped with a stunning new layout. Very good winter golf course.

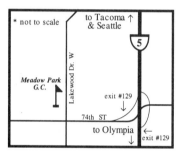

Directions: from I-5 N&S take exit # 129
to S 74th St. Travel westbound for 2.1
miles to Lakewood Drive W. Turn north.
The golf course is located .1 miles ahead
on your left hand side. Look for signs.

Course Yardage & Par:
C-6093 yards, par 71.
M-5763 yards, par 71.
W-5225 yards, par 71.

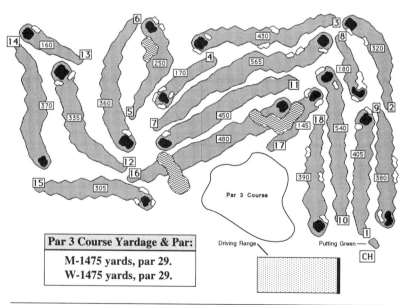

Par 3 Course Yardage & Par:
M-1475 yards, par 29.
W-1475 yards, par 29.

Meadow Springs Country Club (private)
700 Country Club Place; Richland, WA 99352; (509) 627-2321
Pro: Greg Moore, PGA. **18 hole course. Course record:** 63.
Rating/Slope: C 73.3/132; M 71.3/127; M 68.9/123; W 69.2/120.
Green fees: private club; members & guests only; reciprocates; M/C, VISA.
Power cart: private club. **Pull cart:** private club. **Trail fee:** private club.
Reservation policy: private club; members & guests only.
Winter condition: open weather permitting, dry. **Terrain:** relatively hilly.
Tees: grass. **Temporary greens:** no. **Services:** lessons, restaurant, lounge, beer,
wine, liquor, lockers, driving range, pro shop, putting green. **Comments:** a very
challenging course featuring well-placed traps, elevated greens and a fair amount
of water. Meadow Springs is the host course for the Nike Tri-Cities Open.

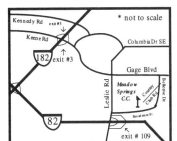

Directions: from I-182 take the exit for
Keene Road #3. Continue to Gage Blvd.
You will run right in to Gage Blvd. Turn
left on Bellerive Drive to Country Club
Place and proceed to the golf course. From
I-82 take exit #109 to Leslie Road. Proceed
to Broadmore Street and turn right. Proceed
to Bellerive Drive and turn left to Country
Club Place. Turn left and proceed to the
clubhouse. Look for signs to the clubhouse.

Course Yardage & Par:
C-6926 yards, par 72.
M-6466 yards, par 72.
M-6125 yards, par 72.
W-5480 yards, par 72.

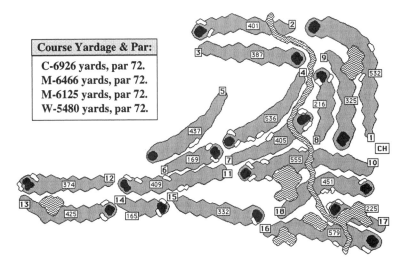

Meadowmeer Golf & Country Club (semi-private)

8530 Renny Lane NE; Bainbridge Island, WA 98110; (206) 842-2218
Pro: Tom Mueller, PGA. Supt.: Gary Duffner. 9 hole course, dual tees.
Rating/Slope: M 67.0/117; W 69.5/121. **Course record:** 62.
Green fees: W/D $15/$11; W/E $18/$14; Jr & Sr rates weekdays; M/C, VISA.
Power cart: $21.50/$13. **Pull cart:** $3/$2. **Trail fee:** $7.
Reservation policy: yes, call up to 1 week in advance, public play is restricted
at certain times. **Winter condition:** course is open all year long, dry.
Terrain: flat, some hills. **Tees:** grass. **Temporary greens:** no, not in use.
Services: club rentals, lessons, snack bar, beer, pro shop, club memberships.
Comments: the course is just 35 minutes from Seattle on the Winslow-Seattle
ferry. Good winter golf course. Easy to walk on even during the summer, so if you
are looking to play golf on your visit to the Olympic Peninsula try Meadowmeer.

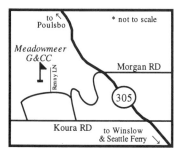

Directions: from the Seattle-Winslow
ferry terminal in Winslow take Hwy 305
northbound to Koura Road. Turn left on
Koura Road. 1/4 mile up you will see
signs for the golf course on your right
hand side. Follow the signs to the golf
course. **Note:** Look for signs marking
your way to the golf course from state
highway 305.

Course Yardage & Par:
M-2968 yards, par 36.
W-22567 yards, par 37.
<u>**Dual tees for 18 holes:**</u>
M-5581 yards, par 71.
W-5170 yards, par 74.

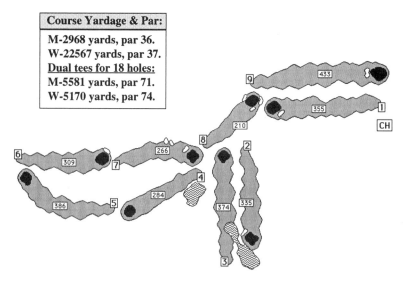

MeadowWood Golf Course (public)

E 24501 Valley Way; Liberty Lake, WA 99019; (509) 255-9539
Pro: Kaye Walker, PGA. 18 hole course, driving range.
Rating/Slope: C 73.1/132; M 71.4/124; W 74.1/137. **Course record:** 64.
Green fees: $20/$10 all week long; VISA, M/C, for merchandise & carts only.
Power cart: $20/$10. **Pull cart:** $5. **Trail fee:** $3 for personal carts.
Reservation policy: yes, call in advance on Tuesday for the week.
Winter condition: the golf course is closed from November to March.
Terrain: rolling terrain, some hills. **Tees:** grass. **Services:** club rentals,
lessons, restaurant, snack bar, beer, wine, pro shop, driving range, putting green.
Comments: designed by Robert Muir Graves. A links-type course, MeadowWood
features mounds, water, and sand bunkers. Four-Star course. Worth a special trip.

Directions: from I-90 E&W take exit # 296. Go through the stoplight 1 mile to Molter Road. Turn right on Molter Road. Proceed for 1 mile and turn left on Valley Way. Proceed to the golf course. Look for signs marking your way to the complex.

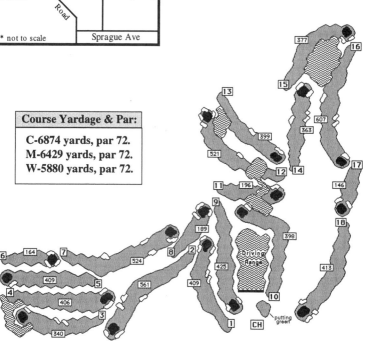

Course Yardage & Par:

C-6874 yards, par 72.
M-6429 yards, par 72.
W-5880 yards, par 72.

Meridian Greens Golf Course & Driving Range (public)
9705 136th Street E; Puyallup, WA 98373; (206) 845-7504
Pro: Rusty Fancher, PGA. **9 hole executive course, covered, lighted range.**
Rating/Slope: M 56.4/84; W 57.9/87. **Course record:** 25.
Green fees: W/D $12/$8; W/E $13/$9; Jr & Sr rates (M-F) $9/$5; VISA, M/C.
Power cart: none available. **Pull cart:** $3. **Trail fee:** not allowed.
Reservation policy: calls up to 1 week in advance, have priority.
Winter condition: open, dry. **Terrain:** flat. **Tees:** grass. **Temporary greens:** no.
Services: lessons, club rentals, pro shop, driving range. **Comments:** flat course
which is easy to walk. Few hazards except six ponds and four bunkers. The golf
course has a practice putting green and a lighted, covered driving range. Mount
Rainier comes into view on several holes. Great course for every level of golfer.

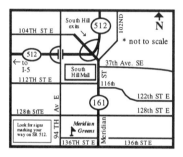

Directions: from I-5 N&S take exit # 127 to
Hwy 512 eastbound. Travel east to the to the
NEW 94th Ave. E exit, turn right a the first
light go 2 miles south (turns into a 2 lane
road), turn left a 136th St. E or travel a little
farther eastbound on Hwy 512 to the South
Hill/ Eatonville exit. Turn right on Meridian E
(Hwy 161). Follow to 136th and turn right to
the golf course which will be on your right
hand side. **Note:** Look for the wooden sign on
(Hwy 161), Meridian marking your turn to the
course. The golf course is located 2 miles
south of the South Hill Mall.

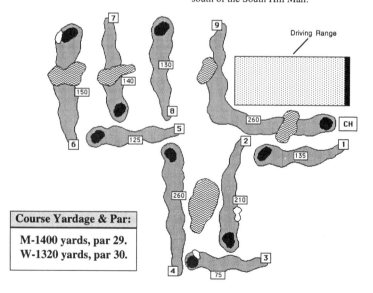

Course Yardage & Par:

M-1400 yards, par 29.
W-1320 yards, par 30.

Meridian Valley Golf & Country Club (private)
24830 136th Avenue SE; Kent, WA 98042; (206) 631-3133
Pro: David Gibson, PGA. Supt.: Craig Benson. 18 hole course, range.
Rating/Slope: C 71.9/127; M 70.5/123; W 73.7/127. **Course record:** M 64, W 62.
Green fees: private club members & guests of members only; reciprocates.
Power cart: private club. **Pull cart:** private club. **Trail fee:** not allowed.
Reservation policy: private club members only. **Winter condition:** damp.
Terrain: relatively hilly. **Tees:** grass. **Temporary greens:** not in use.
Services: lessons, lounge, restaurant, beer, wine, liquor, pro shop, driving range, lockers, showers, club memberships. **Comments:** home of the LPGA Safeco Classic. Demanding layout with well-trapped greens, tree-lined fairways and water. This private course is challenging from every tee. Great private course.

Course Yardage & Par:
C-6635 yards, par 72.
M-6280 yards, par 72.
W-5776 yards, par 72.

Directions: from I-5 N&S take exit # 149 to Hwy 516 eastbound. Travel east for 7.7 miles (through Kent) to 132nd Avenue SE. Turn north and proceed 1.4 miles to SE 247th. Turn east for .1 mile to 136th Avenue SE. Turn south to the golf course.

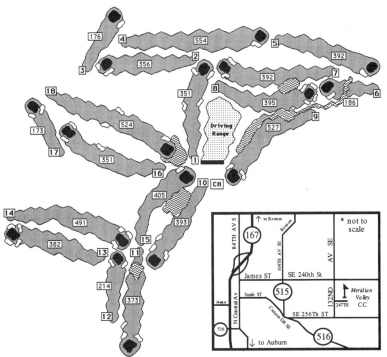

Meriwood Golf Course (public)

4550 Golf Course RD NE; Lacey, WA 98516; (360) 412-0495; 800-55-TEE-IT
Dir. of Golf: Ron Coleman. Pro: Joe Creager, PGA. 18 hole course, range.
Rating/Slope: C 74.6/128; 70.9/123; W 72.8/123. **Course record:** 67.
Green fees: W/D $37 includes cart; W/E $42 includes cart; M/C, VISA
Power cart: included in green fee. **Pull cart:** none. **Trail fee:** not allowed.
Reservation policy: call up to 30 days in advance. **Winter condition:** open, dry.
Terrain: flat, some rolling hills. **Tees:** grass. **Temporary greens:** no, not in use.
Services: club rentals, lessons, lounge, snack bar, beer, pro shop, driving range.
Comments: new golf course that has been well received by all. The track features
rolling terrain tree lined fairways and well bunkered greens. Excellent course that
will challenge you at every turn. Professionaly managed by Golf Resources, INC.

Directions: from the north take exit #111 from
I-5. Turn right a the light. Go approximately 125
yards and turn right (west) on Hogum Bay RD.
Go .3 miles to Meridian Campus Entrance at
Willamette DR, go 2.2 miles to the golf course.
From the south take exit #111 from I-5. Turn left
at the light and go over the freeway. Proceed
through stop light and follow the above directions.

Course Yardage & Par:		
C-7170 yards, par 72.		
M-6579/6159 yards, par 72.		
W-5707/5600 yards, par 72.		

Mill Creek Country Club (private)

15550 Country Club Drive; Mill Creek, WA 98012; (206) 743-5664
Pro: Tom Sursley, PGA. Superintendent: Paul Hoffman. 18 hole course.
Rating/Slope: C 71.6/130; M 70.3/128; W 72.7/130. **Course record:** 62.
Green fees: members only; some reciprocation; no credit cards.
Power cart: private club. **Pull cart:** private club. **Trail fee:** not allowed.
Reservation policy: private club members only. **Winter condition:** damp.
Terrain: relatively hilly. **Tees:** grass. **Temporary greens:** no.
Services: club rentals, lessons, lounge, restaurant, beer, wine, liquor, pro shop,
driving range, lockers, showers, club memberships. **Comments:** rolling terrain,
tree-lined fairways and many hazards put emphasis on shot placement. Greens are
fairly large with undulations throughout. Excellent well kept private facility.

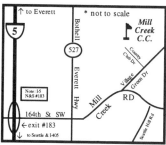

Directions: from I-5 N&S take exit
#183 to Martha Lake Road-(164th St
SW). Travel eastbound for 2 miles to
Mill Creek Road. Turn left and travel .3
miles to Village Green Drive. Turn left
and proceed .3 miles to Country Club
Drive. Turn left to the golf course.

Course Yardage & Par:

C-6331 yards, par 72.
M-6022 yards, par 72.
W-5560 yards, par 72.

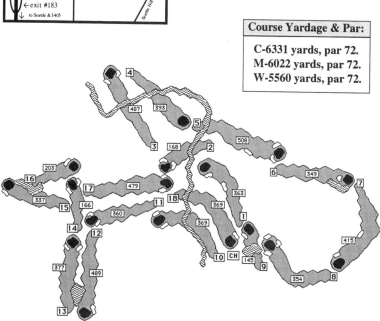

Mint Valley Golf Course (public)
4002 Pennsylvania Street; Longview, WA 98632; (360) 577-3395
Pro: Mahlon Moe, PGA. 18 hole course, putting green.
Rating/Slope: C 71.0/127; M 68.4/119; W 70.0/116. **Course record:** 63.
Green fees: Weekdays $15/$11.50; Weekends $19/$14;
Jr & Sr rates (Monday thru Friday) $11/$9; credit cards for merchandise only.
Power cart: $22/$11. **Pull cart:** $3. **Trail fee:** $10 for personal carts.
Reservation policy: yes, call up to 1 week in advance. **Winter condition:** open,
damp. **Terrain:** flat, very easy to walk. **Tees:** grass. **Temporary greens:** no.
Services: club rentals, lessons, snack bar, beer, wine, pro shop, driving range.
Comments: not overly long, strategically placed bunkers and lakes challenge
any golfers shot making. Greens are in excellent condition and putt well. If you are
looking for a course that is not a back breaker try Mint Valley it will not disappoint.

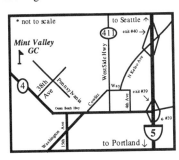

Directions: from I-5 N&S take exit # 39
and proceed west on Hwy 4 (Ocean Beach).
Turn right on 38th, then turn left on Pennsylvania and proceed to the golf course.
Look for signs marking your turns to the
golf course the way is well marked.

Course Yardage & Par:
C-6304 yards, par 71.
M-5800 yards, par 71.
W-5214 yards, par 71.

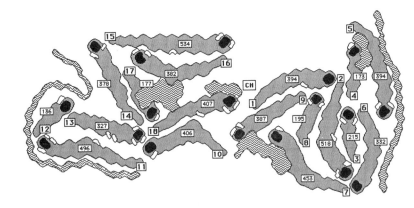

Monroe Golf Course (public)
22110 Old Owen Road; Monroe, WA 98272; (360) 794-8498
Manager: Tom Johnson. 9 hole course, putting green.
Rating/Slope: M 62.5/100; W 66.9/110. **Course record:** 27.
Green fees: W/D $12/$8; W/E $15/$10. Sr. rates on power carts $13/$6.50.
Power cart: $17/$8.50. **Pull cart:** $3. **Trail fee:** $4 per 9 holes.
Reservation policy: yes, please call 7 days in advance for tee-times.
Winter condition: open, dry. **Terrain:** flat, some slight hills. **Tees:** mats.
Temporary greens: yes (winter). **Services:** club rentals, snack bar, pro shop,
lockers, club memberships, pinic area. **Comments:** golf course can play tight due
to many trees lining most fairways. Friendly staff and good food in the club house
can make up for any bad day on the course. Great family golf course.

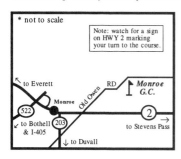

Directions: from I-405 N&S take the exit
for 522 eastbound to Hwy 2 eastbound.
Travel east to Old Owen Road, (the third
light in the town of Monroe) to the golf
course. The golf course will be on your
right. **Note:** Look for a sign on the Hwy 2
marking your turn to the golf course.

Course Yardage & Par:
M-2451 yards, par 33; W-2451 yards, par 33.

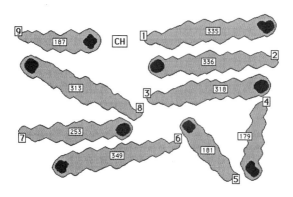

Monument Hill Golf Course (public)

Off 13 NW; PO Box 185; Quincy, WA 98848; (509) 787-3676
Pro: N/A. 18 hole course, driving range, putting green.
Rating/Slope: the golf course has not been rated. **Course record:** N/A.
Green fees: $20. **Power cart:** $20. **Pull cart:** not available. **Trail fee:** N/A.
Reservation policy: call the course for policy. **Winter condition:** N/A.
Terrain: flat, some hills. **Tees:** grass. **Temporary greens:** no.
Services: club rentals, restaurant, fairway lots, pro shop, driving range.
Comments: the expected opening date is summer of 1996. This championship
course will feature undulating fairways, ponds and beautiful desert surroundings.
All holes will offer great views of the Quincy Valley. Excellent new track.

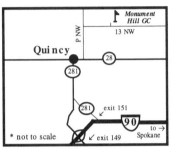

Directions: from I-90 E&W take exit #149
(George exit). Proceed Northbound on Hwy
281 to the city of Quincy. Turn eastbound
at Hwy 28. When you reach PNW RD turn
northbound (left). Proceed for 3.1 miles to
13 NW RD. At 13 NW RD turn right
(eastbound). Proceed for 1 mile to the
course entrance on your left hand side.

Course Yardage & Par:
C-7278 yards, par 72.

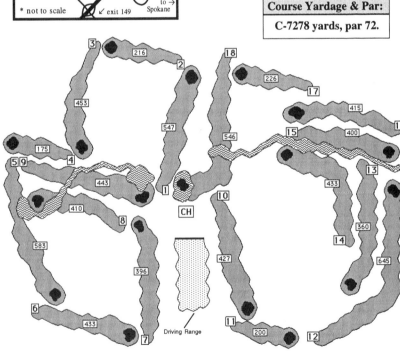

Moses Lake Golf & Country Club (private)

P.O. Drawer G; W Hwy 90; Moses Lake, WA 98837; (509) 765-5049
Pro: Mike Eslick, PGA. Superintendent: Carl Thompson. 18 hole course.
Rating/Slope: C 69.5/111; M 68.5/109; W 73.3/120. **Course record:** 63.
Green fees: private club members & guests only; reciprocates; no credit cards.
Power cart: private club. **Pull cart:** private club. **Trail fee:** private club.
Reservation policy: none. **Winter condition:** golf course closed from December
to January. **Terrain:** flat, some hills. **Tees:** grass. **Temporary greens:** yes.
Services: lessons, restaurant, lounge, beer, wine, pro shop, driving range.
Comments: beautiful lush green fairways and excellent putting surfaces
make this a very enjoyable course. The golf course is very easy to walk.

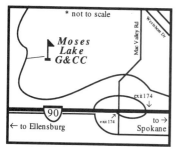

Directions: from I-90 eastbound and
westbound take the first Moses Lake exit
#174. Travel north to the golf course.

Course Yardage & Par:
C-6436 yards, par 71.
M-6187 yards, par 71.
W-5993 yards, par 74.

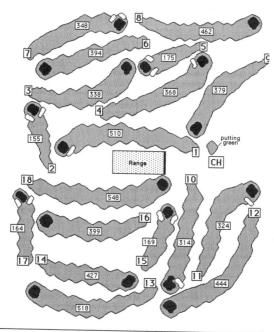

Mount Adams Country Club (semi-private)

1250`Rocky Ford Road; Toppenish, WA 98948; (509) 865-4440
Pro: Scott Galbraith, PGA. **18 hole course, driving range.**
Rating/Slope: C 70.6/121; M 74.1/126; W 73.9/124. **Course record:** 65.
Green fees: $17/$11; Jr. rates, weekdays only; VISA, M/C.
Power cart: $21/$11. **Pull cart:** $2.50/$1.25. **Trail fee:** $3.
Reservation policy: yes, you may call ahead for a tee time. Call prior Thursday
for your weekend reservations. Some other times are restricted by member play.
Winter condition: the golf course is closed from December to February.
Terrain: flat. **Tees:** grass. **Temporary greens:** no. **Services:** lessons, restaurant,
lounge, beer, wine, pro shop, driving range. **Comments:** the course features wide
fairways and small quick greens that can be hard to hold during the summer. This
Eastern Washington course has beautiful views of the Yakima Valley and surrounding countryside from every tee. Great walking golf course.

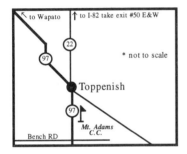

Directions: from I-82 eastbound take
the exit for Highway 97 southbound to
Toppenish. Continue 2 miles south of
Toppenish to the golf course. The golf
course will be located on your left hand
side. The golf course is located right off
of highway 97. Look for signs.

Course Yardage & Par:
C-6524 yards, par 72.
M-6341 yards, par 72.
W-5873 yards, par 73.

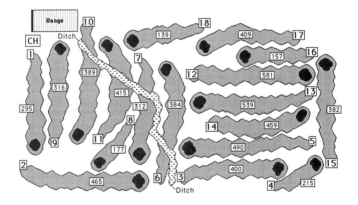

Mount Si Golf Course (public)

9010 Boalch Avenue SE; P.O. Box 2020; Snoqualmie, WA 98065
(206) 391-4926 or 888-1541. 18 hole course. Supt.: Jack Moore, Mike Moore.
Pros: Gary Barter PGA **, John Sanford** PGA, **Matt Campbell** PGA. **Pro: Ron Lee.**
Rating/Slope: C 68.5/116; M 67.4/113; W 68.8/108. **Course record:** 69.
Green fees: W/D $21/$14; W/E $25/$16; Jr & Sr. (M-F) & winter rates.
Power cart: $22/$14. **Pull cart** $3/$2. **Trail fee:** $3 for personal carts.
Reservation policy: yes, no restrictions. **Winter condition:** open, dry.
Terrain: flat, some hills. **Tees:** grass . **Temporary greens:** no, not in use.
Services: club rentals, lessons, snack bar, restaurant, beer, wine, liquor, lockers,
showers, pro shop, club memberships, driving range. **Comments:** Scenic setting
near the base of Mt. Si. Course offers a full service restaurant with fantastic views.
Dramatic changes in the layout make this course even more enjoyable. If you are
looking for a good public golf course with a friendly staff Mt. Si is sure to please.

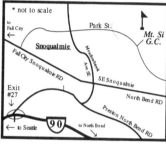

Directions: from I-90 eastbound take exit # 27 to the right. At the stop sign turn left and go 1 mile to the "Snoqualmie Falls" sign. Turn left, then veer right at the fork in the road (past the hospital) to the stop sign. Continue beyond Mt. Si High School to Park St. Turn right on Park St. The golf course will be 1 mile ahead on your left.

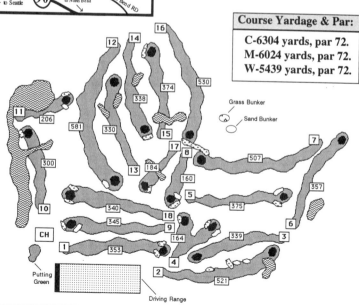

Course Yardage & Par:

C-6304 yards, par 72.
M-6024 yards, par 72.
W-5439 yards, par 72.

New World Pro Golf Center (public)

5022 Guide Meridian; Bellingham, WA 98226; (360) 398-1362.
Pro: none. 9 hole par 3 course, covered driving range.
Rating/Slope: the golf course is not rated. **Course record:** 22.
Green fees: $5/$4 all week long; no credit cards.
Power cart: none. **Pull cart:** $1. **Trail fee: personal carts are not allowed.**
Reservation policy: advance reservations not required, first come first served.
Winter condition: the golf course is closed from November to mMarch.
Terrain: flat, some slight hills. **Tees:** grass. **Temporary greens:** no.
Services: club rentals, limited pro shop, covered driving range.
Comments: fair par 3 golf course with medium to small sized greens. A creek runs through 2 and 9 and does present some challenges. The complex also has a coverd driving range for those wanting to practice their short or long irons.

Directions: From I-5 N&S take exit #256 to Meridian Street. Proceed north on Hwy 539N for 2 miles to the golf course on your right hand side of the highway. Look for a sign indicating your turn.

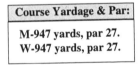

Course Yardage & Par:
M-947 yards, par 27.
W-947 yards, par 27.

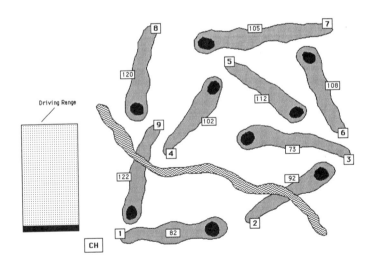

Newaukum Valley Golf Course (public)

3024 Jackson Hwy; Chehalis, WA 98532; (360) 748-0461
Pro: Scott Date, PGA. Supt.: Steve Cox. 27 hole course.
Rating/Slope: C 70.7/126; M 69.0/122; W 71.4/126. **Course record:** 66.
Green fees: W/D $15/$10; W/E $19/$14; Sr rates; M/C, VISA.
Power cart: $18/$9. **Pull cart:** $2/$1. **Trail fee:** $10 for personal carts.
Reservation policy: call in advance, March to September. **Winter condition:** dry.
Terrain: flat, some hills. **Tees:** grass. **Temporary greens:** not in use.
Services: club rentals, lessons, restaurant, beer, wine, pro shop, driving range.
Comments: A full irrigation system keeps the course in great shape all year round. Good public golf course that will be expanding to 27 holes in March of 1996. This new layout should add to what was an already great public course.

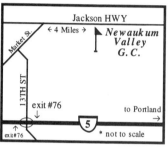

Directions: from I-5 N&S take exit # 76 to 13th St. Go east on 13th to Market St. Turn right on Market which becomes Jackson Highway. Follow for 4 miles to the golf course. Look for signs.

Course Yardage & Par:

C-6512 yards, par 72.
M-6125 yards, par 72.
W-5535 yards, par 72.

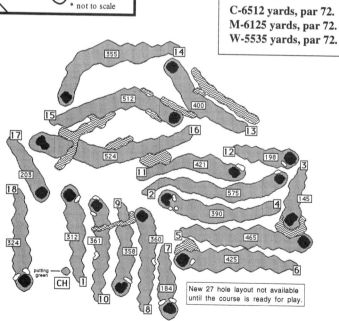

New 27 hole layout not available until the course is ready for play.

Nile Golf & Country Club (semi-private)

500 NE 205th; Edmonds, WA 98020; (206) 776-5154
Pro: Randy Puetz, PGA. Supt.: Davis Korsmoe. 18 hole course.
Rating/Slope: M 67.3/119; W 70.7/124. **Course record:** 63.
Green fees: Shriners $14/$9; guests $24/$14; M/C, VISA, carts & merchandise.
Power cart: $21/$11. **Pull cart:** $2. **Trail fee:** $5 for personal carts.
Reservation policy: up to 1 week in advance for members. Public may reserve 1 day ahead on a "space available basis". **Winter condition:** open, good drainage.
Terrain: very hilly. **Tees:** grass & mats (in winter). **Temporary greens:** yes.
Services: lessons, practice range, well stocked pro shop, club repair, lockers, showers. **Comments:** short, but a test of skill for all players. Beautiful tree-lined, well bunkered course. The new 9 should be ready for play in July of 1996.

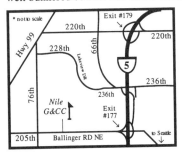

Directions: from I-5 N&S take exit # 177 to 244th SW-205th St-Hwy 104W. Travel westbound for .3 miles to the golf course entrance, which will be on your right.
Note: Look for the Nile Temple entrance and this will take you into the grounds of the golf course and clubhouse

Course Yardage & Par:
M-5000 yards, par 65.
W-5000 yards, par 65.

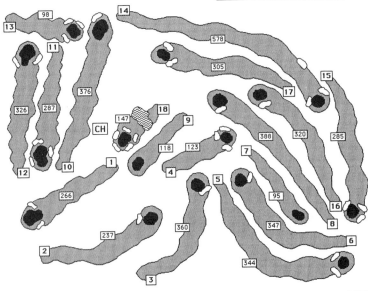

Nisqually Valley Golf Course (public)
15425 Mosman St; Box Q; Yelm, WA 98597; (360) 458-3332 or 800-352-2645
Pros: Chuck Brown, PGA, Eric Olsen, PGA. 18 hole course.
Rating/Slope: C 68.2/116; M 67.3/114; W 71.6/123. **Course record:** 62.
Green fees: $17/$10 (all week long); Jr & Sr rates $10/$5 (M-F); no credit cards.
Power cart: $15/$8. **Pull cart:** $2. **Trail fee:** no trail fee.
Reservation policy: yes, up to 1 week in advance, for weekends times only.
Winter condition: dry, good drainage. **Terrain:** flat, some hills. **Tees:** grass.
Temporary greens: no. **Services:** club rentals, lessons, lounge, restaurant,
beer, wine, liquor, pro shop. **Comments:** very dry and easy to walk golf course
that has very few hazards. Very scenic course with beautiful views of Mount
Rainier and the surrounding countryside. Good public golf course .

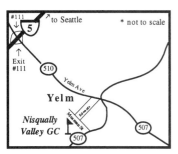

Directions: from I-5 N&S take exit # 111 onto Hwy 510 and travel southeast toward the town of Yelm. When Yelm turn right on Edwards Street. Proceed on Edwards Street for .6 miles to Mosman Street where you will turn to the golf course. Look for signs indicating your turn to the clubhouse.

Course Yardage & Par:
C-6007 yards, par 72.
M-5815 yards, par 72.
W-5751 yards, par 72.

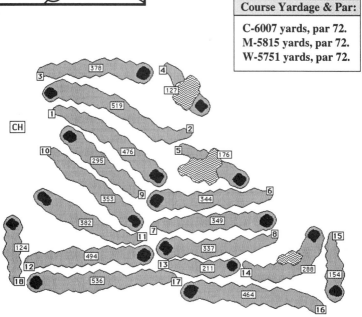

North Bellingham Public Golf Course (public)

205 W Smith Road; Bellingham, WA 98226; (360) 398-8300; 1-800-469-9517
Pro: Howard Russell, PGA. Supt.: Richard Jahnke. 18 hole course, range.
Rating/Slope: C 72.1/124; M 68.9/119; 68.7/112. **Course record:** 68.
Green fees: $26.90/$18.55 all week long; Jr./Sr. rates $25.05/$17.63; winter rates.
Power cart: $10.20/$7.42 (per person). **Pull cart:** $2. **Trail fee:** not allowed.
Reservation policy: please call up to 1 week in advance for tee times.
Winter condition: open weather permitting, dry. **Terrain:** flat, some rolling
hills. **Tees:** grass. **Temporary greens:** no. **Services:** club rentals, lessons,
lounge, restaurant, beer, wine, liquor, pro shop, driving range, putting green.
Comments: newer public golf course. The course is of championship caliber
and length. From the back tees the course plays 6800+ yards and is demanding.
Ponds, grass and sand bunkers dot the entire course. Worth a trip if in the area.

Directions: from I-5 N take exit #256
(Guide Meridian, Hwy 539). Proceed
north on Hwy 539 until you reach W
Smith Road. Turn left on W Smith Road
and proceed to course entrance on your
left hand side. From I-5 S take exit #262
W Axton RD. Proceed east on W Axton
Road to Guide Meridian Hwy 539. Turn
right on Hwy 539. Proceed to W Smith
Road where you will turn right to the golf
course located on your left hand side.

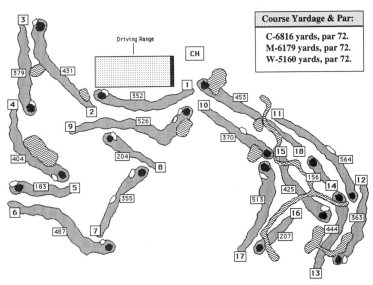

Course Yardage & Par:

C-6816 yards, par 72.
M-6179 yards, par 72.
W-5160 yards, par 72.

North Shore Golf Course (public)

4101 N Shore Blvd. NE; Tacoma, WA 98422; (206) 927-1375; 1-800-447-1375
Pro: David Wetli, PGA. Supt.: Michael Tight. 18 hole course, driving range.
Rating/Slope: C 69.9/120; M 68.6/118; W 74.0/126. **Course record:** 66.
Green fees: Mon. to Tues. $20/$13; Wed. to Thur. $22/$14; Fri. to Sun. $30;
no nine hole rate on Friday thru Sunday; twi-lite rates; VISA, M/C, AMEX.
Power cart: $20/$10. **Pull cart:** $3. **Trail fee:** $20/$10 (Note: add tax to all fees).
Reservation policy: yes, up to 1 week in advance, bankcard number required
for all weekend tee-times. **Winter condition:** open, dry. **Terrain:** relatively hilly.
Tees: grass. **Temporary greens:** yes. **Services:** club rentals, lessons, snack bar,
lounge, restaurant, beer, wine, liquor, well stocked pro shop, lighted and covered
driving range, banquet, tournament facilities available. **Comments:** sand bunkers,
water hazards and undulating terrain make this course a true challenge. Greens
are medium to large in size. This golf course is worth a special trip anytime. The
Northshore pro shop was voted for the seventh straight year as one of the countries
top pro shops by Golf Shop Operations magazine. Excellent golf course.

Directions: from I-5 N&S take exit
142B. Travel westbound for 5 miles.
Turn left on Nassau Avenue. Travel for
1/2 mile to Oakmont. Turn left. Take the
next left onto Northshore Blvd. The golf
course will be 1/10 mile ahead on your
right hand side. Look for signs the roads
to the golf course are well marked.

Course Yardage &Par:
C-6305 yards, par 71.
M-6039 yards, par 71.
W-5442 yards, par 73.

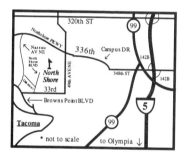

Oakbrook Golf & Country Club (private)
8102 Zircon Drive SW; Tacoma, WA 98498; (206) 584-8770
Pro: Tad Davis, PGA. Superintendent: Jay Griswold. 18 hole course.
Rating/Slope: B 71.6/125; W 69.8/121; Y 73.3/124; R 70.4/117. **Record:** 60.
Green fees: private club, members & guests only; reciprocates.
Power cart: private club. **Pull cart:** private club. **Trail fee:** not allowed.
Reservation policy: private club members & guests only. **Winter condition:** dry.
Terrain: flat, some hills. **Tees:** grass. **Temporary greens:** yes, in winter.
Services: club rentals, lessons, lounge, beer, wine, liquor, lockers, showers,
pro shop, driving range. **Comments:** narrow tree-lined fairways and many
sand bunkers routinely challenge any golfer's game. Greens tend to get firm in
the summer months and can be hard to hold. Excellent private golf course.

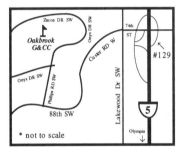

Directions: from I-5 N&S take exit # 129
to S 74th. Go west for 2.3 miles, then S
74th will become Custer Road. Continue
to 88th St. Turn right on 88th. 88th
becomes Steilacoom. At your second light
turn right on Phillips. Stay on Phillips until
you come to the end of the arterial (sign).
Turn left on Turquoise. At the first stop
sign turn right on Zircon. Stay on Zircon
and this should lead to the clubhouse.

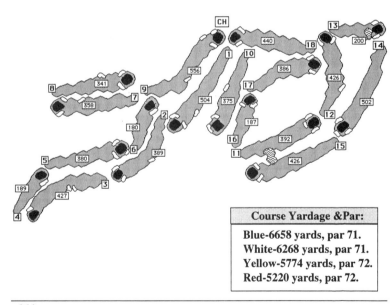

Course Yardage &Par:
Blue-6658 yards, par 71.
White-6268 yards, par 71.
Yellow-5774 yards, par 72.
Red-5220 yards, par 72.

Oaksridge Golf Course (public)

1052 Monte-Elma Road; Elma, WA 98541; (360) 482-3511
Pro: Rich Walker, PGA. 18 hole course.
Rating/Slope: M 65.3/100; W 68.9/108. **Course record:** 61.
Green fees: $16/$9 all week long; Jr. & Sr. rates $10/$5 (M-F); VISA, MC.
Power cart: $16/$9. **Pull cart:** $2. **Trail fee:** $4 for personal carts.
Reservation policy: yes, taken for weekends and holidays only.
Winter condition: open weather permitting, damp. **Terrain:** flat. **Tees:** grass.
Temporary greens: no, not in use. **Services:** club rentals, lessons, pro shop,
driving range, club memberships. **Comments:** flat course which is easy to walk
and has few hazards. For the senior golfer this course is very friendly. During the
week it offers discounted rates on green fees to all seniors.

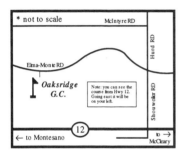

Directions: from I-5 N&S take exit
104 to Hwy 101 and continue to Hwy 8
westbound. Proceed to Highway 12
westbound. Follow to the town of Elma
and turn right on Schouweiler Road.
(watch for your turn because it can come
up very quickly). At Monte-Elma Road
turn west to the golf course which will be
located on your left. **Note:** you will be
able to see the golf course from Hwy 12.

Course Yardage & Par:
M-5643 yards, par 70.
W-5423 yards, par 72.

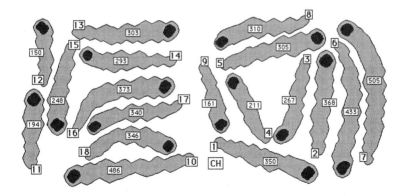

Oasis Park Par 3 (public)
2541 Basin SW; Ephrata, WA 98823; (509) 754-5102
Owners: Mike & Patti Donovan. 9 hole par 3 course.
Rating/Slope: the golf course is not rated. **Course record: 23.**
Green fees: $3.75; all day pass $6.50; Jr & Sr rates.
Power cart: not available. **Pull cart:** $1.25. **Trail fee:** not allowed.
Reservation policy: reservations are not needed or required.
Winter condition: the golf course is closed from November to mid-March.
Terrain: flat, some hills. **Tees:** grass. **Temporary greens:** no, not in use.
Services: club rentals, vending machines, limited pro shop, putting green.
Comments: Treed, well groomed & challenging par 3 course. Holes are fairly
short in length. RV parking is available for those wanting to stay at the park.

Directions: the course is located 1 mile
south of Ephrata on the west side of Hwy
28. Look for signs to the golf course.

Course Yardage & Par:
M-930 yards, par 27.
W-930 yards, par 27.

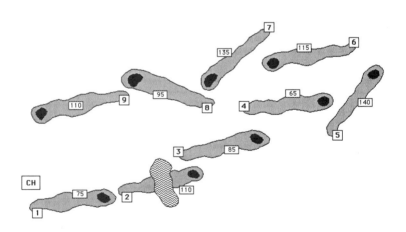

Ocean Shores Golf Course (public)

Box 369; 500 Canal Drive; Ocean Shores, WA 98569; (360) 289-3357
Pros: Ronnie Espedal, PGA. Curt Zander, PGA. 18 hole course.
Rating/Slope: C 70.2/115; M 68.8/113; W 69.6./115. **Course record:** 66.
Green fees: $23/$15 everday; Sr rates $15/$10; winter rates; M/C, VISA.
Power cart: $22/$14. **Pull cart:** $3. **Trail fee:** $7.50/$5.
Reservation policy: call in advance for tee times. No time limit on reservations.
Winter condition: dry. **Terrain:** flat. **Tees:** grass. **Temporary greens:** no.
Services: club rentals, lessons, snack bar, lounge, restaurant, beer, wine, liquor, pro shop, lockers, showers, club memberships. **Comments:** back nine very wooded, front nine winds by the ocean, a very distinctive setting. The golf course can play very tough at times especially if the wind picks up. Excellent facility that is very popular with the summer crowd that vacations at the ocean. Ocean Shores is a fantastic winter golf course because it drains well and stays very dry.

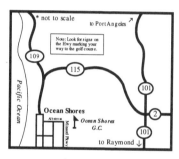

Directions: from I-5 N&S take exit #104 to Hwy 101. Follow Hwy 101. Proceed to Hwy 8 westbound. Then take Hwy 8 to Hwy 12 westbound to Aberdeen/Ocean Beaches. Proceed to Hwy 115. Exit to Hwy 109 southbound and follow the signs to the golf course. The course is located on the Washington coast. **Note:** keep following the signs to Ocean Beaches and this will get you to Aberdeen then Ocean Shores.

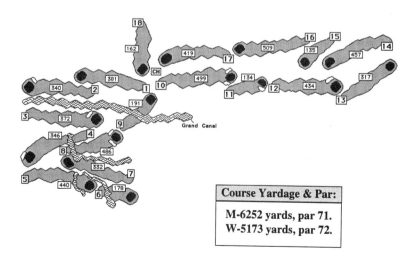

Course Yardage & Par:
M-6252 yards, par 71.
W-5173 yards, par 72.

Odessa Golf Club (public)
off Highway 28; Box 621; Odessa, WA 99159; (509) 982-0093
Manager: Gary Valenta. 9 hole course, dual tees for 18 holes.
Rating/Slope: M 68.8/113; W 72.9/121. **Course record:** 67.
Green fees: W/D $12/$8; W/E $14/$9; W/D $15, W/E $18 all day; M/C, VISA.
Power cart: $5 per person per 9 holes. **Pull cart:** $2. **Trail fee:** $5.
Reservation policy: yes, you may call ahead for a tee time, no restrictions.
Winter condition: the course is closed from Novemeber to February.
Terrain: relatively hilly. **Tees:** grass. **Temporary greens:** no, not in use.
Services: club rentals, snack bar, beer, pro shop, chipping & putting greens,
free RV hook-ups for golfers. **Comments:** a tough medium length golf course
with elevated greens and wide fairways. This track has excellent greens during the
peak golfing season. Adjacent to the golf course is RV parking with power, and
water. Odessa is a great bargin for those wanting to stay and play!!!

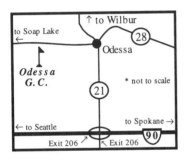

Directions: from I-90 take the exit #206
for Hwy 21 northbound to Odessa. Travel
north to Odessa and once in Odessa exit to
Hwy 28 westbound to the golf course. The
golf course is located west of the city
limits on Hwy 28. Look for signs.

Course Yardage & Par:
M-3070 yards, par 36.
W-2894 yards, par 37.
Dual tees for 18 holes:
M-6248 yards, par 72.
W-5885 yards, par 74.

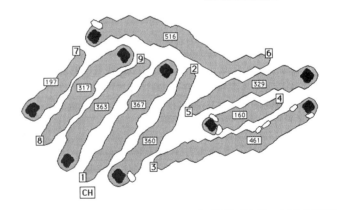

Okanogan Valley Golf Club (semi-private)

Golf Course Drive; Box 1692; Omak, WA 98841; (509) 826-6937
Pro: Bill Sproule, PGA. 9 hole course dual tees for 18 holes.
Rating/Slope: M 69.2/117; W 72.7/125. **Course record:** 65.
Green fees: W/D 15/$10; W/E $20/$15; no credit cards.
Power cart: $20/$11. **Pull cart:** $1.50. **Trail fee:** no charge.
Reservation policy: yes, call 4 days in advance for a tee times.
Winter condition: the course is closed from mid-October to mid-March.
Terrain: flat, some hills. **Tees:** grass. **Temporary greens:** no, not in use.
Services: club rentals, lessons, snack bar, beer, pro shop, putting & chipping green.
Comments: closed to the public Wednesday, men only, Thursday am women only.
Rated by the *National Golf Foundation* as one of the top 9 hole courses in the state.
Well layed out track with water and sand coming into play throughout.

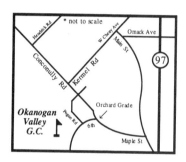

Directions: the golf course is located between Omak and Okanogan. From southbound Hwy 97 take the Hwy 215 exit and enter Omak. Note the signs and turns to the golf course southwest of town.

Course Yardage & Par:
M-3040 yards, par 35.
W-2955 yards, par 38.
Dual tees for 18 holes:
M-6152 yards, par 70.
W-5880 yards, par 76.

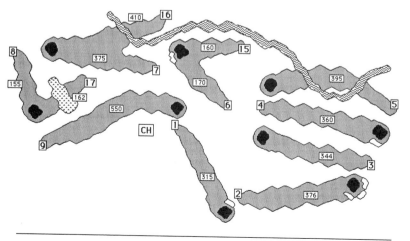

Olympia Country & Golf Club (private)
3636 Country Club Drive NW; Olympia, WA 98502; (360) 866-9777
Pro: Scott Smith, PGA Supt.: Robert Pearsall. 18 hole course.
Rating/Slope: C 69.0/120; M 67.9/118; W 70.6/120. **Record:** 63.
Green fees: private club members & guests only; reciprocates.
Power cart: private club. **Pull cart:** private club. **Trail fee:** not allowed.
Reservation policy: members only club. **Winter condition:** damp.
Terrain: very hilly. **Tees:** grass. **Services:** lessons, lounge, restaurant,
beer, wine, liquor, pro shop, showers, club memberships, driving range, chipping
and putting greens. **Comments:** the front nine is short and tricky demanding shot
placement from the tee. The back nine is long and more difficult. Greens are well
bunkered and can be hard to hold and fast in peak season.

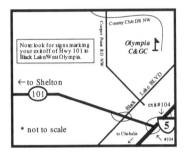

Directions: from I-5 N&S take exit
#104 to Hwy 101 to the Port Angeles-
Aberdeen. Follow to the Black Lake-
West Olympia exit. Turn right off the
exit to Cooper Point Road. Turn left
and travel 4 miles to the golf course.

Course Yardage & Par:
C-6048 yards, par 71.
M-5801 yards, par 71.
W-5265 yards, par 74.
W-5313 yards, par 75.

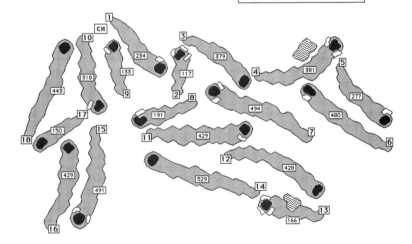

Orcas Island Golf Course (public)
Route 1, Box 85; East Sound, WA 98245; (360) 376-4400
Owner/Manager: Robert Blake. 9 hole course, dual tees for 18 holes.
Rating/Slope: M 67.6/114; W 72.8/125. **Course record:** 65.
Green fees: $25/$17.50 all week long; M/C, VISA.
Power cart: $20/$15. **Pull cart:** $3. **Trail fee:** $5.
Reservation policy: yes, call in advance, no restrictions on tee times.
Winter condition: open, dry, drains well. **Terrain:** relatively hilly. **Tees:** grass.
Temporary greens: no, not in use. **Services:** club rentals $7, snack bar, pro shop,
club memberships, putting green. **Comments:** the course is set in the scenic San
Juan Islands, a very popular area for vacationers in the summer months. The track
features hilly terrain, water and bunkers. One of the best kept secrets in the NW.

Directions: take the Anacortes ferry to
Orcas Island. From the terminal in Orcas
follow the Orcas to Eastsound Road to
the cut-off for the golf course located on
your right hand side. Look for signs
marking your way to the golf course.

Course Yardage & Par:

M-3060 yards, par 36.
W-3000 yards, par 37.
Dual tees for 18 holes:
M-5803 yards, par 71.
W-5464 yards, par 73.

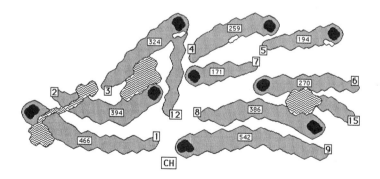

Orchard Hills Golf & Country Club (private)
605 39th Street; Washougal, WA 98671; (360) 835-5444
Pro: Rick Edwards, PGA. 18 hole course, driving range.
Rating/Slope: C 68.3/113; M 67. 4/111; W 70.8/113. **Course record:** 62.
Green fees: private club members & guests only; reciprocates ; M/C, VISA.
Power cart: private club. **Pull cart:** private club. **Trail fee:** private club.
Reservation policy: yes, up to 1 week in advance. **Winter condition:** open, dry.
Terrain: relatively hilly. **Tees:** grass. **Temporary greens:** no not in use.
Services: lessons, snack bar, lounge, restaurant, beer, wine, liquor, pro shop,
lockers, showers, club memberships, driving range, putting & chipping greens.
Comments: the front nine is flat, easy to walk and sports narrow tree lined fair-
ways. The back nine is more wide open but plays much longer than the yardage
indicates. Greens are well bunkered with some being fronted by water hazards.

Directions: from I-5 southbound take
exit # 7 to I-205 southbound. Travel south
to exit # 27, Hwy 14E. Travel eastbound
to the Washougal exit. Follow the signs
to "E" St. and proceed 1.5 miles to 39th.
Turn left on 39th to the golf course.

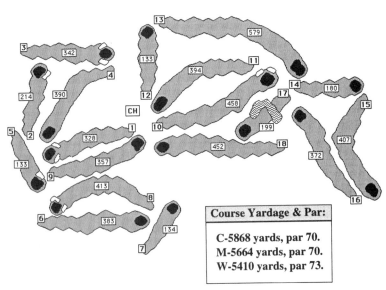

Course Yardage & Par:
C-5868 yards, par 70.
M-5664 yards, par 70.
W-5410 yards, par 73.

Oroville Golf Club (public)

Off Nighthawk Road; Rt. 1, Box G-20; Oroville, WA 98844; (509) 476-2390
Pro: none. **Manager:** Jerry Sneve. **9 hole course, dual tees for 18 holes.**
Rating/Slope: M 67.8/113; W 74.0/126. **Course record:** 62.
Green fees: W/D $15/$10; W/E $18/$12; VISA, M/C.
Power cart: $10 per 9 holes. **Pull cart:** $2. **Trail fee:** $5.
Reservation policy: yes, you may call ahead 7 days for a tee time.
Winter condition: the golf course is closed from November to February.
Terrain: relatively hilly. **Tees:** grass. **Temporary greens:** no not in use.
Services: club rentals, snack bar, beer, pro shop, putting & chipping greens.
Comments: the course is well-conditioned with dual tees for those wanting a
different look for their second nine. Fairways are tree-lined but fairly open and
there are a few sand traps which enter play on approach shots. Good 9 hole track.

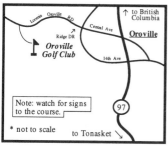

Directions: from Highway 2 westbound
cut-off at Highway 97 northbound via
Hwy 17 northbound. Travel north to
Oroville and Nighthawk Road. Turn left
and proceed 2 miles to the golf course.
Look for signs marking your way to the
golf course.

Course Yardage & Par:
M-2897 yards, par 36.
W-2897 yards, par 37.
Dual tees for 18 holes:
M-5938 yards, par 72.
W-5938 yards, par 74.

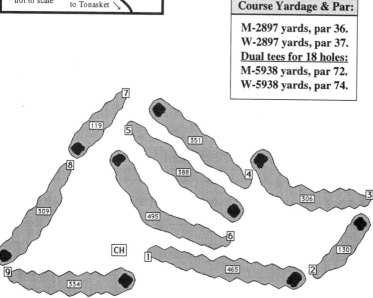

Othello Golf Club (public)

West Bench Road; PO Box 185; Othello, WA 99344; (509) 488-2376
Pro & Owner: Doug Buck, PGA. 9 hole course.
Rating/Slope: M 68.5/110; W 74.2/123. **Course record:** 61.
Green fees: W/D $13/$8; W/E $15/$10; no credit cards.
Power cart: $18/$10. **Pull cart:** $2. **Trail fee:** $5.
Reservation policy: you may call 2 days in advance for a tee time.
Winter condition: dry, course closed sometimes in December and January.
Terrain: flat, easy walking. **Tees:** grass. **Temporary greens:** no not in use.
Services: club rentals, lessons, restaurant, lounge, beer, wine, liquor, pro shop,
lockers, showers, driving range. **Comments:** the course features many mature
trees lining the fairways. Bunkers front many of the greens that are medium to
large in size. Designed by the Trent Jones Corporation this golf course is kept
immaculate. For those traveling in an RV the course provides plenty of RV space.

```
┌─────────────────────────────┐
│   ╭26╮      ●Othello        │
│ ←                      to → │
│ to I-90                Hwy  │
│          ╭24╮          395  │
│                    ╭17╮     │
│                             │
│  Bench  RD                  │
│        ╲                    │
│         ↑                to │
│ Othello Golf Club       Hwy │
│                    * not    395 │
│                    to scale  ↓ │
└─────────────────────────────┘
```

Directions: from Hwy 17 take the exit
for Bench Road. Travel west to the golf
course. The golf course will be located
on your left. The golf course is located
two miles southwest of Othello. Look for
signs marking your way to the course.

Course Yardage & Par:
M-3066 yards, par 35.
W-3066 yards, par 36.

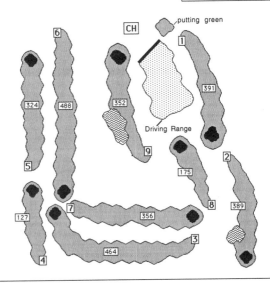

Overlake Golf & Country Club (private)
8000 NE 16th; Bellevue, WA 98004; (206) 454-5031
Pro: Ron Hoetmer, PGA. Supt.: Jeff Gullikson 18 hole course. Record: 65.
Rating/Slope: C 71.2/127; M 69.6/123; M 67.8/117; W 65.8/113.
Green fees: private club members & their guests only; reciprocates; M/C, VISA.
Power cart: private club. **Pull cart:** complimentary. **Trail fee:** not allowed.
Reservation policy: private club members only. **Winter condition:** damp.
Terrain: flat, some hills. **Tees:** grass. **Temporary greens:** no. **Services:** club
rentals, lessons, snack bar, lounge, restaurant, beer, wine, liquor, pro shop, club
memberships, driving range. **Comments:** the course is relatively flat, well
bunkered and wide open. Greens are fast and always in excellent condition.

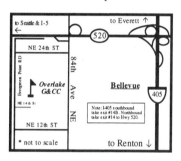

Directions: from I-5 N&S take exit #168B
to Hwy 520E. Travel east to the 84th
Avenue NE exit. Take the exit and go
south for 1 mile to NE 12th. On 12th
travel west for .5 miles to Evergreen Point
Road. Turn north and travel to NE 16th.
On 16th proceed east to the golf course.

Course Yardage & Par:
C-6556 yards, par 71.
M-6150 yards, par 71.
M-5709 yards, par 71.
W-5709 yards, par 71.

Overlook Golf Course (public)

1785 State Highway 9; Mount Vernon, WA 98273; (360) 422-6444
Manager/Owner: Neil Hansen. 9 hole course.
Rating/Slope: C 61.2/101; M 60.4/97; W 60.6/96. **Course record:** 64.
Green fees: W/D $14/$8; W/E $17/$10; Sr rates (weekdays); no credit cards.
Power cart: $18/$9. **Pull cart:** $2. **Trail fee:** no charge for personal carts.
Reservation policy: yes, you may call 14 days in advance for tee times.
Winter condition: good, open. **Terrain:** flat, some hills. **Tees:** grass.
Temporary greens: no not in use. **Services:** club rentals, snack bar, lounge, beer,
pro shop, putting green. **Comments:** very friendly, family-owned facility that is
fun for all. The golf course is fairly open with lovely views of Big Lake and the
surrounding mountains. The course features elevated tees, small greens and fairly
wide open fairways. This course is not a back-breaker so enjoy the peaceful area.

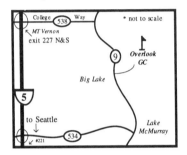

Directions: from I-5 N&S take exit # 227
to Hwy 538 eastbound in Mount Vernon.
Travel east to Hwy 9. Turn southbound
and continue to Big Lake and the golf
course. The golf course is located 7 miles
from I-5. Look for signs marking your turn
to the parking lot.

Course Yardage & Par:
C-2213 yards, par 33.
M-2026 yards, par 33.
W-1809 yards, par 33.

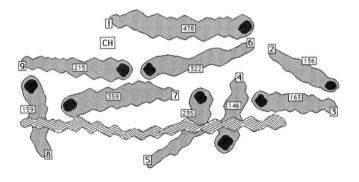

Painted Hills Golf Club (public)

South 4403 Dishman-Mica; Spokane, WA 99206; (509) 928-4653
Pro: Scott Shagool, PGA. 9 hole course, dual tees for 18 holes.
Rating/Slope: M 70.1/120; W 71.0/114. **Course record:** 63.
Green fees: W/D $15/$10; W/E $16/$11; Jr. & Sr. rates Monday thru Thursday.
Power cart: $6 per 9 holes. **Pull cart:** $2. **Trail fee:** $4 (seasonal rates available).
Reservation policy: yes, call ahead any time in advance for a tee time.
Winter condition: the golf course is open all year long Dry conditions.
Terrain: flat (easy walking). **Tees:** all grass. **Temporary greens:** not in use.
Services: lessons, club rentals, restaurant, pro shop, putting green, driving range.
Comments: beautiful fairways, sand traps and water come into play. A well-conditioned golf course. Quality rental clubs for traveling executives. Great course.

Directions: from I-90 E&W take the Argonne/Dishman exit #287 and travel 5 miles south to the golf course. Argonne Road will become Dishman-Mica Hwy just south of Sprague Road.

Course Yardage & Par:
M-3288 yards, par 36.
W-2678 yards, par 36.
Dual tees for 18 holes:
M-6532 yards, par 72.
W-5687 yards, par 73.

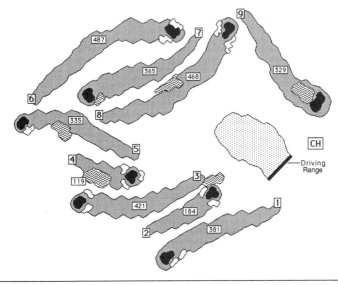

Peaceful Valley Golf Course (public)

8225 Kendall Road; Maple Falls, WA 98226; (360) 599-2416
Pro: none. Manager: Phil Cloward. 9 hole course.
Rating/Slope: M 61/94; W 65.1/103. **Course record:** 64.
Green fees: W/D $11/$8; W/E $13/$10; Jr. & Sr. rates (M-F); VISA, M/C.
Power cart: $15/$10. **Pull cart:** $2. **Trail fee:** no charge for personal carts.
Reservation policy: yes, up to 1 week in advance. **Winter condition:** dry,
course can become closed at certain times. **Terrain:** flat, some hills. **Tees:** grass.
Temporary greens: yes. **Services:** club rentals, snack bar, pro shop, club memberships, putting green. **Comments:** bunkers come into play on five holes, however,
the fairways are quite open. The course is very flat and easy to walk. This track
has excellent views of the nearby mountains and surrounding countryside. A rustic
golf course that is excellent for beginners and families.

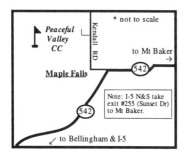

Directions: from I-5 take the exit for the
Mt. Baker Hwy. Travel northeast on the
highway past the 23 mile marker to the
Kendall-Sumas Road. Turn left and
proceed 2.5 miles to the housing development. Left, then right to the golf course.

Course Yardage & Par:
M-2467 yards, par 33.
W-2467 yards, par 34.

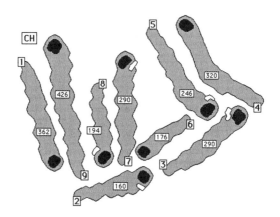

Pend Oreille Golf & Country Club (public)
off of Hwy 31; Box 97; Metaline Falls, WA 99153; no phone.
Pro: none. Manager: none. 9 hole course.
Rating/Slope: the golf course is not rated. **Course record:** 27.
Green fees: $1; $1.50 weekends; student (including college) play for free;
no credit cards. **Power cart:** none. **Pull cart:** none. **Trail fee:** none.
Reservation policy: none. **Winter condition:** closed from October to April.
Terrain: flat, some hills. **Tees:** grass. **Temporary greens:** no.
Services: none. **Comments:** the course is on the honor system. Greens fees
are placed in a honor box. The course features sand greens, rake before and after
putting. The golf course has changed from 6 to 9 holes in the last few years.

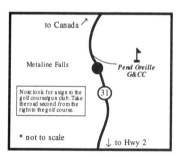

Directions: the golf course is located
4 miles north of Metaline Falls off of Hwy
31. Note the golf course/gun club sign for
the turn off. Take the road second from
the right to the golf course.

Course Yardage & Par:
M-2183 yards, par 31.
W-2183 yards, par 40.

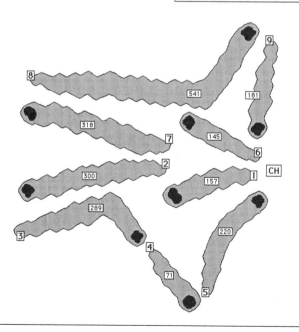

Peninsula Golf Course (public)

Highway's 103 & 97; Box 536; Long Beach, WA 98631; (360) 642-2828
Pro: Bev McCallister. Manager: Jerry Zorich 9 hole course.
Rating/Slope: the golf course is not rated. **Course record:** 28.
Green fees: $13/$9 all week long; VISA, M/C.
Power cart: $15/$9. **Pull cart:** $1. **Trail fee:** $3.
Reservation policy: please call 7 days in advance for tee times.
Winter condition: open weather permitting, damp. **Terrain:** flat, easy walking
golf course. **Tees:** mats. **Temporary greens:** no, not in use at anytime.
Services: club rentals, lessons, snack bar, small pro shop, chipping & putting
greens. **Comments:** located in picturesque Long Beach on the Washington coast,
this course is very flat and easy to walk. Fairways are narrow in scope but greens
have generous landing areas. A great location for a relaxing round of golf.

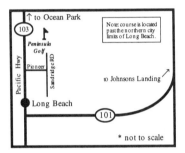

Directions: from I-5 N&S take exit #104
to Hwy 101 W. Follow 101 westbound
to Long Beach. As you approach the
peninsula turn right on Hwy 103
northbound through Seaview. Proceed for
3 miles. The golf course is located just
beyond the northern city limits.

Course Yardage & Par:
M-2148 yards, par 33.
W-2148 yards, par 34.

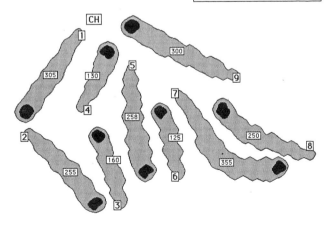

Peninsula Golf Club (private)

824 South Lindberg Road; Port Angeles, WA 98362; (360) 457-6501
Pro: Chris Repass, PGA. Supt.: Merle Pearce. 18 hole course.
Rating/Slope: C 70.3/122; M 69.1/119; W 70.3/120. **Record: 62.**
Green fees: private club members and guests only; reciprocates. M/C, VISA.
Power cart: private club. **Pull cart:** private club. **Trail fee:** private club.
Reservation policy: yes, up to 1 week in advance. **Winter condition:** damp.
Terrain: very hilly. **Tees:** grass. **Temporary greens:** yes (during winter).
Services: club rentals, lessons, snack bar, lounge, restaurant, beer, wine, liquor,
pro shop, driving range. **Comments:** beautiful view of the mountains and the
Strait of Juan de Fuca. This private course which used to be open to the public is
near downtown Port Angeles and sports many unique features. Some of the holes
are cut into a hillside offering a wide variety of lies in the fairway.

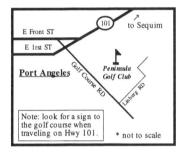

Directions: from Hwy 101. When you
are first entering Port Angeles turn on
Golf Course Road (south toward the
mountains) and proceed .6 miles
to Lindberg Road. Turn left on Lindberg
Road and proceed to the golf course.
These directions can be used if you are
traveling from Sequim or Forks.

Course Yardage & Par:
C-6308 yards, par 72.
M-6235 yards, par 72.
M-5929 yards, par 72.
W-5480 yards, par 72.

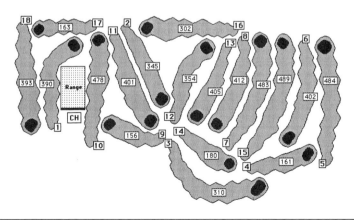

Pine Acres Par 3 Golf Course (public)
11912 N Division; Spokane, WA 99218; (509) 466-9984
Owner/Pro: Jim Tucker, PGA. 9 hole par 3 course, driving range.
Rating/Slope: the golf course is not rated. **Course record:** 22.
Green fees: $9/$7.50 all week long; Jr. & Sr. rates (Monday thru Friday).
Power cart: not available. **Pull cart:** $1. **Trail fee:** not allowed.
Reservation policy: advance reservations for tee times are not required.
Winter condition: damp, the golf course is open weather permitting.
Terrain: flat, slight some hills. **Tees:** mats. **Temporary greens:** N/A.
Services: club rentals, lessons, pro shop, snack bar, driving range, putting green.
Comments: Good par 3 golf course that plays fairly short. Holes range from 85 to 115 yards in length. The facility has a great driving range which has been said to be the "best in the Spokane area".

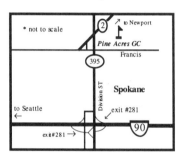

Directions: the golf course is located 7 miles north of Spokane city center off of Hwy 395N. From I-90 east & west exit on Hwy 395 northbound. Proceed on Hwy 395N to the golf course which will be located on your right hand side.

Course Yardage & Par:
M-760 yards, par 27.
W-760 yards, par 27.

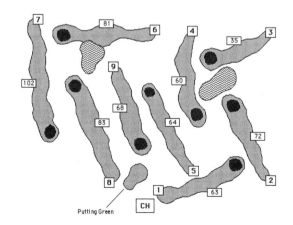

Pine Crest Golf Course (public)

2415 NW 143rd Street; Vancouver, WA 98685; (360) 573-2051
Pro: none. Managers: Mark & Kathy Hart. 9 hole par 3 course.
Rating/Slope: the golf course is not rated. **Course record:** 25.
Green fees: $6.50 all week long; Sr. rates (M-F) $5.50.
Power cart: not available. **Pull cart:** $1.75. **Trail fee:** not allowed.
Reservation policy: advance reservations for tee times are not required.
Winter condition: damp, the golf course is open all year, weather permitting.
Terrain: rolling hills (walkable). **Tees:** mats. **Services:** club rentals, snack bar,
beer, practice green, small pro shop. **Comments:** great par 3 course that will
challenge you at every turn. Several holes are bordered by a steep canyon that
will catch any misguided tee shots. Greens are medium in size and can generally
be found in good condition. Great course for the family golf outing.

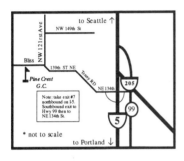

Directions: From I-5 take the 134th Street exit. Proceed westbound for about 2 miles to NW 143rd Street. Turn left on NW 143rd Street and proceed to the golf course. Look for signs marking your way to the golf course.

Course Yardage & Par:
M-1206 yards, par 27.
W-1206 yards, par 27.

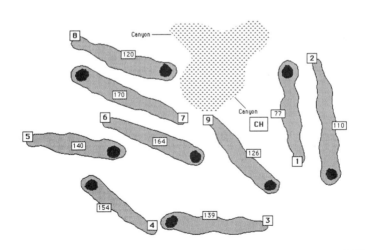

185

Pomeroy Golf Course (public)

1610 Arlington Street; Box 400; Pomeroy, WA 99347; (509) 843-1197
Pro: none. Manager: Ellis Johnson. 9 hole course.
Rating/Slope: M 59.4/94; W 62.5/100. **Course record:** 29.
Green fees: W/D $10/$8; W/E $12/$10; Jr. & Sr. rates; no credit cards.
Power cart: $20/$10. **Pull cart:** $2. **Trail fee:** $3.
Reservation policy: none, some restrictions do apply during league play.
Winter condition: the golf course is closed from mid October through March.
Terrain: relatively hilly. **Tees:** grass & mats. **Temporary greens:** no, not in use.
Services: club rentals, lessons, driving net, putting green, small, limited pro shop.
Comments: this course sports a number of rather hilly holes which increases its difficulty. Greens are very small in size and can be hard to hold. The course is very short in length but the course still can be hard to score on. This rustic course can get somewhat busy during the mid to late summer months

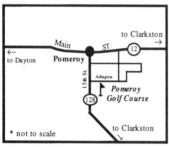

Directions: from Hwy 12 exit on Hwy 128 (15th Street). Proceed to Arlington Street and turn left. Proceed to the golf course. Look for signs marking your way to the golf course.

Course Yardage & Par:
M-2042 yards, par 31.
W-2042 yards, par 32.

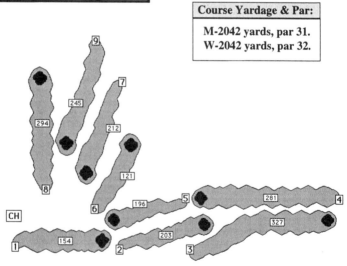

Port Ludlow Golf & Meeting Retreat (public, resort)

751 Highland Dr.; Port Ludlow, WA 98365; (360) 437-0272; 800-732-1239 WA
Director of Golf: Mike Boss. Pro: Al Salvi. Supt.: Jerry Mathews.
27 hole course. Rating/Slope: Tide/Timber C 72.7/131; M 70.3/124; W 72.9/126.
Green fees: peak season $55/$30; off season, winter rates; AMEX, VISA, M/C.
Power cart: $14/$7.50 per person. **Pull cart:** $3/$1.50. **Trail fee:** not allowed.
Reservation policy: resort guests-upon room confirmation; public 5 days ahead.
Winter condition: course is open, dry. **Terrain:** relatively hilly. **Tees:** grass.
Services: club rentals, lessons, snack bar, beer, wine, pro shop, driving range.
Comments: Robert Muir Graves designed course. New 9 "Trail" has been redone.
Facility regarded as one of the nation's best. Plan to stay the whole weekend.

Course Yardage & Par:
Tide 9: 3357 yards, par 36.
Timber 9: 3430 yards, par 36.
Trail 9: 3418 yards, par 36.

Trail/Tide C 73.1/138; M 70.7/128; W 71.3/124.
Trail/Timber C 73.6/138; M 71.4/128; W 70.8/124.

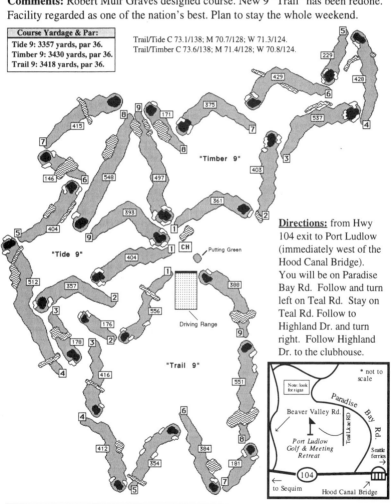

"Timber 9"

"Tide 9"

"Trail 9"

CH

Putting Green

Driving Range

Directions: from Hwy
104 exit to Port Ludlow
(immediately west of the
Hood Canal Bridge).
You will be on Paradise
Bay Rd. Follow and turn
left on Teal Rd. Stay on
Teal Rd. Follow to
Highland Dr. and turn
right. Follow Highland
Dr. to the clubhouse.

* not to
scale

Note: look
for signs

Paradise Bay Rd.

Beaver Valley Rd.

Teal Lkac RD.

Port Ludlow
Golf & Meeting
Retreat

Seattle
ferries →

104

← to Sequim   Hood Canal Bridge

187

Port Townsend Golf Course (public)
1948 Blaine; Port Townsend, WA 98368; (360) 385-0752
Pro: Steve McPherson, PGA. 9 hole course, dual tees for 18 hole play.
Rating/Slope: M 65.8/114; W 70.4/121. **Course record:** 61.
Green fees: $16.18/$10.79; Jr. rates; no credit cards.
Power cart: $19.42/$10.79. **Pull cart:** $4/$2. **Trail fee:** $none.
Reservation policy: yes, call up to 1 week in advance for tee times.
Winter condition: open all year, dry drains well. **Terrain:** relatively hilly.
Tees: grass. **Temporary greens:** no. **Services:** club rentals, lessons, restaurant,
beer, pro shop, club memberships, driving range (grass tees), putting green.
Comments: the course sets atop a hill overlooking the town of Port Townsend
and surrounding inlet. Rolling terrain, sand traps, small greens and water will
challenge your shot making ability. Good public course that gets alot of play.

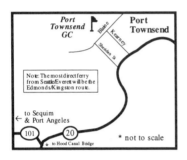

Directions: from Hwy 101 northbound
exit to Hwy 20 eastbound toward Port
Townsend. At Port Townsend turn left
on Kearney Road. Go up the hill to Blaine
Road. Turn right on Blaine road to the
golf course which will be on your left.
Look for signs marking your way.

Course Yardage & Par:
M-2763 yards, par 35.
W-2821 yards, par 35.
Dual tees for 18 holes:
M-5604 yards, par 70.
W-5604 yards, par 71.

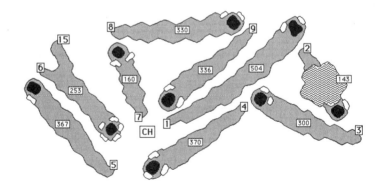

Potholes Golf Course (public)

6897 O'Sullivan Dam Road; Othello, WA 99344; (509) 346-9491
Manager: Gary Santo. 9 hole course, driving range.
Rating/Slope: C 60.2/090; M 59.5/088; W 62.4/093.
Green fees: $15/$11 all week long; Jr. & Sr. rates.
Power cart: $16/$10. **Pull cart:** $1.50. **Trail fee:** $3.
Reservation policy: yes, call up to 1 week in advance for tee times.
Winter condition: the course is open, dry.**Terrain:** flat, easy walking course.
Tees: grass. **Temporary greens:** no, not in use. **Services:** club rentals, lessons,
restaurant (Italian menu), beer, wine, pro shop, driving range, RV spots, putting
& chipping greens. **Comments:** narrow golf course that plays much longer than
the yardage would indicate. RV hookups with full services and cable TV. The
restaurants claim to fame is "We make the best garlic bread in North America".
Good test of golf that can be demanding on your shot making ability.

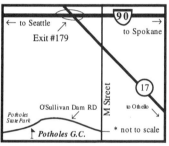

Directions: from Hwy 26 through Royal
City to State RD 262. Turn left. Proceed
14 miles south to the course. From I-90
exit 179 turn left on Hwy 17 to "M" St.
(2 1/2 miles) turn right. Proceed 7-8 miles
to O'Sullivan Dam Road turn right (west)
to the golf course. Look for signs.

Course Yardage & Par:
M-2269 yards, par 33.
W-2167 yards, par 33.
Dual tees for 18 holes:
M-4638 yards, par 66.
W-4334 yards, par 66.

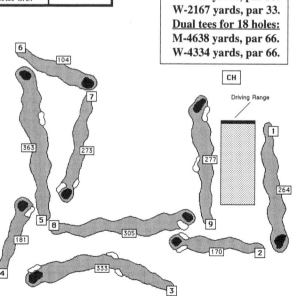

Quail Ridge Golf Course (public)

3600 Swallow's Nest Drive; Clarkston, WA 99403; (509) 758-8501
Pro: Peter Goes. Superintendent: Jason Aerni. 18 hole course.
Rating/Slope: C N/A; M 68.1/1114; W 66.2/107. **Course record:** 63.
Green fees: $13/$10 all week long; annual rates for seniors; M/C, VSIA.
Power cart: $20/$12. **Pull cart:** $3. **Trail fee:** $3 (annual fee available).
Reservation policy: please call 1 week in advance for tee-times.
Winter condition: open, weather permitting, dry. **Terrain:** flat, some hills.
Tees: grass. **Temporary greens:** no. **Services:** club rentals, coffee shop, beer,
pro shop. **Comments:** formerly called Swallow's Nest the golf course has been
expanded to 18 holes recently and is worth a trip. The new nine has spectacular
views of the surrounding countryside and rolling terrain. Good public track.

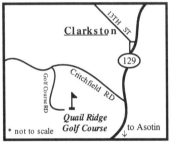

Directions: the golf course is located
south of Clarkston WA. From Hwy 129
Turn westbound on Critchfield RD
(across from the Snake River). Proceed
on Critchfield RD for a 1/4 mile to Golf
Course RD. Turn left. Proceed to the golf
course off of Swallow's Nest Loop.

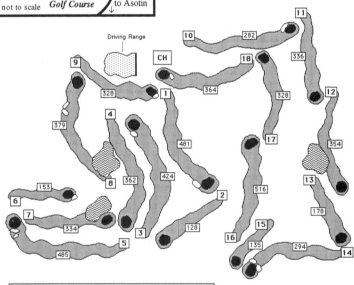

Course Yardage & Par:		
C-5861 yards, par 71. M-5603 yards, par 71.		
W-4720 yards, par 71. W-4637 yards, par 71.		

Quincy Valley Golf (public)
1705 5th NW; Quincy, WA 98848; (509) 787-3244
Managers: Rob & Chuck Anabel. 18 hole course.
Rating/Slope: the golf course will be rerated. **Course record:** 32.
Green fees: W/D $13/$10; W/E $18/$13; Jr/Sr rates (Mon. & Wed.); M/C, VISA.
Power cart: $16/$9. **Pull cart:** $3/$2. **Trail fee:** $3. **Reservation policy:** none,
walk ons only. **Winter condition:** open, when playable. **Terrain:** flat, some hills.
Tees: grass. **Temporary greens:** no. **Services:** snack bar, pro shop, driving net.
Comments: the course is well-conditioned with beautiful fairways and excellent
greens. RV sites are available for those overnighters who want to stay and play golf.
Very friendly golf course. The new 9 holes should open in early to late 1996.

Directions: from Hwy 281 take 5 NW
(White Trail Road) to the golf course.
From I-90 E&W exit at Hwy 281 and
proceed toward Quincy. The golf course
will be off of the Hwy on your left hand
side.

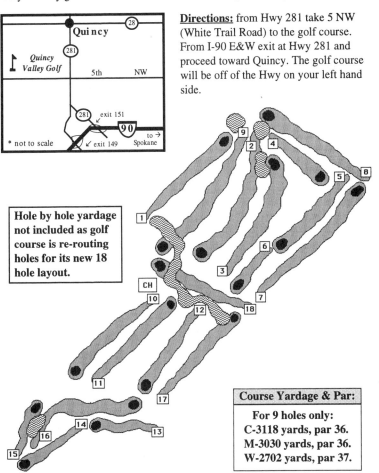

Hole by hole yardage
not included as golf
course is re-routing
holes for its new 18
hole layout.

Course Yardage & Par:

For 9 holes only:
C-3118 yards, par 36.
M-3030 yards, par 36.
W-2702 yards, par 37.

Rainier Golf & Country Club (private)
1856 S 112th; Seattle, WA 98168; (206) 242-2800
Pro: Keith Williams, PGA. Supt.: Ronald Proctor. 18 hole course.
Rating/Slope: C 70.6/125; M 125; W 73.2/126. **Course record:** 63.
Green fees: private club, members and guests only; reciprocates.
Power cart: private club. **Pull cart:** private club. **Trail fee:** not allowed.
Reservation policy: private club, yes, up to 1 week in advance.
Winter condition: damp, new drainage system. **Terrain:** very hilly. **Tees:** grass.
Temporary greens: no, not in use. **Services:** lessons, snack bar, beer, wine, pro
shop, lockers, showers, driving range, puting green. **Comments:** beautiful views
of Mt. Rainier are seen from this course which sports tree-lined fairways, tricky
greens, and many sand traps to contend with. Well kept private facility.

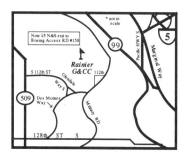

Directions: from I-5 N&S take exit
158B to the South Boeing Access Road.
Go west for .4 miles to Pacific Hwy S.
Turn south on Pacific Hwy S. and follow
for 1.2 miles to S 128th. Turn west on
128th and travel 1 mile to Des Moines
Memorial Way. Turn north. Follow for
1 mile to S 112th. Turn west and proceed
to the golf course.

Course Yardage & Par:
C-6352 yards, par 72.
M-6205 yards, par 72.
W-5913 yards, par 74.

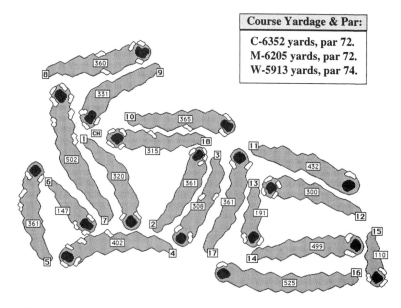

Raspberry Ridge Golf Community (public)
6827 Hannegan Road; Everson, WA 98247; (360) 354-3029
Pro/Owner: Bill Robins. 9 hole course, putting green.
Rating/Slope: C 67.0/106; M 69.8124; W 66.8/110. **Course record:** 63.
Green fees: $15/$9.50; Jr & Sr rates, $13/$8.50; M/C, VISA.
Power cart: $15/$9. **Pull cart:** $2. **Trail fee:** no charge.
Reservation policy: yes, call up to 7 days in advance for tee times.
Winter condition: course is open, dry (drains well). **Terrain:** flat, some hills.
Tees: grass. **Temporary greens:** no, not in use. **Services:** club rentals, snack bar, lounge, restaurant, beer, wine, pro shop, club memberships, putting green.
Comments: beautifully maintained golf course with spectacular views of Mount Baker and the surrounding countryside. Although relatively short, this course will challenge you at every turn. Water and well bunkered greens are every where. Accuracy off the tee is a must for scoring. Worth a special trip if in the area.

Directions: from I-5 N&S take exit # 256A to Hwy 539 northbound and continue 7.7 miles to Hwy 544 eastbound. Turn south on Hannegan Road and proceed to the golf course. Look for a sign marking your turn to the golf course community.

Course Yardage & Par:
C-2825 yards, par 34.
M-2585 yards, par 34
W-2335 yards, par 34.

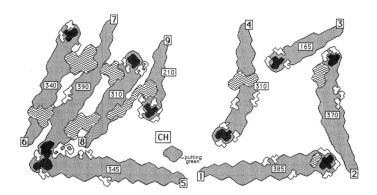

Ritzville Municipal Golf Course (public)
104 East 10th Street; Ritzville, WA 99169; (509) 659-9868
Pro: Ron Barker, PGA. 9 hole course dual tees for 18 holes.
Rating/Slope: M 66.6/114; W 71.8/123. **Course record:** 64.
Green fees: $13/$9; Jr & Sr rates (weekdays only); no credit cards.
Power cart: $18/$9. **Pull cart:** $2. **Trail fee:** no charge.
Reservation policy: advance tee times are not required.
Winter condition: the course is closed from mid November to mid February.
Terrain: flat, some hills. **Tees:** grass. **Temporary greens:** no, not in use.
Services: club rentals, lessons, restaurant, beer, pro shop, putting green.
Comments: a good walking course. Ritzville is fairly flat and in good condition.
The track sports two sets of tees for a different look for 18 holes. Convenient RV
park close by. Some greens are fronted by bunkers and sloping terrain.

Directions: from I-90 take the Ritzville
exit #221 and travel north 2 blocks to the
golf course. The course has great freeway
access. Look for signs marking your turn
to the golf course.

Course Yardage & Par:
M-2812 yards, par 35.
W-2812 yards, par 36.
Dual tees for 18 holes:
M-5597 yards, par 70.
W-5597 yards, par 72.

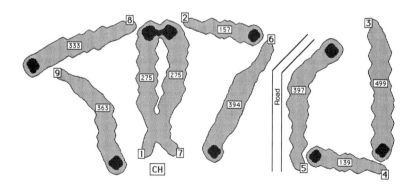

Riverbend Golf Complex (public)

2019 W Meeker; Kent, WA 98032; (206) 854-3673 or (206) 859-4000
Pro: Brett Wilkinson. Superintendent: David Owen, Pete Petersen.
18 hole & 9 hole par 3 golf courses, lighted driving range, mini golf.
Rating/Slope: C 70.1/119; M 68.1/114; W 70.1/114. **Course record:** 64.
Green fees: W/D$19/$13; W/E $23/$15; Jr & Sr rates M-F; M/C, VISA.
Green fees for the par 3 course: W/D $5 1st 9 holes; W/E $6 for 9 holes.
Power cart: $20/$10. **Pull cart:** $4/$2. **Trail fee:** personal carts not allowed.
Reservation policy: 1 week in advance. **Winter condition:** course is open, dry.
Terrain: flat. **Tees:** grass. **Services:** club rentals, lessons, snack bar, beer, chipping
& putting green, driving range, pro shop. **Comments:** championship caliber track.
The course is flat, well-bunkered and water comes in to play on 7 holes. The golf
course is excellent and worth a special trip. Be sure to call ahead for a tee time.

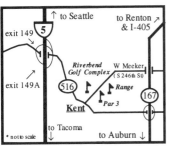

Directions: from I-5 N&S take exit # 149 to
Hwy 516 eastbound. Travel east for 1.3 miles
to W. Meeker. Turn east on Meeker to the golf
course, located on your left, the range and par 3
course will be on your right hand side.

Course Yardage & Par:
C-6603 yards, par 72.
M-6156 yards, par 72.
W-5485 yards, par 72.

Par 3 Course Yardage & Par:
M/W-1260 yards, par 27.

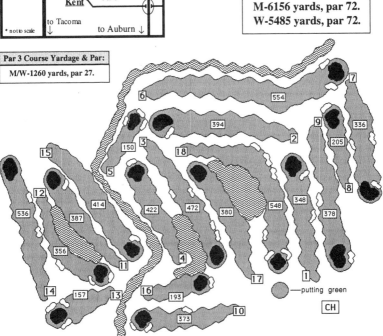

Riverside Country Club (public)

1451 NW Airport Road; Chehalis, WA 98532; (360) 748-8182, 1-800-242-9486
Manager: Nonie Mazza. Supt.: Randy Scafturon. 18 hole course, range.
Rating/Slope: C 69.6/122; M 68.3/117; W 71.0/121. **Course record:** 63.
Green fees: W/D $17/$12; W/E's & Holidays. $22; M/C, VISA.
Senior rates (Monday thru Wednesday); winter rates; winter specials.
Power cart: $20/$15 reserve the cart. **Pull cart:** $2. **Trail fee:** $10/$5.
Reservation policy: yes, please call up to 1 week in advance for tee times.
Winter condition: dry, the golf course is open. **Terrain:** flat, some slight hills.
Tees: grass. **Temporary greens:** no, not in use. **Services:** lessons, snack bar,
restaurant, beer, wine, pro shop, driving range, putting and chipping greens.
Comments: this course winds along the Chehalis River and is noted for its fast,
undulating greens. Fairways are tree-lined with medium to large landing areas.
Great golf course to stop and play anytime of year. Easy freeway access.

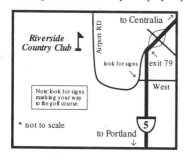

Directions: from I-5 N&S take exit # 79.
Turn right and travel .6 miles to NW
Airport Road. On Airport Road turn right.
The golf course is located .7 miles ahead.
Note: Look for signs marking your way
to the golf course from the road.

Course Yardage & Par:
C-6155 yards, par 71.
M-5771 yards, par 71.
W-5456 yards, par 72.

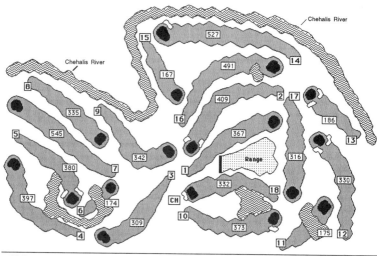

Riverside Golf Course (public)
5799 Riverside Drive; Ferndale, WA 98248; (360) 384-4116
Owner: Jeanne Olson Estie. 9 hole course.
Rating/Slope: C 67.6/104; M 66.9/103; W 70.4/112. **Course record:** 66.
Green fees: W/D $12/$8; W/E & holidays $13/$9; Jr & Sr rates; M/C, VISA.
Power cart: $20/$14. **Pull cart:** $4/$2. **Trail fee:** no charge.
Reservation policy: advance reservations are not taken or required.
Winter condition: the course is open, damp. **Terrain:** flat, easy walking course.
Tees: grass. **Temporary greens:** no not in use. **Services:** club rentals, snack bar,
restaurant, pro shop, putting green, club memberships. **Comments:** the course is
well-kept, particularly the greens. Fairways are wide with generous landing areas.
Greens are of medium size and have few hazards fronting them. A very friendly
staff makes this facility a pleasure to visit and a treat to play. The golf course is
generally flat and easy to walk. Easy freeway access for those traveling on I-5.

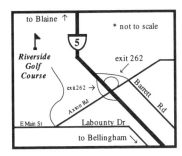

Directions: from I-5 N&S take exit
262. Travel west for 1/10 of a mile
to the golf course. Look for signs that
are posted indicating your turn for the
golf course.

Course Yardage & Par:
M-3000 yards, par 36.
W-2860 yards, par 37.

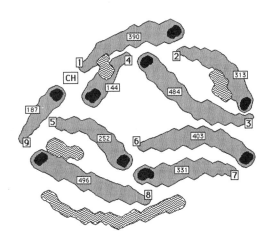

Riviera Golf & Country Club (private)

11019 Country Club Drive; Anderson Island, WA 98303; (206) 884-9634
Manager: Al Hundis. Supt.: Ronald Hall. 9 hole executive course.
Rating/Slope: M 55.3/99; W 56.3/95. **Course record:** 26.
Greens fee: private club, members & guests only; no credit cards.
Power cart: none. **Pull cart:** members & guests only. **Trail fee:** not allowed.
Reservation policy: yes, members may call for weekend tee times.
Winter condition: course is open, wet. **Terrain:** relatively hilly. **Tees:** grass.
Temporary greens: no. **Services:** restaurant, beer, wine, pro shop, putting green.
Comments: friendly private course in set in a beautiful island community of
Washington State. This executive length golf course is a challenge at every turn.
Greens are small and the fronts are well bunkered. Fairways are very narrow.

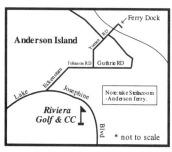

Directions: northbound from Olympia
takethe Dupont/Steilacoom exit from I-5.
Go straight until you reach the ferry dock.
Am ferry leaves at 6am,7:40, 9 and 12pm.
From I-5 southbound take exit 129. Go
westbound to S Tacoma Way. Right to
Steilacoom Boulevard then left to the
ferry dock. Look for signs marking your
way to the golf course.

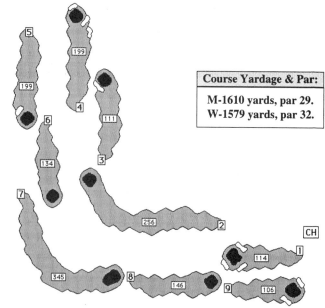

Course Yardage & Par:
M-1610 yards, par 29.
W-1579 yards, par 32.

Rock Island Golf Club (public)

314 Saunders Road; Rock Island, WA 98850; (509) 884-2806
Manager: Pam Orr. 9 hole course, dual tees for 18 holes.
Rating/Slope: M 70.1/112; W 73.4/120. **Course record:** 68 for 18 holes.
Green fees: W/D $15/$10; W/E $15/$10; Jr/Sr rates (Tues & Th); M/C, VISA.
Power cart: $18/$10. **Pull cart:** $2. **Trail fee:** no charge for personal carts.
Reservation policy: yes, you may call ahead for a tee time. No restrictions.
Winter condition: the course is open all year long, weather permitting.
Terrain: very flat. **Tees:** grass. **Temporary greens:** no not in use.
Services: club rentals, lessons, restaurant, lounge, beer, wine, pro shop, driving
range, putting & chipping greens. **Comments:** this course sports large greens with
some bunkers coming into play on approach shots. The course plays long from the
back tees leaving many long irons for your second shots. Water comes into play on
a number of holes. You can usually walk on during the summer months.

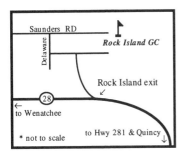

Directions: from Hwy 28 take the Rock
Island exit. At the end of the street, turn
left. Follow to Delaware and turn right.
At the stop sign, turn right on Saunders
Road and follow to the golf course. Look
for signs marking your way

Course Yardage & Par:
M-3396 yards, par 36.
W-2884 yards, par 36.
Dual tees for 18 holes:
M-6467 yards, par 72.
W-5995 yards, par 72.

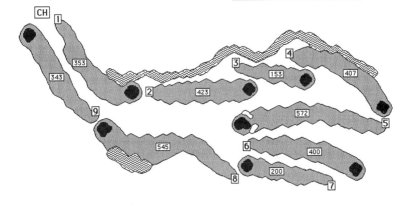

Rolling Hills Golf Course (public)

2485 NE McWilliams Road; Bremerton, WA 98310; (360) 479-1212
Director of Golf: Tedd Hudanich, PGA. Pro: Roger O'Hara. 18 hole course.
Rating/Slope: M 67.9/115; W 71.0/117. **Course record:** 63.
Green fees: W/D $17.58/$12.03; W/E $19.43/$13.88; M/C, VISA.
Power cart: $18.50/$12.95. **Pull cart:** $2. **Trail fee:** $3.
Reservation policy: yes, you may call 7 days in advance for tee-times.
Winter condition: the golf course is open all year long, damp conditions.
Terrain: relatively hilly. **Tees:** grass. **Temporary greens:** occasionally in use.
Services: club rentals, lessons, snack bar, beer, wine, pro shop, driving range,
club memberships, putting green, practice bunker. **Comments:** the course offers
a beautiful view of the Olympic Mountains and Mt. Rainier. Excellent public golf
course with well bunkered greens and medium wide fairways. The golf course also
offers a well stocked pro shop for all your golfing needs.

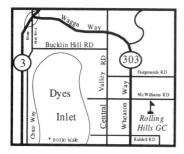

Directions: from the Bremerton ferry
terminal take Washington. Turn north for
.8 miles to Warren. Turn right on Warren
and proceed 3.6 miles to McWilliams
Road. Turn right to the golf course. Look
for signs marking your turn to the course.

Course Yardage & Par:
M-5910 yards, par 70.
W-5465 yards, par 70.

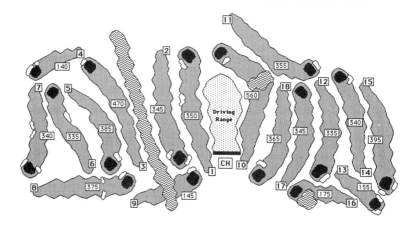

Royal City Golf Course (public)

13702 Dodson Road South; Royal City, WA 99357; (509) 346-2052
Pro: none. Manager: Ed Eilers 9 hole course.
Rating/Slope: M 68.6/113; W 71.9/114. **Course record:** 65.
Green fees: W/D $11/$8; W/E $13/$9; no credit cards.
Power cart: $15/$10. **Pull cart:** $3/$1.50. **Trail fee:** $4.
Reservation policy: please call 1 day in advance for tee-times.
Winter condition: call ahead for golf course conditions, course closed at times.
Terrain: flat, some hills. **Tees:** grass. **Temporary greens:** no not in use.
Services: snack bar, pro shop, driving range, putting green, RV parking.
Comments: newer golf course that varies in terrain. A canal runs through two holes and can present problems with your tee or approach shots. Fairways are wide and firm. RV park is next to the golf course with water and eletric hookups.

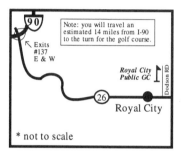

Note: you will travel an estimated 14 miles from I-90 to the turn for the golf course.

Directions: from I-90 E & W take the exit #137 for Hwy 26 to Royal City. Travel eastbound for approximately 14.2 miles to Dodson Road. Turn left. The clubhouse and golf course will be on your left hand side. Signs are posted indicating your turn on Dodson Road to the golf course.

Course Yardage & Par:
M-3106 yards, par 36.
W-2850 yards, par 36.

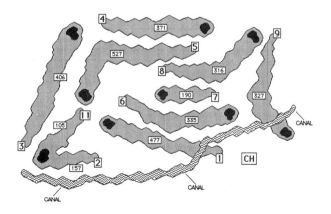

Royal Oaks Country Club (private)

8917 NE Fourth Plain Road; Vancouver, WA 98662; (360) 256-1350
Pro: Steve Bowen, PGA. 18 hole course, driving range.
Rating/Slope: C 73.1/133; M 71.2/125; W 72.6/127. **Course record:** 64.
Green fees: private club members & guests only; reciprocates; no credit cards.
Power cart: private club. **Pull cart:** private club. **Trail fee:** private club.
Reservation policy: no time limit for members, public is not allowed.
Winter condition: the golf course is open all year, dry. **Terrain:** flat, some hills.
Tees: grass. **Temporary greens:** yes, in winter. **Services:** lessons, restaurant,
lounge, beer, wine, liquor, pro shop, lockers, showers, club memberships, driving
range, putting & chipping greens. **Comments:** regarded as one of the state's best,
Royal Oaks fairway's are tight and tree-lined. Greens are well bunkered and hard
to hold. A very difficult layout that is demanding from the tee and on the greens.

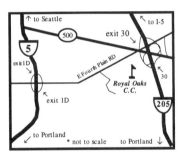

Directions: from I-5 N&S take exit # 1D
(Fourth Plain Blvd E). Travel east just
beyond the 4 mile post to the golf course
which will be on your right hand side.

Course Yardage & Par:
C-6850 yards, par 72.
M-6382 yards, par 72.
W-5895 yards, par 74.

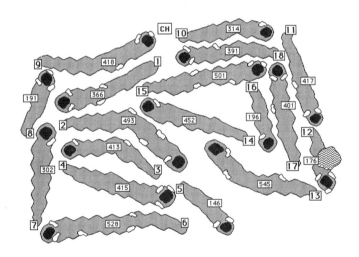

Sage Hills Golf Club (public)

10400 Sage Hills Road SE; Warden, WA 98857; (509) 349-7794
Pro: Mark Fancher. 18 hole course, driving range.
Rating/Slope: C 72.2/124; M 70.0/120; W 72.0/122. **Course record:** 64.
Green fees: W/D $16/$10; W/E $20/$12; Jr & Sr rates (M-F); M/C, VISA.
Power cart: $20/$12. **Pull cart:** $2.50/$2. **Trail fee:** $6 for personal carts.
Reservation policy: yes, you may call 7 days in advance for tee-times.
Winter condition: the golf course is usually closed December to January.
Terrain: flat, some hills. **Tees:** grass. **Temporary greens:** not in use.
Services: club rentals, lessons, restaurant, lounge, beer, wine, pro shop, showers, driving range (with grass tees), putting and chipping greens, RV hookups.
Comments: Good public golf course that can play very difficult if the wind picks up. Greens are medium in size with some being fronted by bunkers. Water comes into play on 5 holes and is a major factor off the tee and on your approach shots. A full service RV park is adjacent to the parking lot for those spending the night.

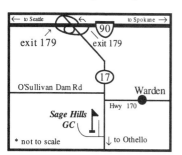

Directions: the golf course is located 2 miles south of the Warden cut-off on the west side of Hwy 17. From I-90 exit #179 to Hwy 17 and proceed southbound to the golf course. Make sure that you look for signs to the golf course from the Hwy.

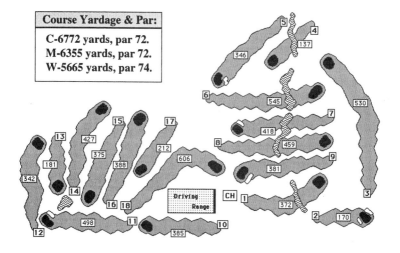

Course Yardage & Par:

C-6772 yards, par 72.
M-6355 yards, par 72.
W-5665 yards, par 74.

Sahalee Country Club (private)

21200 NE 28th Street; Redmond, WA 98053; (206) 453-0484. 27 hole course.
Director of Golf: Rick Acton, PGA. Pro: Jim Pike, PGA. Supt.: Tom Wolff.
Rating/Slope: T 74.0/135; C 73.2/133; M 71.6/130; W 73.6/129.   **Record:** 67.
Green fees: private club members & guests only; reciprocates (very limited).
Power cart: private club. **Pull cart:** private club. **Trail fee:** private club.
Reservation policy: none. **Winter condition:** dry. **Terrain:** relatively hilly.
Tees: grass. **Temporary greens:** no. **Services:** club rentals, lessons, lounge,
restaurant, beer, wine, liquor, pro shop, lockers, showers, club memberships,
driving range, dress code. **Comments:** course record by Jack Nicklaus and is
ranked in *Golf Digest's* top 100 courses in the nation. This course is both demanding and spectacular. Host course of the 1998 PGA Championship. Excellent track.

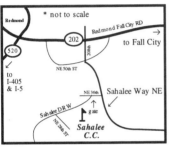

Directions: from I-5 N&S take exit
#168B to Hwy 520 eastbound. Go east
to Hwy 202E (Redmond-Fall City Road).
Travel east for 2 miles to 208th Avenue
NE-Sahalee Way NE. Turn south for 1
mile to NE 36th. Veer left to Sahalee Dr.
W to NE 28th. Turn east to the golf course.

Course Yardage & Par:
(North/South Course)
T-6955 yards, par 72.
C-6749 yards, par 72.
M-6331 yards, par 72.
W-5710 yards, par 72.

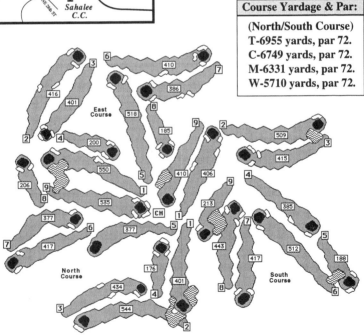

Saint John Golf & Country Club (semi-private)

off Hwy 23; PO Box 232; St. John, WA 99171; (509) 648-3259
Pro: none. Manager: N/A. Superintendent: Curt White. 9 hole course.
Rating/Slope: C 67.0/111; M 66.0/106; W 68.4/109. **Course record:** 21.
Green fees: $10 (all day); non-members welcome; no credit cards.
Power cart: none available. **Pull cart:** none. **Trail fee:** $3.00 all day rate.
Reservation policy: advance tee times are not needed or required.
Winter condition: the golf course is closed from November thru February.
Terrain: very flat easy walking. **Tees:** grass. **Temporary greens:** no not in use.
Services: lessons, (occasionally), limited services. **Comments:** the course is
impeccably maintained with beautiful lush green fairways. A few sand traps and
one creek come into play. Easy walking golf course that is great for the senior.
The clubhouse is often closed so green fees are sometimes on the honor system.
The course has just expanded to 9 holes adding 3 new holes in August of 1995.

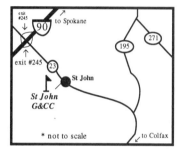

Directions: the golf course is located on
the northwest side of St. John off Hwy
23. Look for signs off of Hwy 23 in St.
John marking your way to the golf course.
The course is located right off Hwy 23.

Course Yardage & Par:
C-2876 yards, par 35.
M-2770 yards, par 35.
W-2564 yards, par 35.

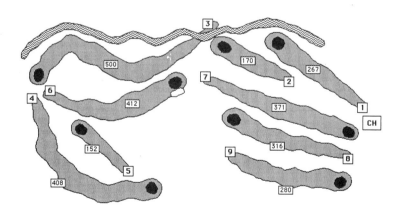

San Juan Golf & Country Club (public)

2261 Golf Course Road; Box 246; Friday Harbor, WA 98250; (360) 378-2254
Manager/Pro: Steve Nightingale. Supt.: Alan Dufur. 9 hole course, dual tees.
Rating/Slope: M 70.9/118; W 70.8/115. **Course record:** 66.
Green fees: $25/$17.50 all week long; twilight rates $10; M/C, VISA.
Power cart: $20/$12. **Pull cart:** $3. **Trail fee:** $5 (for pass unlimited use).
Reservation policy: yes, call 1 day ahead for tee-times June through August.
Winter condition: the course is open all year long, dry. **Terrain:** flat, some hills.
Tees: grass. **Temporary greens:** no not in use. **Services:** club rentals, lessons,
snack bar, lockers, pro shop, club memberships, putting green RV parking.
Comments: set in the scenic San Juan Islands, the course is easy to walk but can
be tough to score on. Tee shots play to medium size landing areas. Two sets of
tees available for full 18 hole play. Excellent golf course that is well maintained.

Directions: from the Anacortes ferry
travel to Friday Harbor. While in Friday
Harbor, take Spring Street. Proceed to
Mullins Road for 3.2 miles to Golf Course
Road. Turn left on Golf Course Road and
proceed to the golf course.

Course Yardage & Par:
M-3194 yards, par 35.
W-2663 yards, par 36.
Dual tees for 18 holes:
M-6508 yards, par 71.
W-5466 yards, par 72.

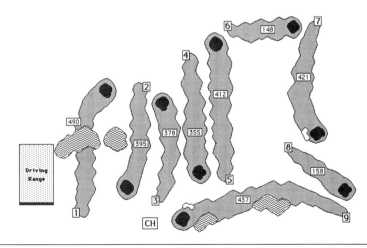

Sand Point Country Club (private)

8333 55th NE; Seattle, WA 98115; (206) 523-4994
Pro: Ron Stull, PGA. Superintendent: Craig Sampson. 18 hole course.
Rating/Slope: C 69.6/123; M 68.2/120; W 72.3/127. **Course record:** 61.
Green fees: private club members and guests only; M/C, VISA.
Power cart: private club members and guests only. **Trail fee:** not allowed.
Reservation policy: no time limit. **Winter condition:** dry. **Terrain:** very hilly.
Tees: grass. **Temporary greens:** no. **Services:** club rentals, lessons, snack bar,
lounge, restaurant, beer, wine, liquor, pro shop, club memberships, driving range.
Comments: the course offers a sweeping view of Lake Washington. Numerous
sand traps, rolling terrain, and many trees provide a great test of golf.

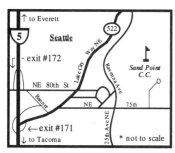

Directions: from I-5 S take exit # 172 to
NE 80th. Turn east to Banner Way NE.
Turn south on Banner which will become
NE 75th. Proceed 2.3 miles to the golf
course. From I-5 N take exit # 171 to NE
73rd. Travel east for .1 mile to 12th NE.
On 12th go north for .1 mile to NE 75th.
Turn east for 1.8 miles to the golf course.

Course Yardage & Par:
C-6004 yards, par 71.
M-5658 yards, par 71.
W-5218 yards, par 72.

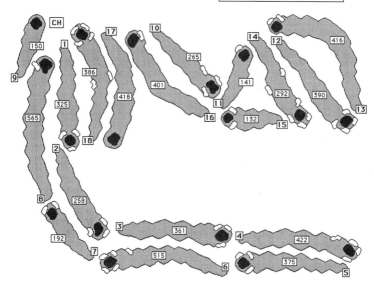

Scott Lake Golf Course (public)

11746 Scott Creek Drive SW; Olympia, WA 98512; (360) 352-4838
Owners: Joel and Karen Boede. 9 hole course, dual tees for 18 holes.
Rating/Slope: M 62.9/94; W 64.4/97. **Course record:** 62.
Green fees: W/D $12/$8; W/E $14/$9; Jr & Sr rates (W/D's); no credit cards.
Power cart: $16/$9. **Pull cart:** $2. **Trail fee:** $2.50.
Reservation policy: yes, call ahead 10 days the during summer and weekends.
Winter condition: the golf course is open, damp. **Terrain:** flat. **Tees:** grass.
Temporary greens: no not in use. **Services:** club rentals, coffee shop, beer, wine,
pro shop, putting green, club memberships. **Comments:** this friendly, family run 9
hole golf course sports dual tees for a full 18 hole round. Greens are medium in size
and sport few undulations. Fairways are tree-lined and well kept. Two lakes come
into play throughout half of the nine hole track. Good course for family outing.

Directions: from I-5 N&S take exit #99.
Travel east on 93rd Avenue SW to Case
Avenue SW. Turn south. Proceed to
Scott Creek Dr. SW and follow to the
golf course. Look for signs to the course.

Course Yardage & Par:
M-2600 yards, par 35.
W-2189 yards, par 36.
Dual tees for 18 holes:
M-5045 yards, par 70.
W-4634 yards, par 72.

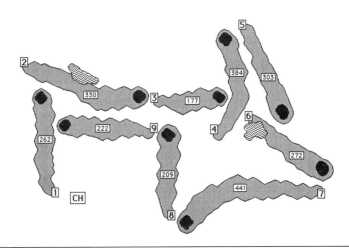

Sea Links   (public)
7878 Birch Bay Drive; Blaine, WA 98230; (360) 371-7933
Owner/Pro: Craig Wood, PGA.   18 hole executive course.
Rating/Slope: M 50.7/67; W 50.7/67. **Course record:** 47.
Green fees: W/D $11/$9; W/E $14; Jr. & Sr. rates (weekdays); M/C, VISA.
Power cart: $15. **Pull cart:** $2. **Trail fee:** no charge.
Reservation policy: yes, up to 1 week in advance. **Winter condition:** dry.
Terrain: flat, some hills. **Tees:** grass. **Temporary greens:** no not in use.
Services: club rentals, lessons, restaurant, beer, wine, pro shop, liquor.
Comments: although short, this executive size layout has many hazards.
Ponds, sand traps, and postage stamp greens challenge golfers of any caliber.
Many of the holes have recently been lengthened from the championship tees.
If you are looking for a change of pace at an excellent facility try Sea Links.

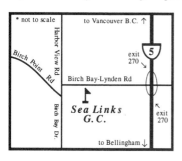

Directions: from I-5 N&S take exit # 270 to Lynden-Birch Bay Road. Travel west for 3.7 miles to Harborview. Turn south. Proceed .2 miles to the bay. Turn left and travel 1/2 mile to the golf course. Look for signs marking your turn to the facility.

Course Yardage & Par:

C-2701 yards, par 54.
M-2320 yards, par 54.
W-2075 yards, par 54.

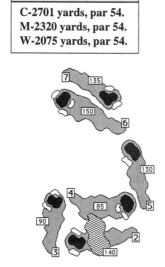

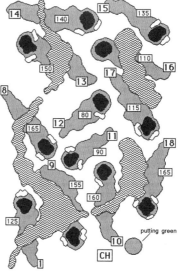

Seattle Golf Club (private)

210 NW 145th; Seattle, WA 98177; (206) 363-8811
Pro: Doug Doxsie, PGA. Superintendent: Peter Wilson. 18 hole course.
Rating/Slope: C 71.8/127; M 69.8/122; W 71.8/126. **Course record:** 63.
Green fees: private course, members only; no credit cards.
Power cart: private club. **Pull cart:** complimentary. **Trail fee:** not allowed.
Reservation policy: private club members only. No outside public is allowed.
Winter condition: the course is open year round, dry. **Terrain:** very hilly.
Tees: grass. **Temporary greens:** no. **Services:** lessons, snack bar, lounge,
restaurant, beer, wine, liquor, pro shop, showers, putting green, driving range.
Comments: a beautiful, stately old course. Mature trees line the fairways.
Greens are well trapped. Water holes can play extremely difficult. Great course.

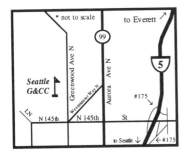

Directions: from I-5 N&S take exit
175 to NE 145th. Turn west and
travel 1.4 miles to the golf course
entrance. The golf course is on your
right hand side.

Course Yardage & Par:
C-6527 yards, par 72.
M-6096 yards, par 72.
W-5595 yards, par 72.

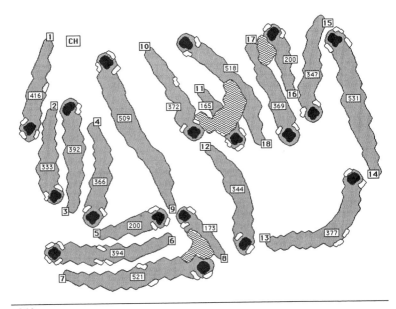

Semiahmoo Golf & Country Club (semi-private resort)

8720 Semi Ah Moo Parkway; Blaine, WA 98230; (360) 371-7005
Pro: Brian J. Southwick, PGA. **18 hole course, range.** **Course record:** 67.
Rating/Slope: T 74.5/130; C 71.9/125; M 69.9/123; W 71.6/125.
Green fees: Monday-Thursday $66/$47; Friday-Sunday $70/$47; (peak season);
winter rates W/D's $32; W/E's $35; VISA, M/C, AMEX.
Power cart: $13.50/$10 per person. **Pull cart:** $4/$2.50. **Trail fee:** not allowed.
Reservation policy: Mon.-Friday 3 days in advance, Friday for Sat. and Sunday.
Winter condition: the course is open, dry. **Terrain:** flat, some hills. **Tees:** grass.
Services: club rentals, lessons, snack bar, wine, beer, pro shop, driving range.
Comments: Arnold Palmer designed layout with numerous bunkers and ponds.
Voted in 1992 as the 18th **Best Resort Course** in the nation by *Golf Digest*. It was
also voted the #1 Resort Course in America by *Golf Digest* when opened in 1987.

Directions: from I-5 N&S take exit
274 to Bell Road. Turn left. The road
becomes Blaine Road. Travel 1 mile to
Drayton Harbor Road. Turn right and
follow to the fork, stay left it becomes
Harbor View Road. Proceed .5 miles to
Lincoln Road. Follow the signs to the
golf course.

Course Yardage & Par:

T-7005 yards, par 72.
C-6435 yards, par 72.
M-6003 yards, par 72.
W-5288 yards, par 72.

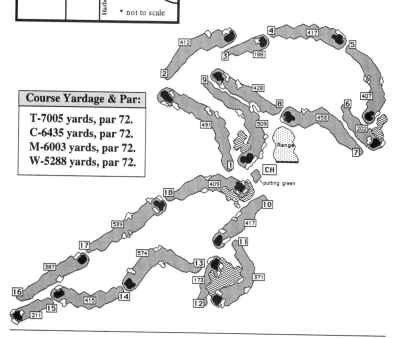

Sham Na Pum Golf Course (public)
72 George Washington Way; Box 14; Richland, WA 99352; (509) 946-1914
Pro: Pat Welch, PGA. 18 hole regulation & 9 hole par 3.
Rating/Slope: M 64.5/106; W 67.2/112. **Course record:** 60.
Green fees: $12/$9*; Jr & Sr rates $9*/$7* (weekdays); M/C, VISA.
Green fees for the par 3 course: $5* all week long.
Power cart: $20/$10*. **Pull cart:** $3*. **Trail fee:** $5*. (*subject to change)
Reservation policy: yes, please call up to 1 week in advance for the weekend.
Winter condition: the golf course is closed during inclement weather.
Terrain: flat, easy walking. **Tees:** grass. **Temporary greens:** no not in use.
Services: club rentals, lessons, cafe, pro shop, lockers, driving range, putting area.
Comments: public course that gets alot of play during the summer months. The facility also has a par 3 course and driving range for all you golfers.

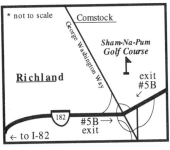

Directions: from I-82 take the exit at George Washington Way in Richland #5B. Turn north and travel to Comstock Road. On Comstock turn right to the golf course. Look for signs marking your way.

Course Yardage & Par:
M-5210 yards, par 66.
W-4870 yards, par 67.

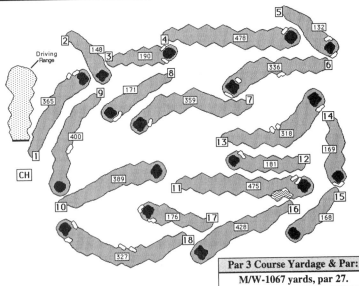

Par 3 Course Yardage & Par:
M/W-1067 yards, par 27.

Shelton Bayshore Golf Club (public)
E 3800 Highway 3; Shelton, WA 98584; (360) 426-1271
Pro: Brian Davis, PGA. Supt.: John Eby. 9 hole course, dual tees.
Rating/Slope: M 69.2/116; W 72.5/121. **Course record:** 63.
Green fees: W/D $15/$10; W/E $18/$12; Sr. rates Mon. & Thur. $12/$8.
Power cart: $22/$13. **Pull cart:** $3. **Trail fee:** $5.
Reservation policy: yes, call 14 days in advance for weekends and holidays.
Winter condition: the course is open, dry (drains well). **Terrain:** flat, some hills.
Tees: grass. **Temporary greens:** at times. **Services:** club rentals, lessons,
pro shop, club memberships, snack bar, wine, beer, putting & chipping greens.
Comments: this golf course is very tight, tricky, and well maintained. Greens are
small and can be hard to hold. Two sets of tees are available for a full 18 hole
round. Good test of golf for any level of player.

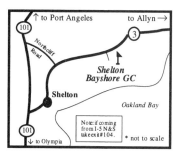

Directions: from I-5 N&S take exit #104
to Hwy 101 toward Shelton. Take the exit
for Hwy 3 (toward Allyn). The golf
course is located 4 miles out of Shelton.
Look for signs marking your way.

Course Yardage & Par:
M-2946 yards, par 36.
W-2752 yards, par 36.
<u>**Dual tees for 18 holes:**</u>
M-6004 yards, par 72.
W-5698 yards, par 73.

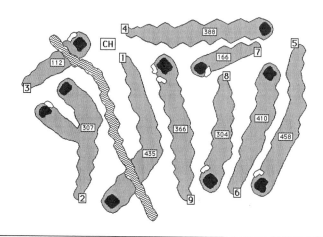

Sheridan Greens Golf Course　(public)

PO Box 454; 380 Sheridan Road; Republic, WA 99166; (509) 775-3899
Pro: none.　9 hole executive course.
Rating/Slope: the golf course is not rated.　**Course record:** 68.
Green fees: $6; $8 all day rate; no credit cards.
Power cart: $8/$5.　**Pull cart:** $1.　**Trail fee:** not allowed.
Reservation policy: non advance reservations are required or needed.
Winter condition: the golf course is closed from October to mid-March.
Terrain: flat, some slight hills.　**Tees:** grass.　**Temporary greens:** no not in use.
Services: club rentals, snacks, pro shop, lounge.　**Comments:** the course is often
on the honor system. The golf course is very easy to walk. It now has expaned to
9 holes so you now can play a some what rustic but regulation golf course.

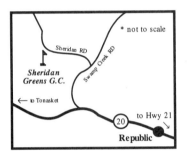

Directions: the golf course is located
2 miles west of Republic off Hwy 20.
Turn right on Swamp Creek Road and
proceed for 1.5 miles to the golf course.
Note the sign for the golf course cut-off
on Sheridan Road.

Course Yardage & Par:
M-2185 yards, par 32. **W-2185 yards, par 32.**

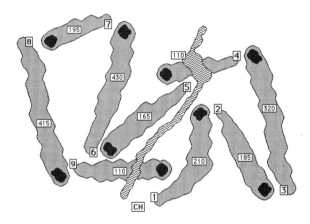

Map 2 Grid A2

Shuksan Golf Club (public)

1500 E. Axton; Bellingham, WA 98226; (360) 398-8888
Director of Golf Rick Verbarendse. **18 hole course, driving range.**
Rating/Slope: C 70.3/128; M 67.3/123; W 68.5/118. **Course record:** 72.
Green fees: Monday thru Thursday $25; Friday thru Sunday $30.
Power cart: $10+tax per person. **Pull cart:** N/A. **Trail fee:** not allowed.
Reservation policy: please call 7 days in advance for a tee time.
Winter condition: open, weather permitting. **Terrain:** flat, some steep hills.
Tees: grass. **Services:** club rentals, lessons, snack bar, restaurant, beer, wine, pro shop, driving range, tournament, banquet facilities. **Comments:** excellent newer course that offers the golfer fantastic golf on every hole. Magestic views of the mountains and surrounding countryside can be seen from nearly every tee. The facility was recently ranked FOUR STAR by *Golf Digest* Places to Play.

Directions: from I-5 southbound take exit #262 (Main St-City Center) eastbound. Travel east on Main which will become Axton Rd. The course is located approximately 7.8 miles ahead on the left. From I-5 northbound take exit #256. Follow Meridian to Axton Rd. and turn right. The golf course will be on your left. Look for signs to the golf course.

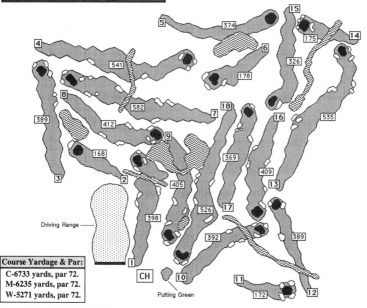

Course Yardage & Par:
C-6733 yards, par 72.
M-6235 yards, par 72.
W-5271 yards, par 72.

Similk Beach Golf Course (public)

1250 Christianson Road; Anacortes, WA 98221; (360) 293-3444
Pro: Dick Freier. Supt.: Earl Morgan. 18 hole course, driving range.
Rating/Slope: M 67.1/107; W 71.1/111. **Course record: 65.**
Green fees: W/D $18/$12; W/E $20/$14; all day rates; no credit cards.
Power cart: $20/$10. **Pull cart:** $2.50. **Trail fee:** no charge for personal carts.
Reservation policy: please call ahead for tee-times, no time limit on reservations.
Winter condition: the course is open all year, damp. **Terrain:** flat, some hills.
Tees: grass. **Temporary greens:** no not in use. **Services:** club rentals, lessons,
snack bar, driving range. **Comments:** the layout of this course is fairly open with
a few water hazards. Greens are medium in size and are usually open in the front.
The golf course has a well stocked pro shop and excellent driving range to serve
you. Good public track that is very popular with the local golfer.

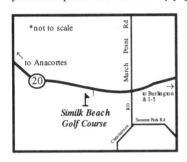

Directions: from I-5 northbound take
exit # 230 to Hwy 20 W (Burlington-
Anacortes). The golf course is located
5 miles east of Anacortes, just off of
Hwy 20. You will be able to see the golf
course from the highway.

Course Yardage & Par:
M-6232 yards, par 72.
W-5934 yards, par 76.

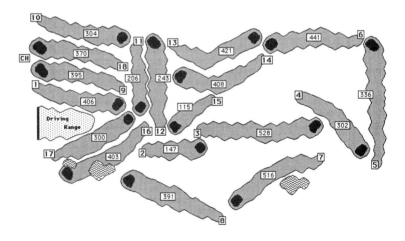

Skagit Golf & Country Club (private)

1493 Country Club Drive; Burlington, WA 98233; (360) 757-4081
Pro: David Bobillot, PGA. Supterintendent: Gregory Miller. 18 hole course.
Rating/Slope: M 68.5/119; W 70.3/120. **Course record:** 65.
Green fees: private club members & guests only; reciprocates.
Power cart: private club. **Pull cart:** private club. **Trail fee:** not allowed.
Reservation policy: summer only 48 hours in advance. **Winter condition:** damp.
Terrain: flat. **Tees:** grass. **Temporary greens:** no. **Services:** club rentals, lessons,
snack bar, lounge, restaurant, beer, wine, liquor, pro shop, lockers, showers,
club memberships, putting green, driving range. **Comments:** the golf course is a
combination of tree-lined and open fairways. Many bunkers front the tracks large
greens. Four ponds come into play off the tee and on your approach shots.

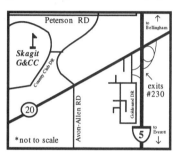

Direction: from I-5 N&S take exit # 230
to Hwy 20 W. Travel west for 2.1 miles
to Avon-Allen Road (the flashing light).
Turn right. Proceed .5 miles to the golf
course.

Course Yardage & Par:
M-6019 yards, par 71.
W-5439 yards, par 73.

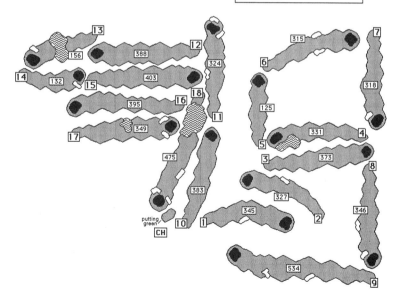

Skamania Lodge Golf Course (public, resort)

PO Box 189; 1131 Skamania Lodge Way; Stevenson, WA 98648
Phone numbers: toll free 1-800-293-0418 or (509) 427-2541.
Pro: Guy Puddefoot, PGA. Supt.: James Medler. 18 hole course, range.
Rating/Slope: C 68.9/127; M 66.7/122; W 65.2/115. **Course record:** 66.
Green fees: W/D $25/$17; W/E $32/$17; Jr. and twilight rates.
Power cart: W/D $24; W/E $27. **Pull cart:** $5/$3. **Trail fee:** not allowed.
Reservation policy: yes, please call up to 2 weeks in advance for tee times.
Winter condition: course is open, weather permitting. **Terrain:** flat, some hills.
Tees: grass. **Temporary greens:** no. **Services:** pro shop, restaurant, wine, liquor,
driving range, lodge facilities. **Comments:** This well kept golf course offers great
views of the Columbia River Gorge and surrounding countryside. If you plan on
vacationing for a few days stay at the Skamania Lodge. The course itself is narrow
in spots with well bunkered greens. Shot placement is a must from the tee. This
full service facility is worth a special trip if you are in the area.

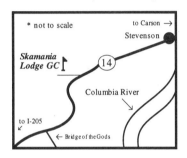

Directions: From Portland take I-84
eastbound to the Bridge of the Gods.
Turn eastbound to Hwy 14 and proceed
1.1 miles eastbound to Stevenson. The
golf course is located on the north side
of Hwy 14. From I-205 exit at Hwy 14
and proceed eastbound to Stevenson and
to the golf course. Look for signs.

Course Yardage & Par:
C-5776 yards, par 70.
M-5351 yards, par 70.
W-4362 yards, par 69.

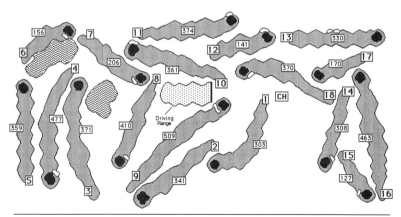

Skyline Golf Course (public)

20 Randall Drive; Cathlamet, WA 98612; (360) 795-8785
Manager: Wayne Cochran. 9 hole course, dual tees for 18 holes.
Rating/Slope: M 62.7/106; W 66.7/111. **Course record:** 62.
Green fees: $12/$8 all week long; no credit cards.
Power cart: $13/$7. **Pull cart:** $1. **Trail fee:** $5.
Reservation policy: please call 1 day in advance for tee-times.
Winter condition: the golf course is open all year long, dry.
Terrain: very hilly. **Tees:** grass & mats. **Temporary greens:** no.
Services: club rentals, snack bar (breakfast & lunch), club memberships.
Comments: the course is short and tight with a friendly atmosphere. Family run and owned. The golf course can play much tougher than it appears.

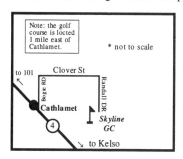

Directions: from I-5 N&S take the exit to Hwy 4 westbound at Kelso to Cathlamet. Turn right on Bogie Road. The road turns right on Clover Street. Turn right at the sign pointing to the golf course. The way is well marked.

Course Yardage & Par:
M-2255 yards, par 35.
W-2012 yards, par 35.
Dual tees for 18 holes:
M-4774 yards, par 70.
W-4205 yards, par 70.

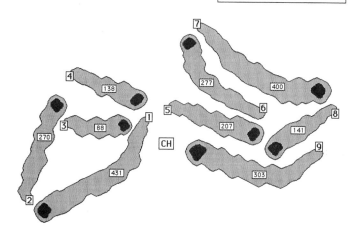

Snohomish Public Golf Course (public)

7806 147th SE; Box 1188; Snohomish, WA 98290; (360) 568-2676, 800-560-2676
Director of Golf: Fred Jacobson. Pro: John Brandvold, PGA.
18 hole course, range. Course record: 63. **Superintendent: George Smith.**
Rating/Slope: C 72.2/124; M 70/121; W 74.1/129.
Green fees: W/D $18/$12*; W/E $23/$14*; Jr./Sr. rates (M-F); M/C, VISA.
Power cart: $21/$12.50*. **Pull cart:** $3/$2*. **Trail fee:** $9*. **(*all add tax).**
Reservation policy: yes, call up to 1 week in advance. **Winter condition:** dry.
Terrain: relatively hilly. **Tees:** grass & mats (winter). **Services:** club rentals,
lessons, snack bar, restaurant, beer, wine, pro shop, club memberships, driving
range. **Comments:** beautiful rural course. Located on a hill the course is surrounded
by trees. The greens are very large and well bunkered. Great public golf course.

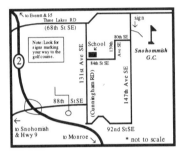

Directions: From I-5 N&S take exit #194 to Hwy 2
going eastbound. Follow Hwy 2 east to Snohomish.
Take the Snohomish exit (look for a sign) to 88th St.
SE. Go east on 88th to 131st Ave SE. Turn left on
131st. Proceed to 84th Ave. SE and turn right. 84th
becomes 139th Ave. SE as you must turn left. At the
T in the road turn right on 80th St. SE. Proceed on
80th to 147th Ave. SE. Turn left. The golf course
entrance will be on your right.

Course Yardage & Par:
C-6858 yards, par 72.
M-6315 yards, par 72.
W-5980 yards, par 74.

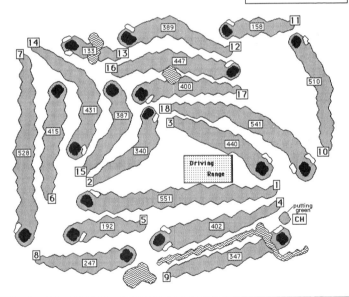

Snoqualmie Falls Golf Course (public)

35109 SE Fish Hatchery Road; Box 388; Fall City, WA 98024
Pro: John Groshell, PGA. Supt.: Lee Baldwin. (206) 222-5244 or 392-1276
18 hole course. Rating/Slope: M 65.3/105; W 68.9/114. **Course record:** 60.
Green fees: W/D $21/$13; W/E $23/$15; Jr /Sr rates (M-F) $16/$10; VISA, M/C.
Power cart: $22/$12. **Pull cart:** $3/$2. **Trail fee:** no.
Reservation policy: yes, call up to 6 days in advance for tee times.
Winter condition: dry, course is open. **Terrain:** very flat. **Tees:** grass & mats.
Temporary greens: no not in use. **Services:** club rentals, lessons, snack bar,
restaurant, beer, pro shop, driving range. **Comments:** situated in the foothills of
the Cascade Mountains, Snoqualmie Falls is easy to walk and fun to play. The golf
course has a well stocked pro shop and great on course restaurant. Good course.

Directions: from I-90 eastbound take exit # 22 to Preston. Turn left over the freeway, then right to the Preston-Fall City Road for 6.2 miles to Hwy 202E. Turn right and proceed approximately .8 miles to SE Fish Hatchery Road (look for a sign at the turn). Turn right to the golf course.

Course Yardage & Par:

M-5413 yards, par 71.
W-5175 yards, par 71.

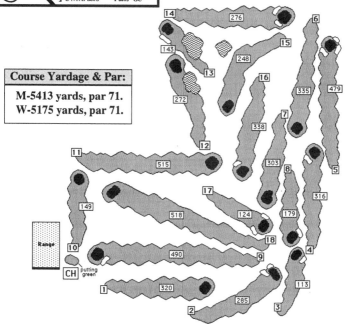

South Campus Golf Course (public)

1475 East Nelson Road; Moses Lake, WA 98837; (509) 766-1228
Owner: Dan Thomas. **9 hole par 3 course, driving range.**
Rating/Slope: the golf course is not rated. **Course record:** 25.
Green fees: $8/$5 all week long; no credit cards.
Power cart: $5 per 9 holes. **Pull cart:** $1. **Trail fee:** information not available.
Reservation policy: reservations are not needed, first come first served.
Winter condition: the golf course is open year round, weather permitting.
Tees: grass. **Terrain:** flat, easy walking course. **Temporary greens:** not in use.
Services: pro shop, club repair, club rentals, driving range, putting green.
Comments: easy to walk nine hole course. Greens are on the small size and can be hard to hold. Fairways are tight and tree-lined. The facility also has driving range for those wanting to get some practice in. Good hole variations.

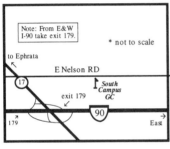

Directions: from I-90 E&W take the Moses Lake/ Highway 17 exit #179. Go northbound on Highway 17. Stay to your right when the road splits. Turn right on East Nelson Road and proceed to the golf course. Look for signs to the course.

Course Yardage & Par:
M-1266 yards, par 27.
W-1266 yards, par 27.

Course layout will change

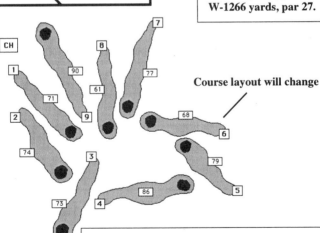

The golf course is undergoing some major revisions.
The course will be changing 2 holes making one a par
4 and one a par 5. The facility will be adding a putting
course that is due to be open sometime in 1996.

Spokane Country Club (private)
W 2010 Waikiki Road; PO Box 18750; Spokane, WA 99218; (509) 466-9813
Pro: Les Blakley, PGA. 18 hole course, driving range.
Rating/Slope: C 72.0/128; M 70.3/125; W 74.4/129. **Course record:** 61.
Green fees: private club members & guests only; reciprocates; no credit cards.
Power cart: private club. **Pull cart:** private club. **Trail fee:** private club.
Reservation policy: members only club, reciprocates call for policy.
Winter condition: open, weather permitting. **Terrain:** flat, some hills.
Tees: grass. **Temporary greens:** no. **Services:** club rentals, lessons, snack bar,
restaurant, lounge, beer, wine, liquor, showers, driving range, putting green.
Comments: this golf course was remodeled in 1988 by Robert Muir Graves. A
very difficult layout that puts a premium on accuracy off the tee. Excellent track.

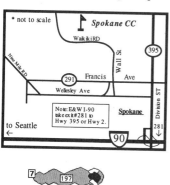

Directions: from I-90 take the exit at
Division Street. Travel northbound on
Division Street to Francis Avenue and
turn left. Proceed on Francis Avenue to
Wall Street and turn right. Then follow
Wall Street to Waikiki Road which will
lead to the golf course.

Course Yardage & Par:
C-6679 yards, par 72.
M-6317 yards, par 72.
W-5556 yards, par 73.

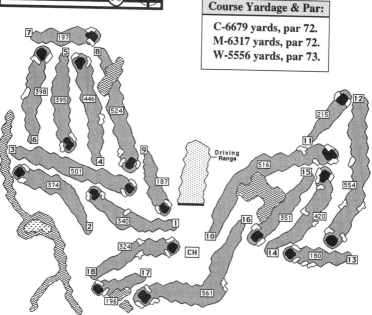

Sudden Valley Golf & Country Club (semi-private)

**2145 Lake Whatcom Blvd. (1001 Sudden Valley); Bellingham, WA 98226
(360) 734-6435. Pro: Greg Paul, PGA. 18 hole course. Supt.: Bryan Newman.
Rating/Slope:** C 72.4/129; M 70.6/126; W 72.5/128. **Course record:** 65.
Green fees: Mon.-Thur. $25+tax; Fri.-Sun. $34+tax; Jr. rates.; M/C, VISA.
Power cart: $23/$13+tax. **Pull cart:** $3. **Trail fee:** personal carts not allowed.
Reservation policy: yes, up to 1 week in advance. **Winter condition:** damp.
Terrain: relatively hilly. **Tees:** grass. **Temporary greens:** rarely (in winter).
Services: club rentals, lessons, snack bar, lounge, restaurant, beer, wine, liquor,
pro shop, showers, driving range. **Comments:** very scenic and challenging golf
course. The front 9 is lake side and flat, the back hilly and forested. Greens are
large in size and well bunkered. This track is worth a special trip anytime of year.

Directions: from I-5 south take exit #253 (Lakeway DR). Take a left at the stop light onto Lakeway DR. Proceed on Lakeway DR (which turns into Lake Whatcom Blvd. for 10.2 miles then you will turn right into Sudden Valley. From I-5 north take exit # 240 (Alger). Turn right at the stop sign and proceed for 1 mile to the next stop sign (Alger Tavern on left). Go straight through this intersection onto Cain Lake RD. Proceed for 8 miles. Turn left onto Lake Whatcom Blvd. Proceed for 3.5 miles to the Sudden Valley G&CC entrance on the right. Look for signs.

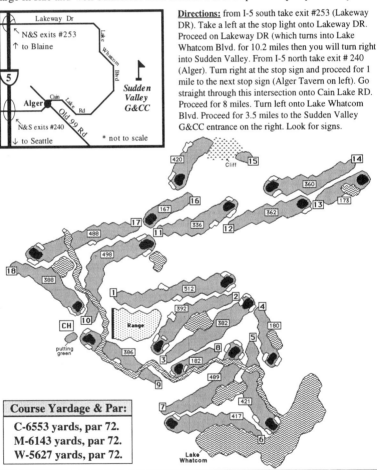

Course Yardage & Par:
C-6553 yards, par 72.
M-6143 yards, par 72.
W-5627 yards, par 72.

Sumner Meadows Golf Links (public)

14802 8th Street E; Sumner, WA 98390; (206) 863-8198; 1-800-959-4344
Director of Golf: Ron Hagen. Superintendent: N/A. 18 hole course, range.
Rating/Slope: the golf course has yet to be rated. **Course record:** N/A.
Green fees: Monday-Thursday $20/$14.50; Friday-Sunday & Holidays $25/$18;
early bird specials, Jr. & Sr. and twilight rates; punch cards VISA, M/C.
Power cart: $20/$14. **Pull cart:** $3/$2. **Trail fee:** personal carts are not allowed.
Reservation policy: please call 7 days in advance for tee times (can get busy).
Winter condition: open all year long, dry. **Terrain:** flat, some hills. **Tees:** grass.
Temporary greens: no. **Services:** club rentals, pro shop, lessons, snack bar,
driving range, putting green. **Comments:** the golf course opened in summer of
1995. This excellent new facility promises to be one of the finest courses in the
Northwest after it matures. This links style track has many challenging holes with
approach shots that carry over the water. Greens are large and well bunkered.

Directions: from Hwy 167 north and
south bound exit in Sumner on the 8th
Street E exit. Proceed eastbound on 8th
Street E for 1 mile to the golf course on
your right hand side. Look for signs
marking your turn to the golf course.

Course Yardage & Par:

T-6693 yards, par 72.
C-6615 yards, par 72.
M-6198 yards, par 72.
M-5726 yards, par 72.
W-5288 yards, par 73.

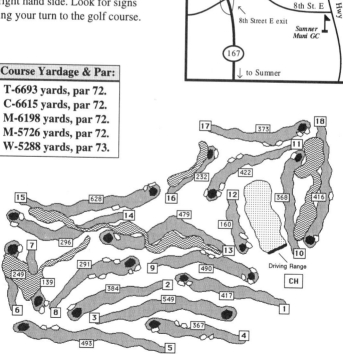

Sun Country Golf Resort (public)

Golf Course Road; PO Box 364; Cle Elum, WA 98922; (509) 674-2226
Manager: Ken Riach. 9 hole course, dual tees for 18 holes.
Rating/Slope: M 68.8/119; W 70.9/124. **Course record:** 33 for 9 holes.
Green fees: W/D $12/$8; W/E $15/$10; no credit cards.
Power cart: $18/$10. **Pull cart:** $1. **Trail fee:** $2 for each 9 holes.
Reservation policy: yes, call ahead 7 days for your tee times.
Winter condition: the golf course is closed from mid October to mid April.
Terrain: relatively hilly (power carts are recommended). **Tees:** grass.
Temporary greens: no not in use. **Services:** club rentals, snack bar, lessons (by appointment), RV park. **Comments:** beautiful setting in the eastern Cascade Mountain foothills. RV park adjacent to the clubhouse for those traveling. Two sets of tees for a full 18 holes of golf. Good course with medium to large greens.

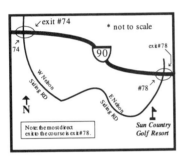

Directions: from I-90 E&W take exit #78 Golf Course Road. Follow signs to the RV park. The golf course is located on the south side of I-90 in the Sun Country Resort signs are posted.

Course Yardage & Par:
M-2861 yards, par 36.
W-2742 yards, par 37.
Dual tees for 18 holes:
M-5715 yards, par 72.
W-5466 yards, par 74.

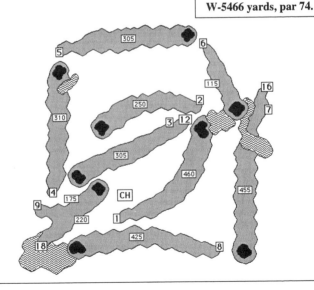

Sun Willows (public)

2035 20th Avenue; Pasco, WA 99301; (509) 545-3440
Pro: Joe Dubsky, PGA. **18 hole course, driving range.**
Rating/Slope: C 72.0/120; M 69.8116; W 71.6/119. **Course record:** 63.
Green fees: $15/$10 all week long; Jr. rates; VISA, M/C.
Power cart: $24/$12. **Pull cart:** $3. **Trail fee:** $5 for personal carts.
Reservation policy: yes, call up to 1 week in advance for tee times.
Winter condition: usually open all year long depending on the weather, dry.
Terrain: flat, easy walking course. **Tees:** grass. **Temporary greens:** not in use.
Services: club rentals, lessons, restaurant, lounge, beer, wine, pro shop, driving range, putting & chipping greens. **Comments:** this excellent public facility has well-trapped greens and gentle rolling terrain. The tree-lined fairways are very wide with large landing areas. Water comes into play on several holes.

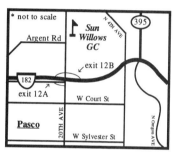

Directions: from I-182/Hwy12 take the 20th St. exit #128 and travel northbound to the course. The golf course is located across from the Red Lion Inn in Pasco. Look for signs indicating your turn.

Course Yardage & Par:
C-6715 yards, par 72.
M-6325 yards, par 72.
W-5665 yards, par 72.

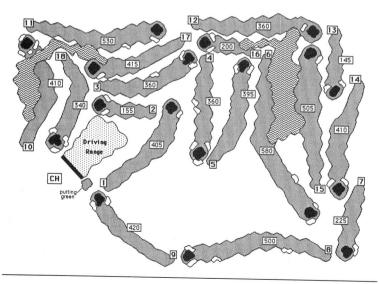

Sundance Golf Course (public)

9725 Nine Mile Road; Nine Mile Falls, WA 99026; (509) 466-4040
Director: Ken Johnston, PGA. Pro: Denny Johnston, PGA. 18 hole course.
Rating/Slope: M 68.1/114; W 73.4/ 119. **Course record:** 65.
Green fees: W/D $12.50/$9.50; W/E $13/$10; Jr. & Sr. rates $9.50/$8.50 (M-F).
Power cart: $20/$10. **Pull cart:** $2.50. **Trail fee:** $3.50.
Reservation policy: yes, you may call ahead for reservations, Saturday for the
following weekend. For weekday tee times call Sunday or any weekday following.
Winter condition: dry, course closed November to March depending on weather.
Terrain: flat, some hills. **Tees:** grass. **Temporary greens:** no not in use.
Services: club rentals, lessons, snack bar, restaurant, lounge, beer, wine, pro shop,
driving range, putting green. **Comments:** this public course sports tree-lined
fairways and very small greens. Well conditioned track that can play tough.

Directions: from I-90 take exit # 280A
to Walnut St. Turn north for 1.5 miles to
Northwest Blvd. Turn left. Travel 5 miles
to Hwy 291. Turn left and proceed 3 miles
to the golf course. Look for signs.

Course Yardage & Par:
M-5960 yards, par 70.
M-5905 yards, par 70.
W-5658 yards, par 72.

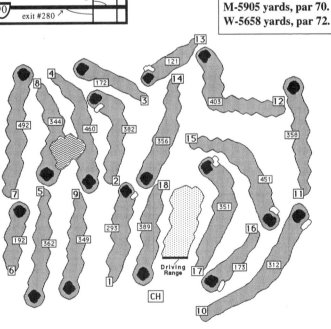

SunLand Golf & Country Club (semi-private)

109 Hilltop Drive; Sequim, WA 98382; (360) 683-6800
Pro: Jeff Lindsey, PGA. Superintendent: Daniel Ratcliff. 18 hole course.
Rating/Slope: C 70.2/121; M 69.0/119; W 71.3/119. **Course record:** 64.
Green fees: W/D $22; W/E $28; M/C, VISA; winter rates November to February.
Power cart: $22/$12. **Pull cart:** $3/$2. **Trail fee:** personal carts not allowed.
Reservation policy: yes, please call ahead for all tee time reservations.
Winter condition: dry, open all year. **Terrain:** flat, some hills. **Tees:** grass.
Temporary greens: yes. **Services:** club rentals, lessons, snack bar, pro shop,
driving range, putting green. **Comments:** the course winds through a variety of
forest and homesites. Greens are well-trapped and water comes into play on 3
holes. Great golf course located in the banana belt of Washington State.

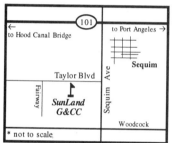

Directions: from Hwy 101 as you enter
Sequim turn right on Sequim Avenue
proceed 2.1 miles to Taylor Blvd. Turn
right and follow to Fairway Dr. Turn left
on Fairway Dr. to the clubhouse. Look for
signs marking your turn to the complex.

Course Yardage & Par:
C-6313 yards, par 72.
M-6051 yards, par 72.
W-5554 yards, par 73.

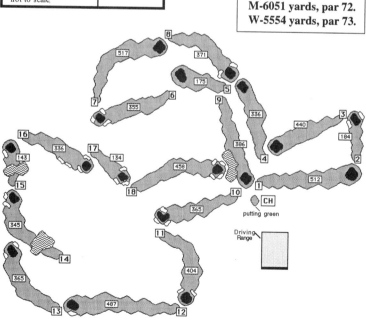

Sunny Meadows Golf & Four Seasons Resort (private)

280 W Chewuck RD; Winthrop, WA 98862; (509) 996-3103, 1-800-433-3121
Owner: Bob Odenthal. 9 hole par 3 course.
Rating/Slope: the golf course is not rated. **Course record:** N/A.
Green fees: private golf course, members & guests only.
Power cart: not available. **Pull cart:** N/A. **Trail fee:** personal carts not allowed.
Reservation policy: yes, please call ahead for all tee time & B& B reservations.
Winter condition: closed during winter. **Terrain:** relatively hilly. **Tees:** grass.
Temporary greens: no. **Services:** the golf course is tied to a bed & breakfast
arrangement with two self-suffucent apartments, limited golf course services.
Comments: this fairly new par 3 course has 3 water hazards, 3 blind holes, and
tough, small elevated greens. This short par 3 course will challenge you at every
turn. Tied to a great bed & breakfast. Plan on staying the whole weekend.

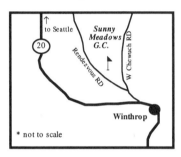

Directions: the golf course is located 2.7
miles north of Winthrop. From Hwy 20
turn on West Chewuck Road to the Bed &
Breakfast and golf course. Look for signs.

Course Yardage & Par:
M-1360 yards, par 27.
W-1134 yards, par 27.

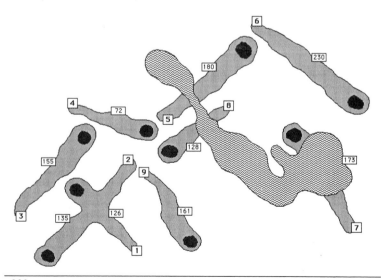

Suntides Golf Course (public)

231 Pence Road; Yakima, WA 98908; (509) 966-9065
Pro: Paul Cobleigh, PGA. 18 hole course, driving range.
Rating/Slope: C 67.8/112; M 67.5/119; W 67.9/122. **Course record:** 63.
Green fees: $17/$10 all week long; winter rates; Jr. rates; VISA, M/C.
Power cart: $20/$10. **Pull cart:** $2/$1. **Trail fee:** $5.
Reservation policy: call Wednesday for Friday through Sunday tee times.
Winter condition: course is open weather permitting. **Terrain:** flat. **Tees:** grass.
Services: club rentals, lessons, snack bar, restaurant, lounge, beer, wine, liquor, pro shop, driving range, putting & chipping greens. **Comments:** a small creek winds through the course which comes into play on numerous holes. A very pleasant course to walk and well-maintained. Golf course has great greens.

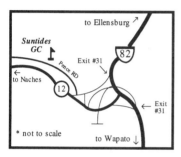

Directions: the golf course is located 3 miles west of Yakima off of Hwy 12. You will find the golf course on the north side of the highway with the exit .5 miles west of the Yakima River. Look for signs.

Course Yardage & Par:
C-6232 yards, par 70.
M-5941 yards, par 70.
W-5509 yards, par 71.

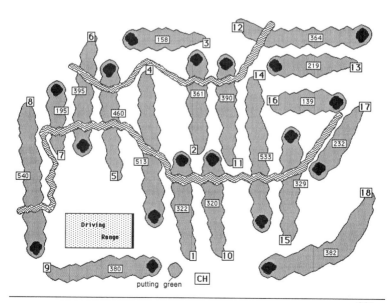

Surfside Golf Course (public)

31508 "J" Place; Ocean Park, WA 98640; (360) 665-4148
Pros: Louis Runge, PGA, Scott Basse, PGA. 9 hole course, dual tees.
Rating/Slope: M 68.6/119; W 72.5/124. **Course record:** 66.
Green fees: $17/$10 all week long; Jr & Sr, winter rates (weekdays); VISA, M/C.
Power cart: $20/$12. **Pull cart:** $2.50/$1.50. **Trail fee:** $10/$5.
Reservation policy: yes, recommended. Call 7 days in advance for tee times.
Winter condition: dry, the golf course is open all year long. **Terrain:** flat.
Tees: grass. **Temporary greens:** not in use. **Services:** club rentals, snack bar,
pro shop, club memberships, lessons, driving range, putting & chipping greens.
Comments: the course is very easy to walk. Water comes into play on four holes
of the nine holes. The wind plays a major factor from the and on your approach
shots. Great place to play when visiting the scenic Washington coast.

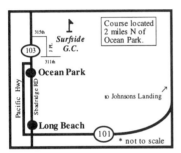

Directions: from I-5 N&S take exit # 104
to Hwy 101 south to Long Beach to Hwy
103. Go north to Ocean Park, following
signs to Surfside. The course is located 2
miles north of Ocean Park. Look for signs
marking your turn to the golf course. The
way is well marked.

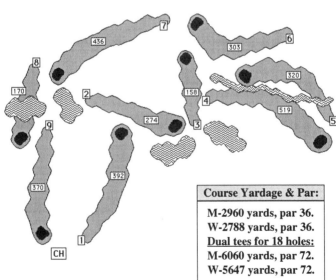

Course Yardage & Par:
M-2960 yards, par 36.
W-2788 yards, par 36.
Dual tees for 18 holes:
M-6060 yards, par 72.
W-5647 yards, par 72.

Tacoma Country & Golf Club (private)

Gravelly Lake Drive SW; Tacoma, WA 98498; (206) 588-0404
Pro: Rich Friend, PGA. Superintendent: Paul Colleran. 18 hole course.
Rating/Slope: C 71.6/124; M 70.1/121; W 72.7/124. **Course record:** 62.
Green fees: members only & guests only; very limited reciprocation.
Power cart: private club. **Pull cart:** private club. **Trail fee:** not allowed.
Reservation policy: private club members & guests of members only.
Winter condition: open, dry. **Terrain:** flat, some slight hills. **Tees:** grass.
Temporary greens: no. **Services:** club rentals, lessons, snack bar, lounge, beer,
wine, liquor, pro shop, lockers, showers, club memberships, driving range.
Comments: the course was built in 1894, the oldest private golf club, west of the
Mississippi. Greens are large with bunkers coming into play on nearly every hole.

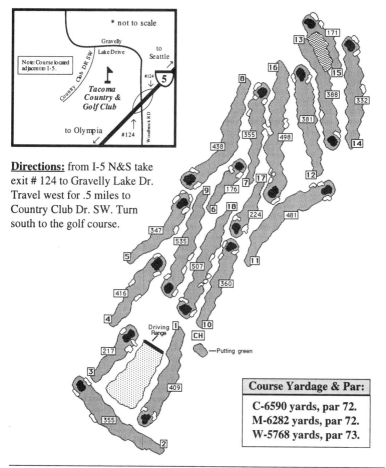

Directions: from I-5 N&S take
exit # 124 to Gravelly Lake Dr.
Travel west for .5 miles to
Country Club Dr. SW. Turn
south to the golf course.

Course Yardage & Par:

C-6590 yards, par 72.
M-6282 yards, par 72.
W-5768 yards, par 73.

Tall Chief Golf Course (public)

1313 West Snoqualmie River Road SE; Fall City, WA 98024
(206) 222-5911 or Seattle (206) 706-1881. 18 hole course, practice area.
Pro: Rick Larson, PGA. Superintendent: Graig Labelle.
Rating/Slope: C 64.4/102; M 63.4/101; W 65.8/105. **Course record:** 62.
Green fees: W/D $20/$13; W/E $23/$14; Sr rates (weekdays); VISA, M/C.
Power cart: $20/$12. **Pull cart:** $3. **Trail fee:** $10 for personal carts.
Reservation policy: yes, call up to 6 days in advance by phone, 7 days in person.
Winter condition: damp, course open all year long. **Terrain:** flat, some hills.
Tees: grass (mats in winter). **Temporary greens:** not in use at any time.
Services: club rentals, lessons, cafe, beer, wine. **Comments:** this course is set in
the foothills of the scenic Cascades. An excellent facility for tournaments and
private functions. Campground adjacent to the course. Friendly golf course that
is worth the trip if you want a fun casual day of golfing with the whole family.

Directions: from I-5 N&S take exit # 168B
to Hwy 520 eastbound. Travel east to Hwy
202 E (Redmond-Fall City Road). Turn
right and travel 10.5 miles to 308th SE.
Turn left and proceed .8 miles, follow the
arterial to W Snoqualmie River Road. Go
left and proceed .9 miles to the golf course.
There are signs on Hwy 202 marking your
turn to the golf course.

Course Yardage & Par:
C-5422 yards, par 70.
M-5218 yards, par 70.
W-4945 yards, par 71.

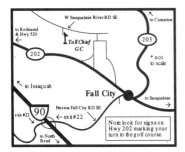

Tam O' Shanter Golf & Country Club (private)

1313 183rd Avenue NE; Bellevue, WA 98008; (206) 746-3502
Pro: John Thorsnes, PGA. Supt.: Tom Corlett. 9 hole course, dual tees.
Rating/Slope: C 70.0/127; M 68.6/124; W 71.3/124. **Course record:** 60.
Green fees: private, members & guests of members only, limited reciprocation.
Power cart: private club members only. **Pull cart:** private. **Trail fee:** not allowed.
Reservation policy: private club members only. **Winter condition:** open, wet.
Terrain: relatively hilly. **Tees:** grass. **Temporary greens:** yes (during winter).
Services: club rentals, lessons, snack bar and grill, lounge, restaurant, beer, wine,
liquor, large pro shop, putting & chipping greens, driving range (for irons only).
Comments: must be a homeowner to gain membership in the golf club. Dual tees
and dual flags are provided for a full 18 hole round. The greens are large, well
bunkered and fast. Well kept private facility that was opened in 1964.

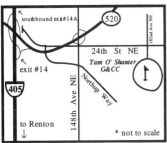

Directions: from I-5 N&S take exit
#168B to Hwy 520 eastbound. Exit at
148th SE. Turn south (right) and make
the first available left which is NE 24th.
Travel east on NE 24th for 2.1 miles to
182nd Ave. NE. Turn south for .7 miles
to the golf course.

Course Yardage & Par:
C-3072 yards, par 36.
M-2984 yards, par 36.
W-2704 yards, par 36.
<u>Dual tees for 18 holes:</u>
C-6168 yards, par 71.
M-5854 yards, par 71.
W-5383 yards, par 72.

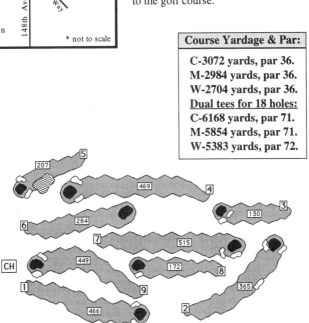

Tapps Island Golf Course (public)

20818 Island Parkway East; Sumner, WA 98390; (206) 862-7011
Pro: Chris Lofthus. Supt.: Mark Seman. 9 hole course, dual tees.
Rating/Slope: M 66.5/117; W 68.1/120. **Course record:** 62.
Green fees: W/D $19/$13; W/E $22/$15; Jr & Sr rates; M/C, VISA.
Power cart: $20/$15. **Pull cart:** $3. **Trail fee:** $5 for personal carts.
Reservation policy: yes, call up to 1 week in advance for tee time reservations.
Winter condition: the course is open all year long, dry. **Terrain:** flat, some hills.
Tees: grass. **Temporary greens:** not in use at anytime. **Services:** club rentals,
coffee shop, beer, wine, lockers, pro shop, putting green. **Comments:** water comes
into play on five holes. Well bunkered greens and narrow tree-lined make this golf
course a real challenge. Do not let the lack of distance fool you this course is very
demanding. Dual tee and flag system are provided for a full 18 hole round. Good
food and challenging golf, make Tapps Island Golf Course worth a special trip.

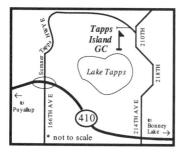

Directions: from I-5S take Hwy 512 to
Hwy 410 into Bonney Lake. Turn left at
214th Avenue and proceed 4 miles to the
golf course. From I-5N take Hwy 18 east
to Auburn/Enumclaw exit. Proceed 1 mile
and veer right onto Howard Street. Then in
1/4 mile turn on "R" Street. Follow "R"
Street for 3 miles to 214th Avenue. Turn
left on 214th Avenue. Golf Course will
located 3 miles ahead on your right. Look
for signs indicating your turn to the course.

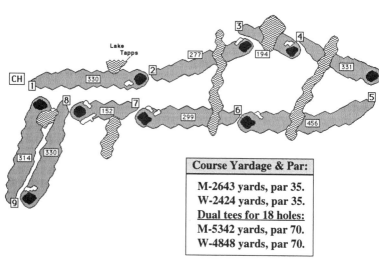

Course Yardage & Par:

M-2643 yards, par 35.
W-2424 yards, par 35.
Dual tees for 18 holes:
M-5342 yards, par 70.
W-4848 yards, par 70.

Tekoa Golf Club (public)

off of Hwy 27; PO Box 809; Tekoa, WA 99033; (509) 284-5607
Pro: none available. Manager: none available. 9 hole course.
Rating/Slope: M 64.2/105; W 68.2/113. **Course record:** 30.
Green fees: W/D $8; W/E & holidays $10; no credit cards.
Power cart: none available. **Pull cart:** none available. **Trail fee:** no charge.
Reservation policy: none required play is on a first come first serve basis.
Winter condition: depending on the weather, but the course is generally closed.
Terrain: flat, some rolling hills. **Tees:** grass. **Temporary greens:** not in use.
Services: the golf course has very limited services, putting green, league play.
Comments: this course features wide open rolling terrain and a few trees. The
golf course plays very short with no hole over 500 yards. Great walking course
for the first time or senior golfer. This course is rustic in design and grooming.

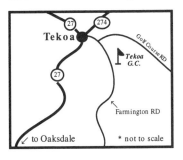

Directions: the golf course is located 1/2
mile south of Tekoa off of Hwy 27. Look
for Farmington Road for your turn to the
golf course. When you get to Golf Course
Road you will turn left. Proceed on Golf
Course Road to the clubhouse. Look for
signs marking your turn to the clubhouse.

Course Yardage & Par:
M-2550 yards, par 35.
W-2550 yards, par 35.

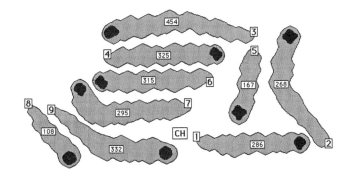

Three Lakes Golf Course (public)
2695 Golf Drive; Malaga, WA 98828; (509) 663-5448
Pro: John Christensen, PGA. 18 hole course, driving range.
Rating/Slope: M 65.2/104; W 70.1/121. **Course record:** 61.
Green fees: $20/$12 all week long; Jr. rates are available.
Power cart: $20/$12. **Pull cart:** $3/$2. **Trail fee:** $5 (annual pass available).
Reservation policy: yes, please call 7 days in advance for a tee time.
Winter condition: closed December to February depending on the weather.
Terrain: relatively hilly. **Tees:** grass. **Temporary greens:** not in use.
Services: club rentals, lessons, restaurant, beer, wine, pro shop, driving range,
putting green. **Comments:** narrow tree-lined fairways make this course a real
challenge. The golf course is well-kept and offers scenic views of the Columbia
River and the surrounding countryside of the Wenatchee Valley.

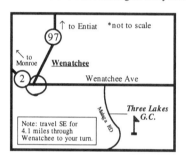

Directions: from Hwy 97 take the
Wenatchee exit. Go through the city
center (on Wenatchee Ave). Travel 4
miles to the golf course turnoff which is
southeast of the city. Turn right at West
Malaga Road. The golf course will be on
your left hand side. Look for signs.

Course Yardage & Par:
M-5276 yards, par 69.
W-5233 yards, par 72.

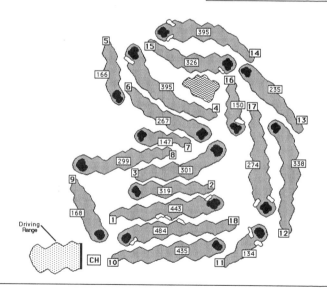

Three Rivers Golf Course (public)

2222 S River Road; Kelso, WA 98626; (360) 423-4653
Pro: Fred Bader, PGA. 18 hole course, driving range.
Rating/Slope: C 71.7/127; M 68.5/116; W 69.4/117. **Course record:** 65.
Green fees: W/D $15/$11; W/E $17/$14; Jr & Sr rates (M-F); no credit cards.
Power cart: $20/$11. **Pull cart:** $2. **Trail fee:** $8 (annual pass available).
Reservation policy: yes, call up to 1 week in advance for tee time reservations.
Winter condition: the golf course is open all year long, dry (drains very well).
Terrain: flat, some slight hills. **Tees:** grass. **Temporary greens:** not in use.
Services: club rentals, lessons, snack bar, lounge, restaurant, beer, wine, lockers, pro shop, club memberships, covered driving range, putting and chipping greens.
Comments: the course is built upon the Mt. St. Helens ash that filled the area, it therefore has excellent drainage. The course is wide open and has large greens.

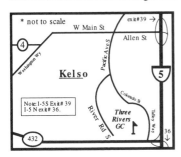

Directions: from I-5 southbound take the first exit in Kelso to Huntington Avenue (I-5 northbound take the last Kelso exit). Travel southwest on Huntington Avenue which becomes Pacific Avenue to "U" St. Turn right at the railroad crossing and follow the signs to the golf course.

Course Yardage & Par:
C-6846 yards, par 72.
M-6161 yards, par 72.
W-5455 yards, par 72.

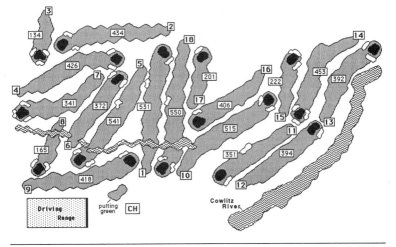

Touchet Valley Golf Course (public)

North Pine Street; P.O. Box 54; Dayton, WA 99328; (509) 382-4851
Owner/manager: Pearl Bickelhaupt. 9 hole course, dual tees for 18 holes.
Rating/Slope: C 67.8/114; M 66.8/115; W 72/122. **Course record:** 30.
Green fees: W/D $12/$9; W/E $15/$12; no credit cards.
Power cart: $14/$7.50. **Pull cart:** $1. **Trail fee:** $5 for personal carts.
Reservation policy: advance reservations are not required, first come first served.
Winter condition: the course is closed from October 16th to March 15th.
Terrain: flat. **Tees:** grass. **Temporary greens:** not in use at any time.
Services: club rentals, snack bar, restaurant. **Comments:** a unique setting within
the grounds of a horse racing track (Columbia County Fairgrounds Racing Track).
The golf course is flat and is very easy to walk. Greens are large and very flat.

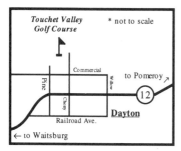

Directions: the golf course is located
in Dayton on the north side of Hwy 12.
You will turn westbound on Main Street.
Then turn right at the Dayton Mercantile
store. Follow this street north for 2 blocks
to the golf course.

Course Yardage & Par:
C-2931 yards, par 36.
M-2841 yards, par 36.
W-2745 yards, par 36.
<u>Dual tees for 18 holes:</u>
C-5862 yards, par 72.
M-5682 yards, par 72.
W-5490 yards, par 72.

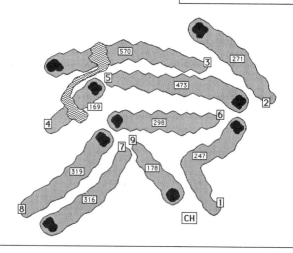

Tri City Country Club (semi-private)

314 North Underwood Street; Kennewick, WA 99336; (509) 783-6014
Pro: Chris Isaacson, PGA. 18 hole course, putting green.
Rating/Slope: C 64.2/114; M 62.5/112; W 65.2/115. **Course record:** 57.
Green fees: W/D $17; W/E $22; reciprocates; no credit cards.
Power cart: $25/$15. **Pull cart:** $2.50. **Trail fee:** $5 for personal carts.
Reservation policy: yes, you may call 2 days ahead for your tee time.
Winter condition: the golf course is open all year long, weather permitting.
Terrain: relatively hilly. **Tees:** grass. **Temporary greens:** not in use.
Services: club rentals, lessons, pro shop, restaurant and lounge (members only).
Comments: the course sports tree-lined fairways and many well-trapped greens.
Water comes into play on three holes. Excellent golf course that can play tough.

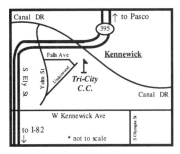

Directions: from Hwy 12 take the exit
Hwy 14 and continue to Yelm St. Turn
left. Travel to Clearwater. Left on
Clearwater and proceed to Underwood
where you turn into the golf course.

Course Yardage & Par:
C-5010 yards, par 65.
M-4693 yards, par 65.
W-4400 yards, par 65.

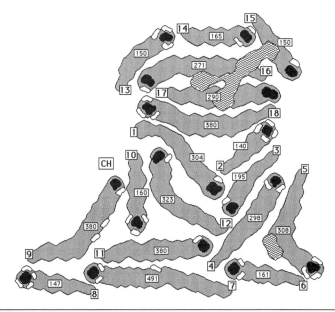

Tri-Mountain Golf Course (public)

1701 NW 299th Street; P.O. Box 55; Ridgefield, WA 98642; (360) 887-3004
Pro: Chuck Disilva. 18 hole course, driving range, putting green.
Rating/Slope: C 71.1/120; M 68.6/117; W 69.8/117. **Course record:** 67.
Green fees: W/D $23/$13; W/E & holidays $29/$16; Sr. rates Mon. thru Fri.
Power cart: $20/$12. **Pull cart:** $3/$2. **Trail fee:** no private carts allowed.
Reservation policy: please call 5 days in advance for a tee time reservations.
Winter condition: the golf course is open all year long, weather permitting.
Terrain: flat, some hills. **Tees:** grass. **Services:** club rentals, lessons, snack bar,
beer, wine, pro shop, driving range. **Comments:** the course offers a number of
challenges such as 86 sand traps, 11 lakes and rolling terrain. This course will be
worth a special trip. This newer track has excellent greens and mature fairways.

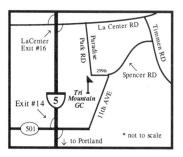

Directions: from I-5 northbound and
southbound take exit #14. Travel eastbound
on Hwy 501 to 11th Ave. Turn left on 11th.
Proceed to 299th. Turn Left on 299th to the
golf course. Look for signs to the course.

Course Yardage & Par:
C-6580 yards, par 72.
M-6091 yards, par 72.
W-5284 yards, par 72.

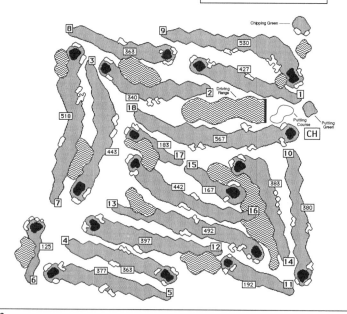

Tumwater Valley Golf Club (public)

4611 Tumwater Valley Drive; Tumwater, WA 98501; (360) 943-9500
Pro: Kevin Myers. Superintendent: Jeffrey Mason. 18 hole course, range.
Rating/Slope: T 73.1/120; C 70.7/115; M 68.8/111; W 70.4/114. **Record: 60.**
Green fees: W/D $17/$12; W/E $24/$15 after 3pm; Jr & Sr rates (weekdays).
Power cart: $20/$14. **Pull cart:** $2. **Trail fee:** $10 for personal carts.
Reservation policy: yes, please call up to 8 days in advance for reservations.
Winter condition: dry, excellent drainage. Course is open all year long.
Terrain: flat, some slight hills. **Tees:** grass. **Temporary greens:** not in use.
Services: club rentals, lessons, snack bar, beer, pro shop, driving range, putting
& chipping green, golf schools available. **Comments:** the course sports quick,
undulating greens, and numerous sand or water hazards on seemingly every hole.
An excellent facility that is worth a trip. Great teaching facility available.

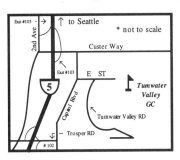

Directions: from I-5 N&S take exit
#103. Proceed southbound for .3 miles
to Custer Way. Turn left and proceed
for .2 miles to Capitol Blvd. Turn right
for .4 miles to "E" Street. Turn left and
proceed for .4 miles to the golf course.
Look for signs marking your way.

Course Yardage & Par:
T-7154 yards, par 72.
C-6523 yards, par 72.
M-6108 yards, par 72.
W-5428 yards, par 72.

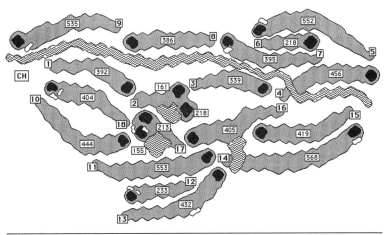

Twin Lakes Golf & Country Club (private)
3538 SW 320th; Federal Way, WA 98023; (206) 838-0345
Pro: Joe Trembly, PGA. Supt.: Dennis Campbell. 18 hole course, range.
Rating/Slope: C 70.3/123; M 68.3/120; W 69.4/118. **Course record:** 62.
Green fees: private club member and guests only; reciprocates (very limited).
Power cart: private club members only. **Pull cart:** private. **Trail fee:** private.
Reservation policy: private club members only & guests of members only.
Winter condition: the course is open all year long, dry. **Terrain:** flat, some hills.
Tees: grass. **Temporary greens:** not in use. **Services:** club rentals, lessons,
lounge, restaurant, snack bar, beer, wine, liquor, lockers, showers, pro shop,
putting & chipping greens, club memberships. **Comments:** sweeping views of
Puget Sound are seen from some fairways. A very tight, tree-lined track. Greens
are large, fast and firm. Bunkers come into play throughout the golf course.

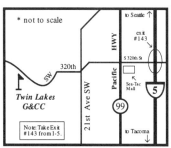

Directions: from I-5 N&S take exit #143
to SW 320th. Travel west for 2.8 miles to
the golf course which will be on your left
hand side. The golf course can be seen
from SW 320th Street which is a main
road in Federal Way. Look for a small sign
indicating your turn into the parking lot.

Course Yardage & Par:
C-6221 yards, par 72.
M-5852 yards, par 72.
W-5123 yards, par 72.

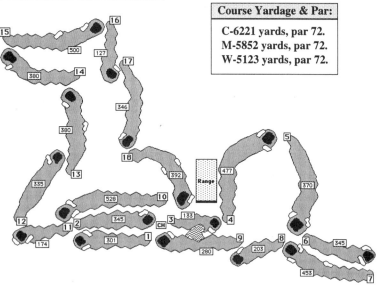

Twin Rivers Golf Course (public)

4446 Preston-Fall City Road SE; Fall City, WA 98024; (206) 222-7575
Pro: Jeff Tachell, PGA. 9 hole course, dual tees for 18 holes, driving range.
Manager: Richard Rutledge. Superintendent: William Shortley.
Rating/Slope: C 71.5/115; M 68.4/106; W 63.7/096. **Course record:** N/A.
Green fees: $22/$13 everyday; Jr. & Sr. rates (M-F). **Power cart:** $20/$10.
Pull cart: $4/$2. **Trail fee:** no. **Reservation policy:** you may call in advance.
Winter condition: open, damp. **Terrain:** flat, easy to walk. **Tees:** all grass.
Temporary greens: no. **Services:** club rentals, snack bar, beer, wine, range.
Comments: The course is built on 81 acres which makes it very open with some trees. Dual set of tees (each hole has 5 tees) creates a real variation for the golfer wishing to play 18 holes. Great newer 9 hole course that is worth a trip.

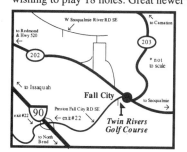

Directions: from I-90 take exit #22. Follow the Preston-Fall City Road approximately 4.5 miles to the course which will be on your right. The course is just outside Fall City. From Redmond travel east on Hwy 202 to Fall City. Turn right (south) on the Preston-Fall City Rd. approximately .5 miles to the golf course entrance which will be on your left. Look for a sign at your entrance.

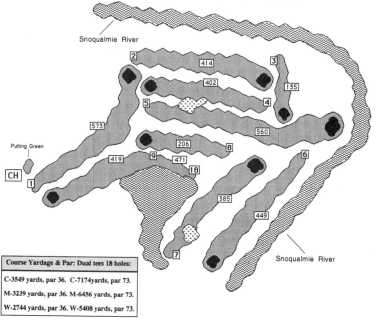

Course Yardage & Par: Dual tees 18 holes:
C-3549 yards, par 36. C-7174 yards, par 73.
M-3239 yards, par 36. M-6456 yards, par 73.
W-2744 yards, par 36. W-5408 yards, par 73.

Tyee Valley Golf Course (public)

2401 S 192nd; Seattle, WA 98188; (206) 878-3540
Pro: Mark Olson. Superintendent: Don Goble. 18 hole course.
Rating/Slope: C 68.8/119; M 67.5/118; W 69.9/123. **Course record:** 63.
Green fees: W/D $18/$12.50; W/E $19/$12.50; Sr./Jr. rates (M-F); M/C, VISA.
Power cart: $18/$10. **Pull cart:** $3/$2. **Trail fee:** $5 for personal carts.
Reservation policy: yes, call up to 1 week in advance for tee time reservations.
Winter condition: the golf course is open all year long, dry (drains well).
Terrain: relatively hilly. **Tees:** grass. **Temporary greens:** not in use.
Services: club rentals lessons, restaurant, beer, wine, putting green, 5-somes OK.
Comments: fairly easy walking course. Greens are guarded by green side
bunkers. The course is fairly wide open. Water comes into play on a few holes.

Directions: from I-5 N&S take exit #152
to S 188th. Proceed west for 1.1 miles to
Pacific Hwy S. (Hwy 99S). Turn south
for 2 miles to S 192nd. Turn west for .3
miles to the golf course. Look for signs
marking your way to the golf course.

Course Yardage & Par:
C-5845 yards, par 71.
M-5812 yards, par 71.
W-5414 yards, par 73.

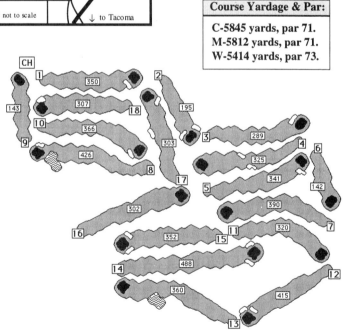

University Golf Club (public)

754 124th South; Tacoma, WA 98444; (206) 535-7393
Pro: Gary L. Cinotto. 9 hole course, dual tees for 18 holes.
Rating/Slope: M 64.4/100; W 69.4/112. **Course record:** 62.
Green fees: $14/$9; Jr & Sr rates (weekdays only); no credit cards.
Power cart: $14/$7. **Pull cart:** $2. **Trail fee:** $3/$2 for personal carts.
Reservation policy: strictly open play, times are on a first come first play basis.
Winter condition: dry, drains well. Open all year long. **Terrain:** very flat.
Tees: grass. **Temporary greens:** yes. **Services:** club rentals, lessons, snack bar,
pro shop, club memberships, putting green. **Comments:** the course is easy to walk
and has excellent greens. The track stays very dry during the winter months due to
its excellent drainage. Greens are medium in size with some guarded by bunkers.

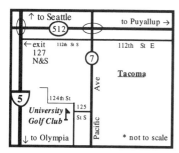

Directions: from I-5 N&S take exit # 127
to Hwy 512 E. Travel east for 2.1 miles
to Hwy 7 south. Proceed southbound on
Hwy 7 for 1 mile to 125th St. S. Turn west
and proced to Yakima Avenue, then turn
right to the golf course. Look for signs.

Course Yardage & Par:
M-2732 yards, par 35.
W-2732 yards, par 36.
Dual tees for 18 holes:
M-5371 yards, par 70.
W-5371 yards, par 71.

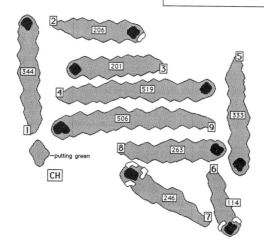

Useless Bay Golf & Country Club (private)

5725 South Country Club Drive; Langley, WA 98260; (360) 321-5958
Pro: Bill Davis, PGA. Supt.: Fred Vanbenschoten. 18 hole course, range.
Rating/Slope: C 70.4/125; M 69.2/122; W 71.0/126. **Course record:** 65.
Green fees: private club members & guests only; reciprocates.
Power cart: private club members only. **Pull cart:** private. **Trail fee:** private.
Reservation policy: private club members & guests of members only.
Winter condition: damp, course is open all year. **Terrain:** flat, some hills.
Tees: grass. **Temporary greens:** yes. **Services:** club rentals, lessons, snack bar,
lounge, restaurant, beer, wine, liquor, pro shop, putting green, club memberships.
Comments: there are many water hazards to contend with, along with a number
of holes defined by out-of-bounds. Greens are large in size and have some undula-
tions. Great private course that is set in a beautiful area of Washington State.

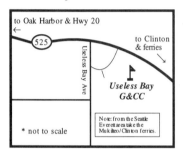

Directions: from the Mukilteo-Clinton
ferry take Hwy 525 for approximately 7
miles to Useless Bay Road. Turn left to
the golf course. Look for signs.

Course Yardage & Par:
C-6389 yards, par 72.
M-6134/6040 yards, par 72.
W-5493 yards, par 74.

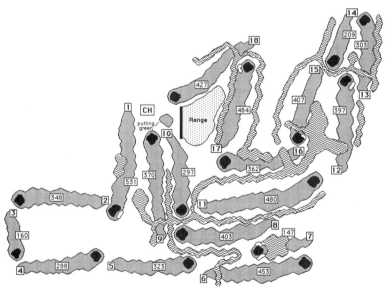

Valley View Golf Course (public)

Liberty Lake Road; PO Box 326; Liberty Lake, WA 99019; (509) 928-3484
Pro: Dennis Reger, PGA. 9 hole executive course, dual tees for 18 holes.
Rating/Slope: M 58/no slope; W 62/no slope. **Course record:** 26.
Green fees: $12/$8; Jr & Sr rates (weekdays); no credit cards.
Power cart: $15/$12. **Pull cart:** $2. **Trail fee:** no charge.
Reservation policy: not required. Times are on a first come first served basis.
Winter condition: the golf course is closed from December to March.
Terrain: flat. **Tees:** grass. **Temporary greens:** not in use at anytime.
Services: club rentals, lessons, restaurant, lounge, beer, wine, driving range.
Comments: Spokane's only executive course. The course is well maintained and easy to walk. Water comes into play on two holes. Two sets of tees.

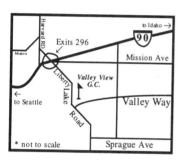

Directions: from I-90 eastbound and westbound take exit # 296 (Liberty Lake). The golf course is located two blocks to the south on Liberty Lake Road. Look for signs marking your way to the golf course.

Course Yardage & Par:
M-2072 yards, par 32.
W-2072 yards, par 32.
Dual tees for 18 holes:
M-4095 yards, par 62.
W-4095 yards, par 62.

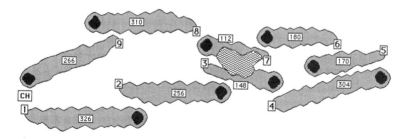

Vashon Island Golf & Country Club (private)
Box 370; 24615 75th Avenue SW; Vashon, WA 98070; (206) 463-2006
Pro: Steve Englund, PGA. 9 hole course, dual tees for 18 holes.
Rating/Slope: M 68.0/117; W 70.3/120. **Course record:** 63.
Green fees: private club members only; reciprocates. **Power cart:** private club.
Pull cart: private. **Trail fee:** private. **Reservation policy:** private club with
limited outside play. Call pro for verification. **Winter condition:** dry. **Terrain:**
very hilly. **Tees:** grass. **Temporary greens:** yes. **Services:** lessons, lounge,
restaurant, beer, wine, liquor, pro shop, putting green, club memberships.
Comments: dual tees available for a full 18 hole round. Few hazards to contend
with. The course is tree lined with bunkers guarding the greens. Excellent track.

Directions: from the West Seattle ferry
follow Vashon Island Hwy for 6.1 miles
to SW 204th. To east for 1 mile to George
Edwards Road. Turn south for 12 miles
to SW 228th. Turn east for .1 mile to
Portage-Dockton Road. Turn south and
proceed 1 mile to the golf course.

Course Yardage & Par:
M-3006 yards, par 35.
W-2618 yards, par 36.
Dual tees for 18 holes:
M-5890 yards, par 70.
W-5195 yards, par 72.

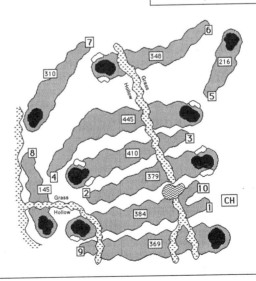

Veteran's Memorial Park Golf Course (public)
201 E Rees, Box 611; Walla Walla, WA 99362; (509) 527-4507
Pro: Pat Welch, PGA. 18 hole course, driving range.
Rating/Slope: C 70.7/115; M 69.2/111; W 69.5/111. **Course record:** 63.
Green fees: $16/$11.50 all week long; Jr & Sr rates; M/C, VISA.
Power cart: $22/$12. **Pull cart:** $3/$2. **Trail fee:** $5 (annual pass available).
Reservation policy: yes, please call Monday for the following weekend.
Winter condition: the golf course is open all year long weather permitting, dry.
Terrain: flat, some hills. **Tees:** grass. **Temporary greens:** not in use.
Services: club rentals, lessons, snack bar, lounge, beer, wine, liquor, pro shop,
lockers, putting green, driving range. **Comments:** consistently rated in Golf
Digest's top 100 public courses. Veteran's Memorial is well-kept with tree-lined
fairways and excellent greens. If you are looking for a great course in eastern
Washington try Veteran's Memorial you will not be disappointed.

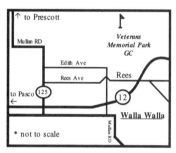

Directions: the golf course is located east
of the city of Walla Walla off of Hwy 12.
Take the Rees RD exit to the golf course.
Go westbound for 1 block and turn right
on Rees RD. Proceed and turn left to the
golf course. Look for signs at your turn.

Course Yardage & Par:
C-6650 yards, par 72.
M-6311 yards, par 72.
W-5963 yards, par 76.

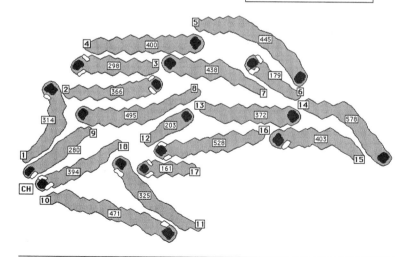

Vic Meyer's Golf Course (Sun Lakes, public)

34228 Park Lake RD NE; Box 141; Coulee City, WA 99115; (509) 632-5738
Pro: none. Superintendent: John Johanson. 9 hole course.
Rating/Slope: C 70.9/105; M 67.9/102; W 70.8/108. **Course record:** 69.
Green fees: W/D $13/$9; W/E $14/$10; VISA, M/C.
Power cart: $20/$10. **Pull cart:** $2. **Trail fee:** $5 for personal carts.
Reservation policy: yes, call ahead for a tee time. (especially in summer).
Winter condition: the golf course is closed from mid-October to mid-March.
Terrain: relatively hilly. **Tees:** grass. **Temporary greens:** not in use at anytime.
Services: club rentals, snack bar, pro shop, showers, putting green, RV parking.
Comments: the course is a part the the Sun Lakes recreation area. The golf course
is set atop the cliffs over looking Sun Lakes. Fairways are bordered by desert.

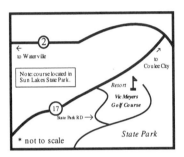

Directions: the golf course is located off
Hwy 17 north of Ephrata and Soap Lake
at the Sun Lakes State Park Resort. From
Hwy 17 turn at the park entrance and
follow signs to the golf course.

Course Yardage & Par:
C-3123 yards, par 35.
M-2897 yards, par 35.
W-2702 yards, par 35.

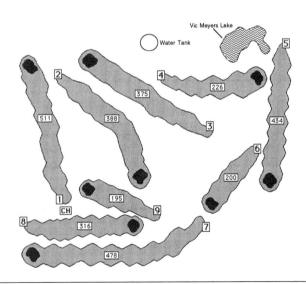

Village Greens Golf Course (public)

2298 Fircrest Drive SE; Port Orchard, WA 98366; (360) 871-1222
Pro: Doug Hathaway, PGA. 18 hole executive course.
Rating/Slope: M 55.7/87; W 58.4/90. **Course record:** 52.
Green fees: $10/$8 all week long; Jr & Sr rates and military rates.
Power cart: $15/$10. **Pull cart:** $2. **Trail fee:** no trail fee.
Reservation policy: yes, call ahead for a tee time. **Winter condition:** dry.
Terrain: flat, some hills. **Tees:** grass. **Temporary greens:** yes.
Services: club rentals, lessons, snack bar, pro shop, club memberships,
putting & chipping greens, driving range. **Comments:** narrow tree-lined fairways
and small greens make this short course very difficult. Varied terrain gives the
golfer a wide variety of lies. Worth a trip if you want a change of pace.

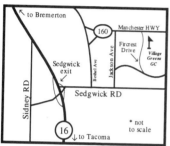

Directions: from I-5 N&S take the exit for
Hwy 16 W. Exit Hwy 16 at the 2nd Port
Ochard exit, (sign will read Tremont and
old Clifton RD). Stay on Tremont through
four stop lights and continue until you
reach a stop sign. Turn right and proceed
for 11/2 blocks and then turn left on
Fircrest. You should now see the course.

Course Yardage & Par:

M-3255 yards, par 58.
W-3255 yards, par 62.

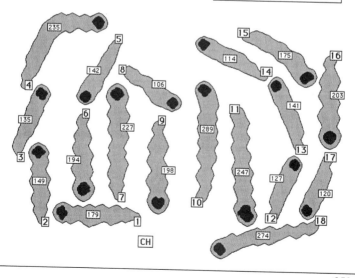

Walla Walla Country Club (private)

1390 Country Club Road; Box 2246; Walla Walla, WA 99362; (509) 525-1562
Pro: Steve Stull, PGA. 18 hole course, driving range.
Rating/Slope: M 70.8/125; W 71.9/125. **Course record:** 63.
Green fees: private club members only; reciprocates; no credit cards.
Power cart: private club. **Pull cart:** private club. **Trail fee:** private club.
Reservation policy: private club members only & guests only.
Winter condition: varies on the weather. **Terrain:** relatively hilly. **Tees:** grass.
Temporary greens: no. **Services:** club rentals, lessons, restaurant, lounge, beer, wine, liquor, pro shop, lockers, showers, driving range, putting & chipping greens.
Comments: The course features sand and grass bunkers, narrow tree-lined fairways, and water. This well kept private facility is one of the state's finest.

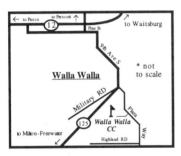

Directions: from Hwy 12 follow the Pendleton signs off of Hwy 12 to Plaza & 9th. Turn south on 9th to Country Club RD. Turn right and proceed to the course.

Course Yardage & Par:
M-6429 yards, par 72.
W-5809 yards, par 74.

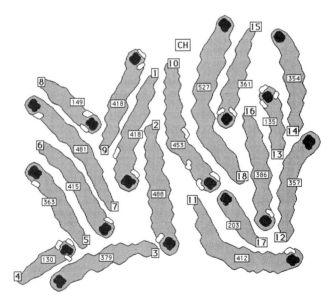

Walter E. Hall Memorial Golf Course (public)

1226 W Casino Road; Everett, WA 98204; (206) 353-4653
Pros: Bob Whisman, PGA, Bruce Weir, PGA. Supt: Barry Glade.
Rating/Slope: C 69.6/117; M 68.46115; W 71.6/115. **18 hole course.**
Green fees: Everett resident $12.50/$9.75; non-resident $17/$14.25; no C.C.
Power cart: $20/$10. **Pull cart:** $3. **Trail fee:** call for trail fee.
Reservation policy: call up to 1 week in advance. **Winter condition:** open, dry.
Terrain: flat. **Tees:** grass. **Temporary greens:** yes. **Services:** club rentals,
lessons, restaurant, beer, wine, pro shop, lockers, showers, club memberships.
Comments: the course is very busy during the summer. An easy walking
course. Walter E. Hall hosts a creek which winds through most of the back nine.

Directions: from I-5 N&S take exit
189 to Hwy 526 W. Turn west and
travel .6 miles to Evergreen Way. Turn
south. Proceed 1/10 of a mile to West
Casino Road. On W Casino Road turn
west and travel 1 mile to the golf course.

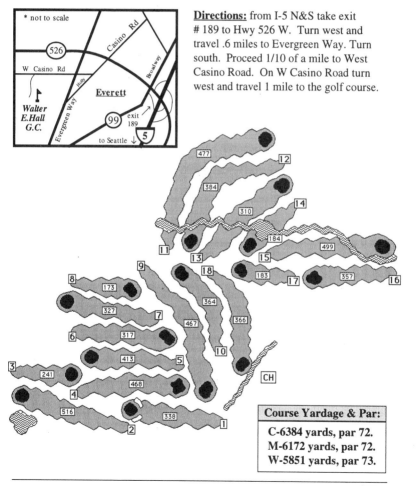

Course Yardage & Par:

C-6384 yards, par 72.
M-6172 yards, par 72.
W-5851 yards, par 73.

Wandermere Golf Course (public)

North 13700 Division Street; Spokane, WA 99208; (509) 466-8023
Pro: Bob Ross, PGA. 18 hole course, driving range.
Rating/Slope: M 68.6/119; W 72.2/126. **Course record:** 62.
Green fees: W/D $15/$11; W/E $16/$11; Jr. & Sr. rates (M-F); VISA, M/C.
Power cart: $20/$10. **Pull cart:** $3. **Trail fee:** $6.
Reservation policy: call 7 days in advance for W/E's, 1 day in advance for W/D's.
Winter condition: the golf course is closed from December to late February.
Terrain: flat, some hills. **Tees:** grass. **Temporary greens:** not in use at anytime.
Services: club rentals, lessons, restaurant, lounge, beer, wine, pro shop, driving
range, putting green. **Comments:** the course features rolling fairways in which a
creek comes into play on two holes. Greens are small, firm and hard to hold.

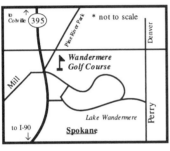

Directions: the golf course is located 10
miles north of Spokane off of Hwy 395.
Take the Division St exit off of I-90
eastbound and westbound. This will
turn into Hwy 395. Proceed on Hwy 395
northbound. The golf course will be located
on your right hand side when traveling
northbound on Hwy 395.

Course Yardage & Par:
M-6095 yards, par 70.
W-5760 yards, par 74.

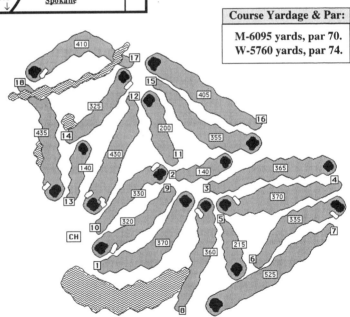

Washington Golf Club (private)

At Covington-Sawyer Road & 207th; Kent, WA 98032; (206) 286-8686
Pro: Kelly O'Meara, PGA. 18 hole course, driving range.
Rating/Slope: the golf course is not rated until opening. **Course record:** N/A.
Green fees: private club members and guests only; reciprocates,; M/C, VISA.
Power cart: members only. **Pull cart:** members only. **Trail fee:** not allowed.
Reservation policy: private club members only. **Winter condition:** open, dry.
Terrain: flat, some hills. **Tees:** all bentgrass. **Temporary greens:** not in use.
Services: lessons, lounge, liquor, lockers, showers, pro shop, driving range.
Comments: 7000 + yard tournament golf course. Fantastic layout, tentatively
scheduled to open in late summer of 1996. Greens will be large undulating and
fronted by either bunkers or water hazards. This course will be worth a the trip.

Directions: from I-405 N&S, exit at Maple
Valley (Hwy 169) to Four Corners. Take a
right on Kent Kangley (272nd). Proceed
for about 2 miles, then take a left at 216th.
Turn right on Covington -Sawyer RD, then
a left on 207th to the golf course.

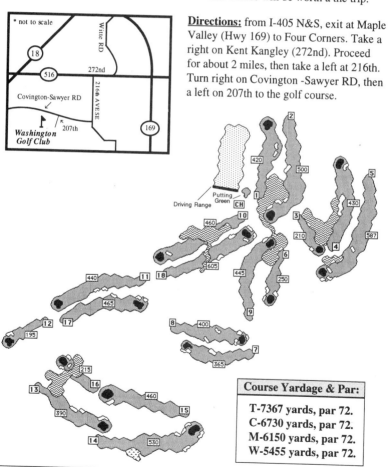

Course Yardage & Par:

T-7367 yards, par 72.
C-6730 yards, par 72.
M-6150 yards, par 72.
W-5455 yards, par 72.

Washington State University Golf Course (public)

North Fairway Drive; CUB 337; Pullman, WA 99163; (509) 335-4342
Pro: Christine L. Burkhart, PGA. **9 hole course, dual tees for 18 holes.**
Rating/Slope: M 65.4/110; W 69.8/119. **Course record:** 29.
Green fees: $8/$7.50 (student) all week long; VISA, M/C.
Power cart: $20/$12. **Pull cart:** $3/$2. **Trail fee:** $3.
Reservation policy: yes, you may call 14 days in advance for a tee time.
Winter condition: the golf course is closed from November to mid-March.
Terrain: relatively hilly. **Tees:** grass & mats. **Temporary greens:** not in use.
Services: club rentals, lessons, pro shop, driving range, putting & chipping greens.
Comments: this is a well-conditioned, scenic course located in the heart of the
Palouse on the campus of Washington State University. The terrian varies from
being flat on the first few holes then becoming very steep on the inward holes.

Directions: from Hwy 270, turn into
the main WSU campus entrance. Follow
Stadium Way to Fairway Drive. Turn
right on Fairway Drive to the golf course.
The golf course is located on the Washington State University campus. Look for
signs marking your way.

Course Yardage & Par:
M-2880 yards, par 36.
W-2623 yards, par 36.
Dual tees for 18 holes:
M-5785 yards, par 72.
W-5256 yards, par 72.

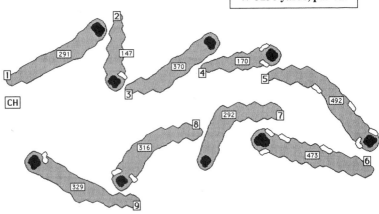

Wayne Golf Course (public)

16721 96th NE; Bothell, WA 98011; (206) 486-4714 or 485-6237
Pros: Dave Richards, PGA. Steve Richards. Superintendent: Richard Gettle.
Rating/Slope: M 60.6/97; W 64.5/105. **Course record: 57. 18 hole course.**
Green fees: W/D $15/$12; W/E $17/$13; Jr & Sr rates (Monday thru Friday).
Power cart: $18/$12. **Pull cart:** $2/$1.50. **Trail fee:** no charge (summer only).
Reservation policy: yes, call up to 1 week in advance for tee time reservations.
Winter condition: the course is open all year long, wet. **Terrain:** relatively hilly.
Tees: grass & mats. **Temporary greens:** not in use. **Services:** club rentals,
lessons, snack bar, beer, pro shop, club memberships, putting green, practice net.
Comments: the course is split by the Lake Washington-Sammimish Slough which
winds through the course. A unique layout sporting 8 par 3 holes. Greens are very
small and can be a challenge to any level of golfer. Course can get very busy.

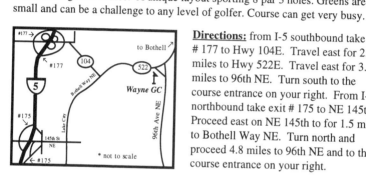

Directions: from I-5 southbound take exit # 177 to Hwy 104E. Travel east for 2.5 miles to Hwy 522E. Travel east for 3.1 miles to 96th NE. Turn south to the course entrance on your right. From I-5 northbound take exit # 175 to NE 145th. Proceed east on NE 145th to for 1.5 miles to Bothell Way NE. Turn north and proceed 4.8 miles to 96th NE and to the course entrance on your right.

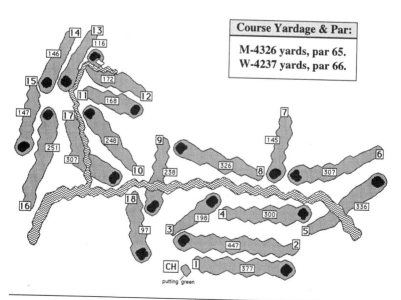

Course Yardage & Par:

M-4326 yards, par 65.
W-4237 yards, par 66.

Wellington Hills Golf Course (public)

7026 Wellington Heights Drive; Woodinville, WA 98072; (206) 485-5589
Managers: Mimi Racicot, Jan Japar. Supt.: Rick McDow. 9 hole course.
Rating/Slope: M 64.8/106; W 68.8/115. **Course record:** 30 for 9 holes.
Green fees: W/D $12/$9; W/E $14/$10; Sr rates (weekdays); M/C, VISA.
Power cart: $20/$10. **Pull cart:** $2. **Trail fee:** no charge.
Reservation policy: yes, weekends only, call up to 1 week in advance.
Winter condition: the golf course is open all year long, with damp conditions.
Terrain: relatively hilly. **Tees:** mats. **Temporary greens:** yes (during winter).
Services: club rentals, snack bar, restaurant, beer, wine, pro shop, putting green,
club memberships. **Comments:** course is under new management. While the long-
term range is uncertain, the "Golf Operations Co." and superintendent McDow
have planned many improvements over the next three years. The pro shop will be
expanded, featuring top of the line golf merchandise and apparel. At present time
the course plans to operate indefinitely. This track has rolling terrain, one pond and
tree-lined fairways. Look for Wellington Hills to be much improved over last year.

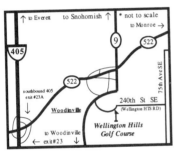

Directions: from I-405 N&S take exit
23 to Hwy 522 eastbound. Travel east
to Hwy 9S. Turn south. At Wellington
Heights Road turn east to the golf course.
Watch for signs to the golf course from
the exit from Hwy 522.

Course Yardage & Par:
M-2735 yards, par 34.
W-2735 yards, par 35.

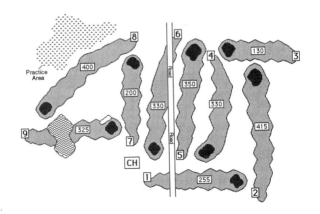

Wenatchee Golf & Country Club (private)

1600 Country Club Drive; East Wenatchee, WA 98802; (509) 884-7050
Pro: Patrick Welch, PGA. 18 hole course, driving range.
Rating/Slope: C 70.1/123; M 68.9/120; W 71.3/120. **Course record:** 62.
Green fees: private club members only; reciprocates; no credit cards.
Power cart: private club members only. **Pull cart:** private. **Trail fee:** private.
Reservation policy: private club members & guests of members only.
Winter condition: open, in good weather. **Terrain:** relatively hilly. **Tees:** grass.
Temporary greens: not in use. **Services:** club rentals, lessons, lounge, restaurant,
beer, wine, showers, grass driving range, locker room, putting & chipping greens.
Comments: narrow fairways and quick greens characterize this course. Greens
are well fronted by bunkers. Great private golf course that is a challenge to all.

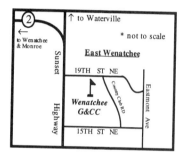

Directions: from Hwy 2, after crossing
the Columbia River traveling toward East
Wenatchee, turn right at the Sunset Hwy
to 19th Street. Turn left. Follow to
Country Club Drive and the golf course.

Course Yardage & Par:
C-6347 yards, par 72.
M-6086 yards, par 72.
W-5515 yards, par 73.

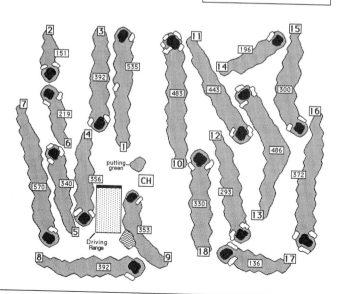

West Richland Municipal Golf Course (public)

4000 Fallon Drive (PO Box 41); West Richland, WA 99352; (509) 967-2165
Pro: Rod Marcum, PGA. 18 hole course, driving range.
Rating/Slope: M 67.7/114; W 70.3/114. **Course record:** 61.
Green fees: $9.75/$8; Jr & Sr rates (weekdays only); VISA, M/C.
Power cart: $20/$10. **Pull cart:** $2/1.50. **Trail fee:** $5.
Reservation policy: call ahead 7 days for a tee time. **Winter condition:** dry.
Terrain: very flat. **Tees:** grass & mats. **Temporary greens:** not in use.
Services: club rentals, lessons, restaurant, pro shop, putting green, driving range.
Comments: this is a good course to walk due to its flat terrain. The Yakima
River borders the course and comes into play on numerous holes.

Directions: from I-82 take the West
Richland exit #96 and enter town. Turn left
on Fallon Road (by the Yakima River)
to the golf course. Look for signs.

> **Course Yardage & Par:**
>
> **M-6103 yards, par 70.**
> **W-5516 yards, par 71.**

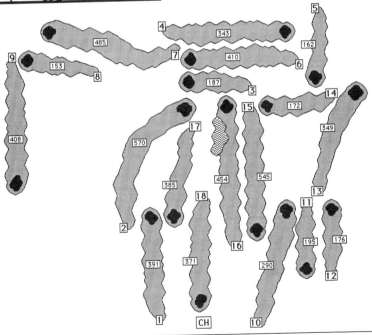

West Seattle Golf Course (public)

4470 35th SW; Seattle, WA 98126; (206) 935-5187; Tee-Times 301-0472
Pro: Matt Amundsen. Supt.: Vern Rollin. 18 hole course.
Rating/Slope: C 70.8/118; M 69.2/116; W 72.1/120. **Course record:** M 63; W 69.
Green fees: $15* all week long (*subject to chnage); M/C, VISA.
Power cart: $18/$13*. **Pull cart:** $3*. **Trail fee:** $4* for personal carts.
Reservation policy: yes, call up to 1 week in advance for your tee times.
Winter condition: the golf course is open all year long, damp.
Terrain: relatively hilly. **Tees:** all grass. **Temporary greens:** yes (at times).
Services: club rentals, lessons, snack bar, lounge, restaurant, beer, wine, liquor,
beverages, pro shop, lockers, putting & chipping green, club memberships.
Comments: the course sports a terrific view of the Seattle skyline. Fairways are
tree-lined with a creek meandering throughout. Greens are large with bunkers
guarding the front. Good track that can get very busy during the peak season.

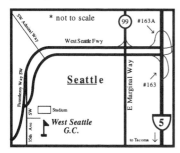

Directions: from I-5 N&S take exit # 163
to the West Seattle Freeway. Travel west
for 2.5 miles to Fauntleroy Way. At 35th
SW (the first light), turn left to the golf
course. The golf course is next to the West
Seattle Stadium. Look for a sign marking
your turn to the golf course.

Course Yardage & Par:
C-6635 yards, par 72.
M-6221 yards, par 72.
W-5685 yards, par 72.

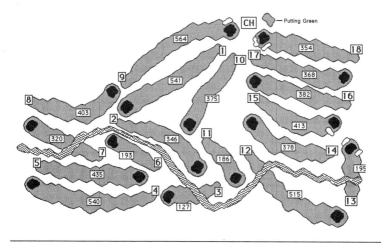

Westwood West Golf Course (public)

6408 Tieton Drive; Yakima, WA 98908; (509) 966-0890
Pro: N/A. 9 hole course, dual tees for 18 holes.
Rating/Slope: M 64.3/104; W 69.1/110. **Course record:** 29.
Green fees: $18/$11.50; monthly Senior rates; no credit cards.
Power cart: $20/$10. **Pull cart:** $2. **Trail fee:** no charge.
Reservation policy: call 7 days in advance for a tee time reservations.
Winter condition: the golf course is closed from mid-November to mid-February.
Terrain: flat, some slight hills. **Tees:** grass. **Temporary greens:** occasionally.
Services: club rentals, lessons, pro shop, putting green, covered driving range.
Comments: course is built in a unique setting, within an old apple orchard. The course offers rolling terrain and small greens to challenge your play. For those wanting to practice the course features a covered driving range with grass tees.

Tieton Dr

Directions: from I-82 take the exit at Nob Hill Road #34. Travel west to S 64th Avenue. Turn right and follow to Tieton Drive and the golf course. From Hwy 12 exit onto 40th Avenue S for 2.3 miles. Proceed to Tieton Drive and turn right to the golf course. Look for signs.

Course Yardage & Par:
M-2691 yards, par 35.
W-2607yards, par 36.
Dual tees for 18 holes:
M-5378 yards, par 70.
W-5252 yards, par 72.

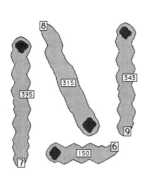

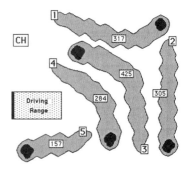

Whidbey Golf & Country Club (private)

1411 W Fairway Lane; Oak Harbor, WA 98277; (360) 675-4546
Pro: Chuck West, PGA. Supt.: Henry Goodwin. 18 hole course, range.
Rating/Slope: C 71.1/125; M 69.6/123; W 71.2/125. **Course record:** 63.
Green fees: private club members and guests only; reciprocates.
Power cart: private club, members only. **Pull cart:** $2.50. **Trail fee:** $5.
Reservation policy: yes, call up to 7 days in advance for tee time reservations.
Winter condition: course is open all year long, dry. **Terrain:** flat, some hills.
Tees: grass. **Temporary greens:** not in use at anytime. **Services:** lessons, snack
bar, restaurant, driving range, putting & chipping greens. **Comments:** the course
has excellent greens all year long. A very demanding layout with numerous sand
traps and ponds to contend with. Good private golf course that is a challenge.

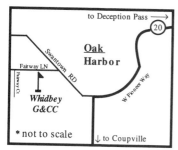

Directions: from I-5 N&S take exit 230
to Highway 20 West. Travel through Oak
Harbor. Turn right at Swan Town Road to
the golf course. Look for a sign at the turn.

Course Yardage & Par:
C-6392 yards, par 72.
M-6059 yards, par 72.
W-5342 yards, par 72.

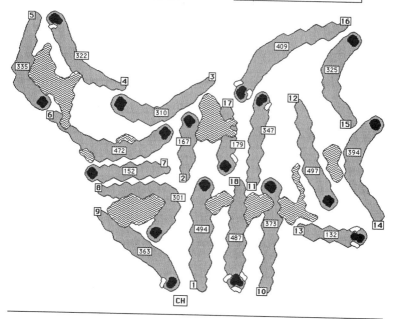

Whispering Firs Golf Club (private)
NAFFMB Box Drawer C; McChord AFB 98438; (206) 984-2053
Manager: James Tompkins. Supt.: Terry Beck. 18 hole course, range.
Rating/Slope: C 71.0/123; M 70.2/121; W 73.3/122. **Course record:** 62.
Green fees: private military club; All military ID holders, call for rates.
Power cart: private club military only. **Pull cart:** military only. **Trail fee:** N/A.
Reservation policy: no time limit. **Winter condition:** course is open all year, dry.
Terrain: flat, some hills. **Tees:** grass. **Temporary greens:** yes (a certain times).
Services: club rentals, lessons, snack bar, pop, beer, wine, pro shop, lockers,
showers, club memberships, covered driving range, putting & chipping greens.
Comments: the course is well-kept all year long. Narrow tree-lined fairways and
numerous sand traps make this a very difficult course. Great military golf course.

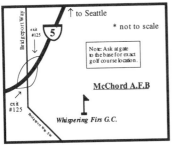

Directions: from I-5 southbound take
the exit at Lake McChord. Turn left at
Bridgeport and travel straight to the AFB
where the golf course is located. You
will take exit #125 and head toward the
main gate. Ask at the Main gate for exact
directions to the golf course once you are
inside the base.

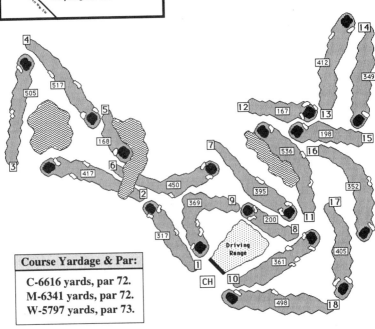

Course Yardage & Par:

C-6616 yards, par 72.
M-6341 yards, par 72.
W-5797 yards, par 73.

Willapa Harbor Golf Course (public)
Route 3; Box 441; Fowler Street; Raymond, WA 98577; (360) 942-2392
Pro: Louis Runge, PGA. 9 hole course.
Rating/Slope: M 68.8/119; W 72.7/123. **Course record:** 64.
Green fees: $16/$10 (7 days a week); M/C, VISA.
Power cart: $20/$12. **Pull cart:** $2.50/$1.50. **Trail fee:** $10/$7.
Reservation policy: call 7 days in advance for tee times during the summer.
Winter condition: the course is open all year long. Good playing conditions.
Terrain: flat, some hills. **Tees:** grass. **Temporary greens:** not in use at anytime.
Services: club rentals, lessons, snack bar, coffee shop, beer, club memberships, pro shop, driving range, putting green, chipping area. **Comments:** this golf course plays rather difficult with tree-lined, narrow fairways. There are also pot bunkers to contend with. RV hook-ups on site. Good course that is very easy to walk.

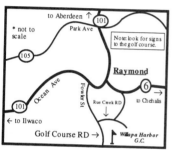

Directions: from I-5 N&S take exit #104 to Hwy 101. Follow 101 to Raymond. Turn west on Fowler Road and travel 1 mile to the golf course. Look for signs indicating your turn to the golf course.

Course Yardage & Par:
M-3004 yards, par 36.
W-2878 yards, par 36.

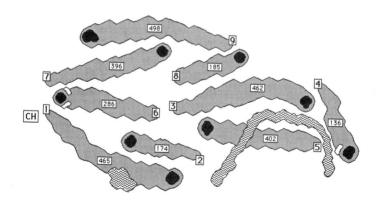

Willows Run Golf Club (public)

10442 Willows Road NE; Redmond, WA 98052; (206) 883-1200 or for western Washington 1-800 833-4787. **18 hole course, covered driving range.**
Pro: Travis Cox, PGA. Superintendent: Ben Nelson.
Rating/Slope: C 71.6/119; M 68.5/113; W 71.1/116. **Course record:** 66.
Green fees: Monday to Thursday $29/$16; Friday to Sunday $39/$22.
Power cart: $22/$11. **Pull cart:** $4. **Trail fee:** personal carts are not allowed.
Reservation policy: 2 weeks in advance in summer. 1 week in advance in winter.
Winter condition: dry, course open weather permitting. **Terrain:** flat, some hills.
Tees: grass. **Temporary greens:** not in use. **Services:** club rentals, lessons, beer, lounge, restaurant, snack bar, beer, pop, wine, pro shop, covered driving range.
Comments: This excellent newer facility has a metropolitan location and is fast becoming one of the finest new courses in the entire Northwest. Great golf course.

Directions: from I-405 N&S take the 124th St. exit (Totem Lake). Travel eastbound on 124th Street for 1.4 miles to Willows Road NE. Turn right on Willows Road NE. Proceed on Willows Road NE for 1 mile to the golf course which will be on your left hand side.

Course Yardage & Par:

C-6851 yards, par 72.
M-6229 yards, par 72.
W-5633 yards, par 72.

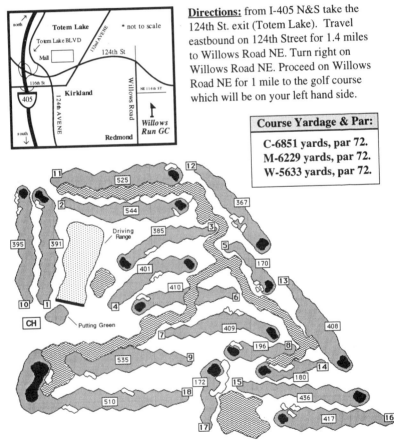

Wing Point Golf & Country Club (private)

811 Cherry Ave.; Box 10460; Bainbridge Island, WA 98110; (206) 842-7933
Pro: Jim Swagerty Jr., PGA. Supt.: Bill Schilling. 18 hole course.
Rating/Slope: C 67.7/124; M 66.9/122; W 70.8/122. **Course record:** 63.
Green fees: private club, members & guests of members only; reciprocates.
Power cart: private club members only. **Pull cart:** private. **Trail fee:** private.
Reservation policy: private club, members & guests of members only.
Winter condition: the golf course is open all year weather permitting, damp.
Terrain: flat, some hills. **Tees:** grass. **Temporary greens:** not in use.
Services: club rentals, lessons, lounge restaurant, beer, wine, liquor, pro shop,
lockers, putting & chipping greens, practice area, club memberships available.
Comments: the back 9 is fairly open with numerous traps. Front 9 winds through
tree lined fairways. The layout is designed to be challenging, target style golf.

Directions: from the Seattle-Winslow ferry terminal travel north for .2 miles to Winslow Way. Turn right and proceed .5 miles to Ferncliff. Turn left. Continue .3 miles to Wing Point Way. Turn right and travel another .5 miles to Cherry NE. Turn left on Cherry NE to the golf course clubhouse which will be on your left.

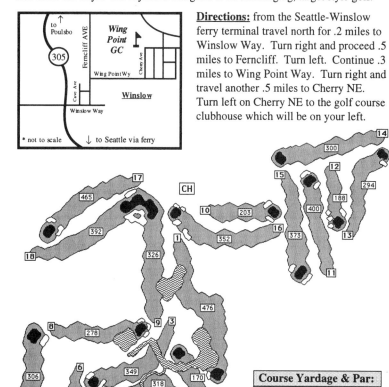

Course Yardage & Par:

C-5625 yards, par 70.
M-5473 yards, par 70.
W-5153 yards, par 71.

Yakima Country Club (private)

500 Country Club Drive; Yakima, WA 98901; (509) 452-2266
Pro: Jim Gilbert, PGA. 18 hole course. Rating/Slope: M 69.4/120; W 72.6/126.
Course record: 67. **Green fees:** private club members only; no credit cards.
Power cart: private club. **Pull cart:** private club. **Trail fee:** not allowed.
Reservation policy: private club, members & guests of members only.
Winter condition: open, weather permitting. **Terrain:** flat, some hills.
Tees: grass. **Temporary greens:** no. **Services:** lessons, restaurant, lounge, beer,
wine, liquor, showers, driving range. **Comments:** nicely treed well kept private
course. Back nine plays very tight places making it tough to score on. Good course.

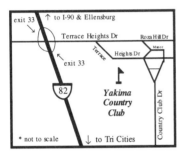

Directions: from I-82 take exit # 33 and
travel eastbound. Turn north on Terrace
Heights Drive to Country Club DR. Turn
right on Country Club Drive. Proceed on
Country Club DR to the golf course which
will be located on your right hand side.

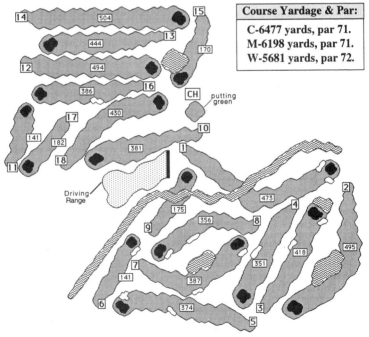

Course Yardage & Par:

C-6477 yards, par 71.
M-6198 yards, par 71.
W-5681 yards, par 72.

Yakima Elks Golf & Country Club (private)

Golf Course Road; Selah, WA 98942; (509) 697-7177
Pro: Stuart Kitzmiller, PGA . 18 hole course, driving range.
Rating/Slope: C 71.1/121; M 68.6/113; W 74.2/126. **Course record:** 64.
Green fees: private club, members & guests only; reciprocates.
Power cart: private club. **Pull cart:** private club. **Trail fee:** private club.
Reservation policy: private club members & guests of members only.
Winter condition: the golf course is open all year, weather permitting.
Terrain: flat. **Tees:** grass. **Temporary greens:** not in use at anytime.
Services: club rentals, lessons, restaurant, lounge, beer, wine, liquor, lockers,
showers, driving range. **Comments:** this is a well conditioned, easy walking
course with tree lined fairways and a number of water hazards to contend with.

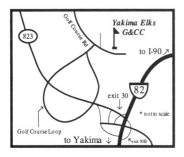

Directions: from I-82 take the Selah exit
(#30A) proceed eastbound to Golf Course
Loop (the first right). Turn right and
follow this to the golf course.

Course Yardage & Par:
C-6586 yards, par 71.
M-6057 yards, par 71.
W-6057 yards, par 74.

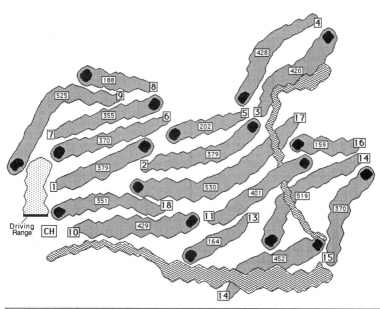

Ashford Driving Range
29716 SR 706 E.; Ashford, WA 98304
(360) phone # N/A; Pro: Rich Mulholland.
Hours: 10am-7pm, Summer until dusk.
Lights: no. **Covered:** no.
Putting & chipping: no.
Services: store, RV Park 23 hook ups, propane.
Directions: The range is located in Ashford
on SR 706E on the north side of the Hwy.
<u>Map 2; Grid E3</u>

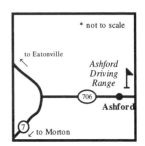

Batstone Hill Practice Golf
321 Mason Lake Road; Shelton, WA 98584
(360) 426-4276. Pro: Jeff Jackson, PGA.
Hours: 10 am to dusk. **Lights:** no. **Covered:** yes.
Putting & chipping: putting only.
Services: lessons, vending machines.
Directions: 5 miles north of Shelton on Hwy 3
to Mason Lake Road. The range is located .25
miles up Mason Lake Road on the left.
<u>Map 1; Grid D4</u>

Beacon Hill Golf Center
4848 Valley Spring Road; Spokane, WA 99207
(509) 482-0622 (not in winter). **Pro:** N/A.
Hours: N/A. **Lights:** N/A. **Covered:** N/A.
Putting & chipping: not available.
Services: lessons, small pro shop.
Directions: from I-90 E&W take the Freya/Thor
exit. Go north for 3 miles to Euclid Avenue. Go
right for 3 blocks to Freya. Turn left to the range.
<u>Map 4; Grid C3</u>

Birdies Golf Place *New Range*
1111 E Westview Court; Spokane, WA 99218
(509) 468-5000. Pro: Clint Wallman, PGA.
Hours: summer 9am-10pm; winter 10am-5pm.
Lights: yes. **Covered:** yes & 22 stalls heated.
Putting & chipping: yes. **Services:** video lessons,
swing analysis, track trainer, club repair, pro shop.
Directions: from Hwy 395 (Division) north turn
right on Francis, then turn left on Nevada. The
range is located @ 9500 block. **Map 4; Grid C3**

Cooper's Golf Range
1899 S Burlington Blvd.; Burlington, WA 98233
(360) 757-1854. Pro: Ken Harrsch, PGA.
Pro: Mark Flitton.
Hours: 9am to dusk; extended summer hrs.
Lights: no. **Covered:** yes. **Putting &chipping:** no.
Services: pro shop, basic club repair, lessons.
Directions: I-5S take exit 229 to stop sign.
Turn right, the range is located 100 yards ahead.
Map 2; Grid B2

Crystal Springs Golf Center
405 Ohme Gardens RD; Wenatchee, WA 98801
(509) 663-6300. Pro: Greg Knight.
Hours: varies. **Lights:** yes. **Covered:** yes.
Comments: 18 hole putting course ready in 1996.
Services: lessons, range will offer a full range
of services. **Directions:** from Hwy 2 exit to
Ohme Gardens Road. Proceed to the driving range.
You can see the driving range from the Hwy.
Map 3; Grid D1

Eagle View Golf Center
8000 72nd Lane SE; Olympia, WA 98513
(360) 493-1000. Master Golf Pro: Joe Thiel, PGA
Hours: hours vary depending on the season.
Lights: yes. **Putting & chipping:** yes, 3 hole course.
Services: golf camps, lessons, pro shop, snack bar,
indoor facility, 3 hole course. **Directions:** from I-5
N&S exit at College St. exit. Proceed for 3.4 miles
on College Street to the Yelm Hwy. Turn left. Go
to Spurgeon Crk RD turn right. **Map 1; Grid E4**

Evergreen Golf Center
16703 SE 1st; Vancouver, WA 98684
(360) 253-3184. Manager: Garret Koster.
Hours: Monday-Sunday 9am-9pm. **Lights:** yes.
Covered: yes. **Putting & chipping:** yes, grass
tees. **Services:** lessons, club repair, custom clubs,
full service pro shop. **Directions:** From I-205 take
the Mill Plain E exit to 164th. Turn north on 164th
proceed to the stoplight which is 1st. Turn right on
1st to range. **Map 1; Grid G4**

Fore-Ten Driving Range
22719 SR 410; Buckley, WA 98321
(206) 862-8496 Pro: N/A
Hours: N/A. **Lights:** N/A.
Covered: N/A.
Putting & chipping: N/A.
Services: N/A
Directions: range is located right off Hwy
410 in Buckley.
Map 2; Grid E2

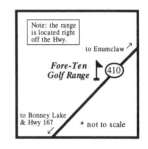

Gateway Driving Range
Hwy 12 on Port Drive; Clarkston, WA 99403
(509) # not listed. Pro: N/A.
Hours: to be determined. **Lights:** yes.
Covered: yes. **Putting & Chipping:** no.
Services: to be determined. **Comments:** the
range is due to be open in the summer of 1996.
Directions: the range is located next to the
Quality Inn on Port Drive, just off Hwy 12.
Map 4; Grid F4

Gold Creek Tennis & Sports Club
15327 140th PL NE; Woodinville, WA 98072
(206) 487-1090. Pro: Juanita Reinhardt.
Hours: M-F 6 am - 10 pm, Sat-Sun 8am - 9pm.
Lights: yes. **Covered:** yes.
Putting & chipping: yes. **Services:** lessons.
Directions: the range is located off of Hwy 202
in Woodinville. Look for the signs to the tennis &
sports club.
Map 2; Grid D2

Golf Park
9116 212th Street; Kent, WA 98032
(206) 850-8300. Pro: Jim Hill, PGA.
Hours: 7am to 9pm daily. **Lights:** yes.
Covered: yes. **Putting & Chipping:** putting.
Services: full service pro shop, lessons, video
teaching, deli, heated tee line. Managed by Golf
Resources, INC. **Directions:** the range is located
at the intersections of Hwy 176 & 212th.
Off of Hwy 167, exit at 212th. **Map 2; Grid D2**

Grand Mound Driving Range
20525 Old Highway 9; Centralia, WA 98531
(360) 273-9335. Pro: Denny Densmore.
Hours: 8am to dusk, 7 days a week.
Lights: no. **Covered:** yes. **Putting & chipping:** yes.
Services: custom clubs, used clubs, practice bunker.
Directions: from I-5 N&S take exit #88 (Hwy 12).
Procced west for 1 block to Old Hwy 99 and turn
south. Procced to Old Hwy 9 and turn left to range.
Map 1; Grid F4

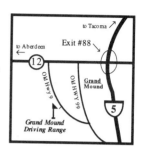

H&H Driving Range
11405 NE 72nd Avenue; Vancouver, WA 98661
(360) 573-3315. Pro: Jeff McRae.
Hours: 9am to 9pm daily. **Lights:** yes.
Covered: yes. **Putting & chipping:** yes.
Services: lessons, simulated golf course with
water hazards, sand traps and grass tees.
Directions: from I-5 take exit #4 and proceed
east on NE 78th to NE Andresen RD. Turn left on
Andresen and proceed to range. **Map 1; Grid G4**

Iron Eagle Sports Center
16651 Currie Road; Monroe, WA 98272
(360) 794-0933. Pro: Chris Aoki, PGA.
Hours: 10am-10pm Mon.-Fri.; 8am-10pm Sat.;
9am-8pm Sun. **Lights:** yes. **Covered:** yes.
Putting & chipping: putting only.
Services: pro shop, lessons, heated stalls.
Directions: From Hwy 522 take the 164th St. exit.
Left off exit (under highway). Take first right on
Curry Road to the range. **Map 2; Grid C2**

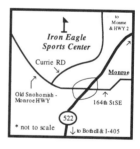

Kaddyshack Golf Center Driving Range
4003 204th SW; Lynnwood, WA 98036
(206) 775-8911. Pro: Pete Dixon, PGA.
Hours: 7:30am to Midnite, 7 days a week.
Lights: yes. **Covered:** yes, heated tee-line.
Putting/chipping: yes and practice sand trap.
Services: club repair, lessons, discount pro shop.
Directions: I-5 N take 44th St. (Lynnwood) exit.
Straight through light at the bottom of hill and
follow for .5 miles to range. **Map 2; Grid C2**

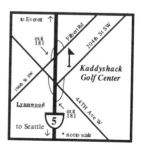

Linksman Golf Center (The)
708 122th Street E; Tacoma, WA 98445
(206) 537-3037. Pro: Graham Dornan, PGA.
Hours: hours vary, please call. Range has
extended summer hours. **Lights:** yes.
Covered: yes, heated, raised target greens.
Services: club repair, lessons, video lessons,
pro shop. **Directions:** from Hwy 512 take Pacific
Avenue exit.Turn left on 112th St. The range will
be located 1/2 mile on the right.   **Map 2; Grid E1**

Longest Drive (The)
6311 W Clearwater Ave.; Kennewick, WA 99336
(509) 735-6072. Pros: 3 to serve you.
Hours: 10am-10pm; 11pm-8pm winter.
Lights: yes. **Covered:** yes and heated.
Services: lessons, pro shop, snack bar, miniature
golf, club repair. **Directions:** from Hwy 395 turn
right on Clearwater Avenue. The range is located
up Clearwater Avenue 2.5 miles on the left hand
side of the street.   **Map 3; Grid G3**

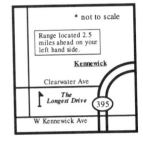

Longshots Driving Range
1215 80th Street SW; Everett, WA 98203
(206) 355-2133. Pro: Bob Osgood, PGA.
Hours: summer 8am-9pm; winter 9am-8pm.
Lights: yes. **Covered:** yes.
Putting & chipping: yes. **Services:** restaurant,
beer, wine, discount pro shop. **Directions:** From
Hwy 99 go west on Casino RD to 5th Ave. North
on 5th. Take first left on 80th. The range is 4
blocks up on the right hand side. **Map 2; Grid C2**

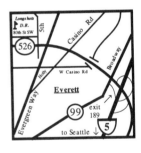

Marysville Golf Center
7431 64th Drive NE; Marysville, WA 98270
(360) 653-2000. Pro: Gary Niklason.
Hours: 8am-10pm, summer 9am-9pm winter.
Lights: yes. **Covered:** yes. **Putting &**
chipping: yes. **Services:** club repair, lessons, pro
shop. **Directions:** From I-5 N&S take exit #199,
go east on 4th St .3 miles to State Ave. Left on
State for .8 miles to Grove St. Right. Follow 1.9
mi to 64th Ave. SE. Right. **Map 2; Grid C2**

North West Golf Range
368 NE Bucklin Hill Rd; Bremerton, WA 98310
(360) 692-6828. Pro: John Chafin.
Hours: Monday-Sunday 9 am-10 pm.
Lights: yes. **Covered:** yes.
Putting & chipping: putting only.
Services: lessons, club repair, club fitting,
pro shop. **Directions:** range is located between
Bremerton and Silverdale just off Wagga Way.
Take the Schold Road exit. **Map 2; Grid D1**

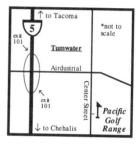

Pacific Golf Range
8080 Center Street SW; Tumwater, WA 98502
(360) 786-8626. Pro: N/A.
Hours: 9am-10pm, summer may vary. **Lights:** yes.
Covered: yes. **Putting & chipping:** yes, bunker.
Services: club repair, custom clubs, pro shop,
lessons, heated stalls. **Directions:** from I-5 N&S
take exit #101(Airdustrial). Proceed eastbound to
the first stoplight. Right on Center St. Proceed for
1/2 mile, the range is on the left. **Map 1; Grid E4**

Pasco Golfland
2901 Road 40; Pasco, WA 99301
(509) 544-9291. Pro: Jeff Hendler, PGA.
Hours: hours vary depending on the season.
Lights: yes. **Covered:** yes. **Putting & chipping:** yes.
Services: club repair, lessons, pro shop, facility is
planning a par 3 course. **Directions:** from I-182 take
the 20th Ave. exit.. Proceed north to Agren. Left on
Agren to Road 40. Range is located on your right
hand side. Look for signs. **Map 1; Grid E4**

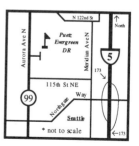

Puetz Evergreen Golf Range
11762 Aurora N; Seattle, WA 98133
(206) 362-2272. Pro: 6 pro's to serve you.
Hours: Mon.-Sat. 9 - 9; Sun. 9 - 8; summer hours.
Lights: yes. **Covered:** yes. **Putting & chipping:**
yes. **Services:** club repair, lessons, video lessons,
pro shop. **Directions:** From I-5 N&S take exit 173
to NE Northgate Way W. West for .7 mi to Aurora
Ave. (Hwy 99). Turn right on Aurora Ave. N for 1
mile to the range on the right. **Map 2; Grid D2**

Rainbow Golf Driving Range
2723 Harrison Avenue; Centralia, WA 98531
(360) 330-0585. Pro: N/A.
Hours: Monday thru Sunday 12pm-8pm; check
for summer hours. **Lights:** yes. **Covered:** yes.
Putting & chipping: yes. **Services:** pro shop,
lessons. **Directions:** from I-5 N&S take exit #82
to Harrison Avenue. Proceed westbound on
Harrison for approximately 2 miles. The range is
located on your left. **Map 1; Grid F4**

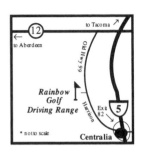

Red Wood Golf Center
13029 Red-Wdnl Road NE; Redmond, WA 98052
(206) 869-8814. Head Pro: Scott Williams, PGA.
6 PGA pro's to serve you. Hours: W/D 9am-10pm;
W/E 8am-10pm. **Lights:** yes. **Covered:** yes & heated.
Putting & chipping: yes. **Services:** complete service
pro shop, private, group, video and Jr. lessons, custom
clubs, club repair. **Directions:** from I-405 N&S take
exit 20B (NE 124th St). Follow 124th east 3 miles
to Hwy 202, turn left to the range. **Map 2; Grid D2**

Rodarco Golf Range
8020 Kickerville Road; Blaine, WA 98230
(360) 332-2665. Pro: Roger D. Cook, PGA.
Hours: summer 7-9 daily. **Tees:** 30 grass tees.
Lights: no. **Covered:** 3 stalls with mats.
Putting & Chipping: yes, practice bunker.
Services: club repair, lessons, pro shop, snack bar.
Directions: From I-5 N&S take exit #270 to Birch
Bay-Lynden RD. West for 2 miles to Kickerville
RD, Turn south to range.   **Map 2; Grid A1**

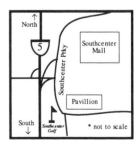

South Center Golf *New Range*
18791 Southcenter Pkwy; Tukwila, WA 98188
(206) 575-7797. Pro: Jim Bennett.
Hours: Mon.-Fri. 8 am-8 pm; W/E's 7am-8pm.
Lights: yes. **Covered:** yes.
Putting/chipping: N/A. **Services:** club repair,
lessons, pro shop, video studio, custom clubs.
Directions: proceed straight on Southcenter Pkwy
beyond the Pavillion thru the intersection to the
range located 2 blocks ahead. **Map 2; Grid C2**

Steamboat Golf *New Range*

3605 Steamboat Is. Road; Olympia, WA 98502
(360) 866-4653. Pro: Scott Geroux.
Hours: 7am to 12 midnite, 7 days a week.
Lights: yes. **Covered:** yes, grass tees.
Putting/chipping: yes. **Services:** lessons,
pro shop, competitions, tourneys, ladies night.
Directions: from Hwy 101 exit for Steamboat
Island Road. The range is located 1/4 mile east on
the left, btwn. Shelton & Olympia. **Map 2; Grid C2**

Super Range

511 128th SE; Everett, WA 98208
1-800-478-4887, (206) 742-5790, (206) 338-2424
Pro: Kevin Mackay, PGA. Mgr.: Bob Rielly.
Hours: 7 am-11 pm; extened summer hours.
Lights: yes. **Covered:** 50 stalls (heated).
Putting/chipping: 18 hole par 2 scramble course.
Services: club repair, lessons, pro shop, snack bar.
Directions: I-5 N&S take exit 186. Go east for .5
miles to the range on your left. **Map 2; Grid C2**

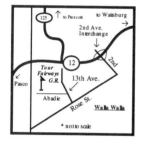

Tour Fairways Golf Range

1150 Abadie, Walla Walla, WA 99362
(509) 529-5810. Pro: Jim Henderson.
Hours: 8am-10pm daily. **Covered:** 12 covered,
grass tees. **Putting & chipping:** yes. **Lights:** yes.
Services: full service pro shop, lessons, custom
clubs, club repair, automated batting cage.
Directions: from Hwy 12 exit at 2nd Ave. South to
Rose St. Turn right on Rose. Go to 13th. Right on
13th. Left on Abadie to range. **Map 4; Grid D1**

University of Washington Driving Range

1/2 mi north of stadium; Seattle, WA 98195
(206) 543-8759. Pro: John Krebs, PGA.
Hours: 10am-8pm (winter) 9am-10pm (summer).
Lights: yes. **Covered:** yes.
Putting & chipping: yes. **Services:** lessons.
Directions: I-5 N&S take exit 169 to NE 45th.
Go east for 1.8 miles to Union Bay Pl NE. E for
.1 mile to Clark Road. West to range. The range is
located right off Montlake Blvd. **Map 2; Grid D2**

Vanco Golf Range
703 N Devine; Vancouver, WA 98661
(360) 693-8811 or (503) 253-0902.
Pros: Scott Blake, PGA. Chuck Milne, PGA.
Hours: 9am-11pm (summer). 9am-9pm(winter).
Lights: yes. **Covered:** yes. **Putting/chipping:** yes.
Services: club repair, lessons, pro shop, miniature
golf. **Directions:** From I-5 N&S take exit 1C to
Mill Plain Road E for 4.1 miles to Devine RD.
Range is on your left.   **Map 1; Grid G4**

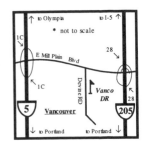

Woodalls World Driving Range
8400 NE W Kingston Road; Kingston, WA 98436
(360) 297-4653. Pro: Ted Wurtz, PGA.
Hours: 8am-10pm summer; 9am-7pm winter.
Lights: yes. **Covered:** yes. **Services:** lessons,
custom clubs, retail pro shop. **Directions:** from
Kingston turn left at Country Corners (Millers Bay
Suquamish RD). Proceed for 1 mile to the first left
(West Kingston RD) turn left. Range 1/4 mile on
your left . Look for signs.   **Map 2; Grid C1**

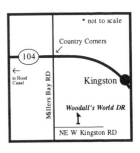

Aberdeen Golf Repair
2950 McLeod Road; Bellingham, Wa. (360) 647-0351
Services: club repair, custom clubs, club refinishing

Action Golf
1066 Lakeway Drive; Bellingham, Wa. (360) 676-5766
Services: lessons

Alexander's Discount Golf
7261 West Belfair Valley Road; Gorst, Wa. (360) 674-2363
Services: club repair, custom clubs, club refinishing

Bogey's Golf
2019 Hewitt Avenue; Everett, Wa. (206) 258-5300
Services: club repair, club refinishing

Caddy Shack Golf Shop
2614 A West Nob Hill Boulevard; Yakima, Wa. (509) 575-6461
Services: club repair, indoor driving range, sport tech swing analyzer, lessons

Cascade Athletic Academy
9805 NE 116th; Kirkland, Wa. (206) 821-8372
Services: golf instruction

Clarke-Stephens Golf
E. 116 Nora; Spokane, Wa. (509) 325-5905
Services: club repair, custom clubs, club refinishing, lessons

Club 72
210 S. 26th; Pasco, Wa. (509) 547-6461
Services: club repair, custom clubs, club refinishing

Cooper's Golf Outlet
1582 S. Burlington Boulevard; Burlington, Wa. (360) 757-GOLF
Services: club repair, lessons at the range

Doug McDonald's Golf in the 80's
7531 Lake City Way NE; Seattle, Wa. (206) 522-8940
Services: lessons, video lessons

Eagle Golf
1135 NW Gillman Boulevard; Issaquah, Wa. (206) 391-9497
Services: golf merchandise, club repair, regrip, reshaft, mail order catalog

Fairway Golf Club Repair
27239 132nd SE; Kent, Wa. (206) 639-0740
Services: club repair, custom clubs, club refinishing

Foster's Golf
2016 James Street, Suite C; Bellingham, Wa. (360) 671-5416
Services: club repair, custom clubs, club refinishing

Golf Academy, The
249 SW 41st; Renton, Wa. (206) 251-8515
Services: teaching facility only

Golf Club Company
2423 Harrison Avenue NW; Olympia, Wa. (360) 352-1331
Services: club repair, hand-crafted custom clubs, club refinishing

Golf USA
31830 Pacific Highway S; Federal Way, Wa. (206) 839-6488
Services: club repair, club refinishing, lessons

Golf USA
1300 N. Miller Wenatchee, Wa. (509) 662-7714
Services: club regripping, retail store, apparel, indoor range

Henderson Golf Shop
P.O. Box 1484; Walla Walla, Wa. (509) 529-5810
Services: club repair, custom clubs, alterations

Indoor Golf Club of Seattle
15620 Hwy 99, Suite 7; Lynnwood, Wa. (206) 742-4653
Services: indoor golf course

Jorgensen Golf *Julius Jorgensen, Owner/Pro* **1-800-218-2373**
11700 Mukilteo Spdwy; STE 407; Mukilteo, Wa.; (206) 349-1347 or 787-9186
Services: indoor video lessons, club repair, upscale pro shop, USGA GHIN G.C.

Kitsap Indoor Golf
1351 Bay Street; Port Orchard, Wa. (360) 876-9401
Services: indoor golf course, club repair, lessons, pro shop

Leading Edge Golf
1000 NE 135th; Seattle, Wa. 98125 (206) 363-4747
Services: club repair, custom club fitting, golf instruction, golf tours

Marlows Golf Tech & Family Golf Learning Center *New Shop*
22703 Bothell Everett Hwy; Bothell, Wa. (206) 481-3199, 290-5769, 324-7981
Services: indoor video lessons, discount pro shop, Marlows School of Golf

National Golf
5114 Dartmouth Road; Spokane, Wa. (509) 927-GOLF
Services: discount golf merchandise, club repair

National Golf
8701 N Division; Spokane, Wa. (509) 468-0660
Services: discount golf merchandise, club repair

Nevada Bob's
6409 Tacoma Mall Boulevard; Tacoma, Wa. (206) 474-8288
Services: club repair, club refinishing

Nevada Bob's
6855 W. Clearwater Avenue; Kennewick, Wa. (509) 783-1112
Services: club repair, custom clubs

O'briens Golf Shop
11860 Des Moines Memorial Drive South; Seattle, Wa. (206) 243-3110
Services: club repair, club refinishing, custom clubs, lessons

Olsen's Golf Shop
7612 Beverly Boulevard; Everett, Wa. (206) 355-9241
Services: club repair, club refinishing

Oshman's Super Sports *New Shop*
1101 Supermall Way; STE 1333; Auburn, Wa. (206) 735-7447
Services: custom clubs, regripping, retail store, lessons

Pro Golf Discount
14121 NE 20th; Bellevue, Wa. (206) 641-6766
Services: club repair, club refinishing, discount pro shop

Pro Golf Discount
301 Tukwila Parkway (Southcenter); Tukwila, Wa. (206) 431-0100
Services: club repair, club refinishing, discount pro shop

Pro Golf Discount
10746 5th Avenue NE (Northgate); Seattle, Wa. (206) 367-3529
Services: club repair, club refinishing, discount pro shop

Pro Golf Discount
18905 33rd Avenue W.; Lynnwood, Wa. (206) 525-5518 or 771-2131
Services: club repair, club refinishing, discount pro shop

Pro Golf Discount
5015 Tacoma Mall Boulevard, Suite C; Tacoma, Wa. (206) 473-4290
Services: club repair, club refinishing, discount pro shop

Pro Golf Discount
4225 Meridian Street; Bellingham, Wa. (360) 738-7101
Services: club repair, club refinishing, discount pro shop

Pro Golf Discount
905 S 1rst Street; Yakima, Wa. (509) 248-0800
Services: club repair, club refinishing, discount pro shop

Puetz Golf Superstore
402 Strander Blvd.; Tukwila, Wa. (206) 439-1740
Services: club repair, club refinishing, discount pro shop, brand name clubs

Puetz Golf Superstore
1645 140th Avenue NE; Bellevue, Wa. (206) 747-0664
Services: club repair, club refinishing, discount pro shop, brand name clubs

Puetz Golf Superstore
11762 Aurora Avenue N.; Seattle, Wa. (206) 362-2272
Services: club repair, refinishing, discount pro shop, lessons, video lessons, range

Puetz Golf Center
7231 S Tacoma Way; Tacoma Wa. (206) 475-1989
Services: club repair, club refinishing, discount pro shop, brand name clubs

Puget Sound Golf Shop
2708 Locust Avenue W; Tacoma, Wa. (206) 566-1934
Services: club repair, regrip, custom clubs, limited instruction

Redbird Sports
4860 Beacon Avenue South; Seattle, Wa. (206) 725-7872
Services: club refinishing, custom clubs

Richmark Golf
14668 NE 95th; Redmond, Wa. (206) 881-6947
Services: custom clubs, regrip, club manufactruing

Sporthaus
326 N. Columbia Center Boulevard; Kennewick, Wa. (509) 735-7555
Services: club repair, custom clubs

Studio Fore
12003 NE 12th, Suite 56; Bellevue, Wa. (206) 454-6766
Services: lessons

The Golfer's Edge
P.O. Box; 222 Poplar Avenue; Wenatchee, Wa.; (509) 662-2032
Services: club repair, custom clubs, re-gripping

The Golfing Gallery
11200 Kirkland Way; Kirkland, Wa. (206) 242-PUTT
Services: collectable golf art, prints, limited editions

The Old Duffer
847 NE Northgate Way; Seattle, Wa. (206) 367-5907
Services: club repair, custom clubs, club refinishing, club regrips

Tim O'brien's Club Crafters, Inc.
12003 NE 12th, Suite 57; Bellevue, Wa. (206) 453-8255
Services: custom clubs

Tom Wells Golf Company
7806 Aurora Avenue N.; Seattle, Wa. (206) 523-7124
Services: club repair, club refinishing, custom clubs, lessons

Ultimate Golf
11200 Kirkland Way; Kirkland, Wa. (206) 827-3641
Services: indoor golf, pro shop, call for additional services

Ultimate Golf of Tacoma
5401 6th Avenue; Suite 501;Tacoma, Wa. (206) 752-4440
Services: indoor golf

Wide World of Golf
N. 4921 Division; Spokane, Wa. (509) 489-4653
Services: club repair, custom clubs

Wiffi's Place
PO Box 766; Darrington, Wa. (360) 436-1221
Services: lessons

Our newest section in *Golfing in Washington* is called **Weekend Getaways.** We have received calls from people using the book for suggestions on weekend trips and my family and I personally enjoy going golfing in the morning and seeing other attractions in the afternoon. We have designed this section, therefore, to give you some ideas of short weekend trips you could take in the area and you can tailor them to your taste! Any further information you would like on specific lodging availability the Chamber of Commerce in the destination city would be eager to provide. Some of our suggestions may be seasonal so it is always best to call ahead.

Burlington: Avalon Golf Course is situated a short distance from I-5 and offers a lovely restaurant for your "after golf" meal. Burlington itself has one of the first and largest outlet malls and is the gateway to the North Cascades Hwy. This is a very popular and scenic drive highlighting many beautiful sights in the Cascades. Make sure the Highway is open, however, because it is closed during the winter. Another very beautiful trip is State Route 11 from Burlington called Chuckanut Drive. This trip provides panoramic views of the San Juans as you wind your way to Bellingham following the Washington coastline. The Skagit Valley would be another destination to travel to from Burlington and, if you timed it right, you could see the Tulip Festival. The waterfront town of LaConner also offers shopping and dining. It is located south of the Burlington Highway on Skagit Bay.

Lake Chelan/Orondo: This vacation location offers two golf courses, Lake Chelan Golf Course and Desert Canyon in Orondo. Desert Canyon is located at a resort which has full amenities. This is a desert course similar to those of Palm Springs. South of Orondo is the Rocky Reach Dam which is open for the public to tour. Lake Chelan has the full gamut of activities available as any resort town. There is boating, lodging right on the lake, shopping in town, and other water activities. If your time allows you might like to take the Lady of the Lake trip from Chelan to the remote village of Stehekin, 55 miles northwest. This breathtaking trip will take you through steep cliffs, waterfalls, and beautiful mountain scenery. Stehekin and the Lake Chelan National Recreation area are not accessible by road.

Leavenworth: The Bavarian village of Leavenworth is located east of Stevens Pass and Lake Wenatchee. There are two golf courses in the area, Leavenworth and Kahler Glen. Leavenworth offers lodging, extensive gift shopping, and restaurants in a scenic unique mountain setting. All of the storefronts are Bavarian style. The town often has special events happening including art exhibits, folk dancing, and the Octoberfest. If you prefer, Lake Wenatchee offers a large campground with swimming and kayaking on the Wenatchee River. There are guided river trips available.

Ocean Shores: A trip to Ocean Shores is always a treat. There is plenty of lodging and dining available. The golf course is located right in the heart of Ocean Shores. Other activities include horseback riding, kite flying, mopeds, bike riding and beachcombing. During limited seasons clam digging and other fishing activities are within a stones throw of Ocean Shores. A day could easily be spent driving the coastline and visting such communities as Klaloch, Copalis, Forks and even Lake Crescent.

Port Orchard/Bremerton/Gig Harbor: This is a widespread area has many golf courses available for play. McCormick Woods, Horseshoe Lake, Gig Harbor, Madrona Links, Rolling Hills, Clover Valley, and Gold Mountain. There are dining and lodging facilities in any of the towns. There is art gallery shopping in Gig Harbor, the Bremerton Naval Museum, or drive up to Poulsbo "Little Norway" for a waterfront Scandinavian adventure in shopping. *Or* take the ferry from Seattle to Bremerton, play golf and enjoy the afternoon in Kitsap Co., return to Seattle that evening and stay downtown. The following day could include a trip to the Pike Place Market and visiting the other beautiful Seattle sights.

Port Townsend: The Port Townsend area has three golf courses, the Port Townsend Golf Course, Chevy Chase, and The Port Ludlow Golf & Meeting Retreat. Port Ludlow offers full resort accommodations, a restaurant, lounge, tennis courts and marina. Golf packages are available. Chevy Chase is the oldest resort golf course in the state of Washington having been built and continually operated since 1925. The accommodations reside on a bluff overlooking Discovery Bay. The amenities available with cabin rental are: swimming pool, tennis court and a clam rich private beach. Port Townsend is famous for its many bed and breakfast inns housed in old Victorian mansions built in the historical town. The downtown waterfront has many galleries and small shops as well as waterfront dining. There are numerous sites at Fort Wordon State Park including a Marine Science Center, The Rothschild House (a 1868 home owned by a Port Townsend merchant with mostly original furnishings) and a Commanding Officer's House which has been restored to reflect actual officers quarters of the Victorian period. There is also a museum of yesteryear located in Port Townsend.

San Juan Islands: The San Juans are home to three golf courses, Orcas Island, San Juan and Lopez Island. A trip to the San Juans is breathtakingly beautiful, peaceful, and a real break from the hustle and bustle of city life.
Orcas Island: Rosario Resort offers fine cuisine and lodging. Moran State Park features a stone tower, fishing, and beachcombing. The Orcas Island Historical Museum focuses on early pioneer and indian life on the island. **San Juan:** Whale watching is available at Lime Kiln State Park (west of Friday Harbor, daytime only), and the Whale Museum featuring art exhibits and the natural habitat and history of whales and dolphins. **Lopez Island:** Bring your bicycles and ride the

Lopez Loop covering 13 miles around the island (this route sees the minimum of traffic). The Washington State Ferry System provides service to the San Juans, call them for further detail and schedules.

Semiahmoo/Blaine/Bellingham: The Washington-Canadian border is rich with golf courses and historical sites. The Semiahmoo Resort is a wonderful getaway just for the Arnold Palmer designed golf course and the peaceful surroundings of the resort. Bellingham also offers lodging and dining. There is a myriad of things to do. Vancouver British Columbia is a beautiful city and is only an hour from Blaine. There is the famous Stanley Park, the former Expo site, Gastown and exquisite dining. Attractions in the Bellingham area you might enjoy for the afternoon include the Lake Whatcom Railway which provides views of everything from the San Juan Islands to Mt. Baker. Hovander Homestead (Ferndale) is a restored 1903 homestead furnished with antiques and antique farm equipment. Pioneer park (Ferndale) has a number of restored log cabins on site. The Whatcom Museum of History and Art (Bellingham) focuses on Northwest, maritime, and indian artifacts

Sequim: Sequim offers two golf courses, Dungeness and SunLand (semi-private). You can check with the Dungeness Golf Course for the packages they offer with local motels. Located nearby is the Olympic Game Farm, and the Dungeness Spit (a beautiful, peaceful, beach trail on the Straits of Juan de Fuca). The 3 Crabs Restaurant is also located right on the beach and serves excellent fresh seafood. A nice addition to this trip would be a drive to Port Angeles and up to Hurricane Ridge which is located in the heart of the Olympic Mountains. There is a visitor center with spectacular views of the Olympics. If you have an extended weekend you can take the ferry from Port Angeles to Victoria and all the sites of this lovely city which could include the Butchart Gardens, downtown shopping, the British Columbia Museum of Natural History, the Empress Hotel and Capitol Building. Don't forget to bring your golf clubs as Vancouver Island is host to many fine golf courses.

Snoqualmie: The Salish Lodge located at Snoqualmie Falls is a beautiful and peaceful hide-a-way only 30 minutes from Bellevue. There are many golf courses located in all directions from the Salish. Mt Si Golf Course, Twin Rivers Golf Course, Snoqualmie Falls Golf Course, Tall Chief Golf Course and Carnation Golf Course. There are trails at the lodge leading to scenic views of the falls. Some of the other activities in the area include the most popular hike in Washington up Mt Si, North Bend has an outlet mall, Remlinger Farm located in Carnation is a family operated farm offering a restaurant, nursery, gift shop, fresh produce and farm products, a working steam train, as well as seasonal events. Boehm's Candies in Issaquah offers a tour of the home, chapel, candy making and an art gallery. The Puget Sound & Snoqualmie Railroad provides a very scenic train ride covering approximately a 10 mile route. Snoqualmie also has the Snoqualmie Winery open for wine tasting and tours.

Spokane: The Spokane area has many fine golf courses, check the geographical index for the listing. This major city offers superb lodging and dining. Other attractions include: Finch Arboretum (includes nature trail), Manito Park featuring formal and Japanese gardens, Crosby Library on Gonzaga University's campus (Bing Crosby memorabilia), the Cathedral of St. John the Evangelist (constructed over a 50 year time period), Fort Spokane (a previously active army post) with a walking trail and four original buildings, the Museum of Native American Cultures, the Walk in the Wild (a walk through wooded acreage includes wide variety of wildlife), and the Riverfront Park, the site of the Spokane world's fair which includes a science center, kiddie rides, IMAX theater and more.

Stevenson: The Skamania Lodge offers full amenities and is home to the Bridge of the Gods Golf Course which opened in 1993. The Columbia River Gorge is nearby as well as the Skamania Co Historical Museum. If you don't mind the drive this would be a great time to see the new visitor center at Mt. St. Helens and hike the trails there.

Union: The Alderbrook Inn is located right on Hood Canal in Union. The Inn offers fine dining, dancing, a lounge, and a covered swimming pool along with many other activities on Hood Canal. The Alderbrook Golf Course is right across the street up the hill. You might also like to take the drive to Hoodsport and play the Lake Cushman Golf Course, visit the town of Hoodsport and the Hoodsport Winery which is open for wine tasting.

Yakima: Dubbed the "Palm Springs of Washington" this town has a wonderful climate. Apple Tree Golf Course (with the famous 17th island green shaped as a Washington apple), Westwood West, and Suntides are the local public regulation golf courses. The city is thriving in the midst of many apple orchards and has all amenities. After your round of golf you might enjoy taking the "Wine Country Road" which is approximately a 50 mile trip from Yakima to Prosser. There are 8 wineries along the way which all offer vineyard or winery tours and wine tasting. Yakima also has a large arboretum with Japanese gardens. The Yakima Valley Museum features a restored Victorian farmhouse, or take a ride on the Yakima Trolleys which travel over everything from an old trestle to steep rock cliffs.

We hope you have found this new section useful. Above all else enjoy yourself, the peace and quiet that a round of golf provides, and the majestic beauty of the State of Washington.

Desert Aire: Desert Aire Golf & Country Club
Ellensburg: Ellensburg Golf Club
Elma: Oaksridge Golf Course
Enumclaw: Enumclaw Golf Course
Ephrata: Oasis Park Par 3
Everett: Everett, Harbour Pointe, Hat Island, Legion Memorial, Longshots, Super Range, Walter E. Hall Memorial,
Everson: Evergreen, Peaceful Valley, Raspberry Ridge
Fall City: Carnation, Snoqualmie Falls, Tall Chief, Twin Rivers
Federal Way: Christy's Golf Course & Driving Range, Twin Lakes G&CC
Ferndale: Riverside Golf Course, Sandy Point GC
Fort Lewis: Fort Lewis Golf Course
Freeland: Holmes Harbor Golf Club
Gig Harbor: Canterwood, Gig Harbor, Madrona Links
Glenoma: Ironwood Green Golf Course
Goldendale: Goldendale Country Club
Gorst: Gold Mountain Golf Course
Grand Coulee: Banks Lake, Big Bend, Vic Meyer's
Grand Mound: Grand Mound Driving Range
Harrington: Harrington, Odessa
Hood Canal: Alderbrook, Batstone Hill Gold Mountain, Lake Cushman, Lake Limerick, Lakeland Village, Shelton Bayshore
Kelso: Three Rivers
Kennewick: Badger Mountain GC, Canyon Lakes, Longest Drive, Tri-City (see Tri-Cities for additional listings)
Kent-Renton: Fairwood, Golf Park, Lake Wilderness, Maplewood, Meridian Valley, Riverbend, Southcenter Golf, The Course @ Taylor Creek, Washington National
Kingston: Woodall's World Driving Range
Lacey: Eagle View Golf Center, Meriwood (see Olympia & Tumwater)
Leavenworth: Kahler Glen, Leavenworth
Liberty Lake: Liberty Lake, MeadowWood, Valley View (see Spokane)
Long Beach: Peninsula, Surfside
Longview: Golf Green, Longview, Mint Valley
Lynden: Homestead, Raspberry Ridge (see Everson)
Lynnwood: Lynnwood Municipal, Kaddyshack Golf Center
Manson: MA 8+1 Golf
Maple Falls: Evergreen, Peaceful Valley, Raspberry Ridge
Maple Valley: Elk Run, Lake Wilderness, The Course at Taylor Creek
Marysville: Battle Creek, Cedarcrest, Kayak Point, Marysville Golf Center
McChord A.F.B: Whispering Firs Golf Club
Metaline Falls: Pend Oreille
Monroe: Blue Boy West, Iron Eagle Sports Center, Monroe Golf Course

Seattle: Ballinger Park, Broadmoor, Foster, Glen Acres, Green Lake, Interbay, Jackson, Jefferson, Nile, Puetz, Rainier, Sand Point, Seattle, Tyee Valley, U of W, West Seattle
Sedro-Wooley: Gateway
Selah: Suntides, Yakima Elks
Sequim: Dungeness, SunLand
Shelton: Batstone Hill Driving Range, Lake Cushman, Lake Limerick, Shelton Bayshore
Snohomish: Flowing Lake, Kenwanda, Lobo, Snohomish
Soap Lake: Lakeview
Spanaway: Brookdale, The Classic, Lake Spanaway, University
Spokane: Beacon Hill Golf Center, Birdies Golf Place, Buckhorn Par 3, The Creek @ Qualchan, Downriver, Esmerelda, Fairways, Hangman Valley, Indian Canyon, Liberty Lake, Manito, MeadowWood, Painted Hills, Pine Acres, Spokane, Sundance, Valley View, Wandermere
Stanwood: Camaloch, Kayak Point
Stevenson: Skamania Lodge Golf Course
Sumner: High Cedars, Sumner Municipal GC, Tapps Island GC
Sunnyside: Lower Valley, Mount Adams
Tacoma: Allenmore, Brookdale, Christy's, Fircrest, Ft. Lewis, Ft. Steilacoom, Highlands, Lake Spanaway, Linksman, Meadow Park, North Shore, Oakbrook, Tacoma, Twin Lakes, University, Whispering Firs
Tekoa: Tekoa
Toppenish: Lower Valley, Mount Adams
Tri Cities: Columbia Park, Canyon Lakes, Horn Rapids, Meadow Springs, Pasco, Sham Na Pum, The Longest Drive, Tri City, West Richland
Tumwater: Eagle View GC, Meriwood GC, Olympia Golf &CC, Pacific Golf Range, Scott Lake GC, Steamboat Golf, Tumwater Valley (see Olympia & Laceyfor additional listings)
Union: Alderbrook G&YC
Vancouver: Bowyer's, Cedars, Evergreen Golf Center, Fairway Village, Green Meadows, H&H Driving Range, Lakeview, Orchard Hills, Pinecrest, Royal Oaks G&CC, Vanco DR
Vashon Island: Vashon Golf & Country Club
Walla Walla: Memorial Park, Tour Fairways DR, Walla Walla CC
Warden: Moses Lake, Sage Hills, South Campus
Washougal: Orchard Hills G&CC
West Richland: West Richland Golf Course
Wenatchee: Crystal Springs, Desrt Canyon, Rock Island, Three Lakes, Wenatchee Golf & Country Club
Whidbey Island: Gallery Golf Course, Island Greens Golf Course, Lams Golf Links, Useless Bay Golf & Cuntry Club, Whidbey G&CC
Whidbey Island Naval Air Station: Gallery Golf Course

Order Form Information

Please send:

_____ *Golfing in Washington $10.95 ea.*.............. _____
with layouts, map grids and detailed golf course information.

_____ *Golfing in Oregon $8.95 ea.*........................ _____
with layouts, map grids and detailed golf course information.

_____ *Golfing in Idaho & Montana $10.95ea.*...... _____
with layouts, map grids and detailed golf course information.

_____*Golf Courses of the Pacific N.W. $19.95 ea.*.. _____
A book covering the unique aspects and history of over
500 golf courses in the Pacific Northwest. By **Jeff Shelley**

_____*The Northwest Golfers Almanac $7.95 ea.*.... _____
Bits and pieces of northwest golf history, golf stories and facts.
A must for any golf historian. Published by **Fairgreens Media**

Add $2.75 per book for postage & handling _____

Add $2.50 for Canadian Funds...................... _____
(please send US funds)
                    Total Enclosed................. _____

Washington residents add 8.2% for sales tax

Send Check or Money order to:
Mac Productions
PO Box 655
Carnation, WA 98014 USA

M_A_C Productions
Golf Guides Since 1986

Send to:

_____

Name of Recipient

_____

Address

_____

City, State or Province, zip or postal code